Mathematical Methods in Physics and Engineering

INTERNATIONAL SERIES IN PURE AND APPLIED
MATHEMATICS

William Ted Martin, *Consulting Editor*

Mathematical Methods in Physics and Engineering

John W. Dettman

Assistant Professor of Mathematics
Case Institute of Technology

1962
McGRAW-HILL   BOOK   COMPANY,   INC.
New York   San Francisco   Toronto   London

MATHEMATICAL METHODS IN PHYSICS AND ENGINEERING

16596

Dedicated to My
Mother and Father

Preface

Students of physics and engineering, after having completed the standard course in calculus through differential equations, are faced with the problem of deciding what additional mathematics to take. Some leave mathematics out of their curriculum altogether, only to discover, after they have embarked on a program of graduate study, that they must go back and take undergraduate courses in order to acquire the mathematical background and maturity necessary to understand work being done in modern physics and engineering. Others, in their haste to pick up additional techniques not covered in the elementary calculus course, take courses in advanced engineering mathematics which cover such topics as Fourier series, Laplace transforms, partial differential equations, boundary-value problems, and complex variables. These topics are often presented in a very heuristic fashion, because the students lack a solid background in analysis. In fact, many of these mathematical techniques are taught in the same heuristic manner in courses in physics and engineering when they are needed in specific applications. Eventually, however, most graduate students will need a thorough understanding of applied mathematics if they are going to be able to read the literature in their own field and use mathematics effectively in their own work.

It is my opinion that a student who intends to do graduate work in physics or in some branches of engineering should develop a broad mathematical base for his graduate studies when he is an undergraduate. He should do this by taking a course in what has traditionally been called advanced calculus, followed by an introduction to mathematical physics based on the advanced calculus. Without the burden of presenting applications, advanced calculus can be a course which carefully develops the concepts of function, limit, continuity, differentiation, integration, infinite series, improper integrals, and possibly functions of a complex variable. Then, with this as a background, the applications can be presented in the mathematical physics course, and the students will be capable of understanding thoroughly the mathematics involved. This book has been written to fill the need for a textbook for the latter course.

The student is assumed to have had elementary calculus through differential equations, some elementary mechanics, plus the kind of advanced calculus course described above, including vector analysis. Some knowledge of functions of a complex variable is very helpful but not essential. The bulk of material can be understood without prior knowledge of complex variable analysis. The necessary higher algebra is developed from the beginning, so that no more than elementary college algebra is needed.

This material is taught in a course at Case Institute of Technology to seniors majoring in mathematics and physics and to some graduate students studying engineering and physics. For most students of physics this could very well be a terminal mathematics course, for it gives them the necessary maturity and background to do graduate work in quantum mechanics and modern theoretical physics. For the mathematics student it acts as a survey of some of the methods of applied mathematics and will, I hope, interest some in doing graduate work in applied mathematics. It should not take the place of pure mathematics courses in real and complex variables, modern algebra, ordinary and partial differential equations, functional analysis, etc., but on the other hand, it is adequate preparation for most beginning graduate courses in elasticity, plasticity, and fluid mechanics. Thus a student of applied mathematics would be in a position to develop early his interests in these fields.

Chapter 1 presents the **algebraic preliminaries** necessary for the development of the rest of the book. It includes determinants, linear equations, matrices through the simultaneous reduction of a pair of hermitian forms, eigenvalues and eigenvectors, and the concept of a vector space, which is important to the understanding of linear problems. There is also an introduction to infinite-dimensional vector spaces, Hilbert space, and Fourier analysis. Chapter 2 discusses the **calculus of variations** and its applications. Hamilton's principle is used to introduce the methods of the calculus of variations into the study of small vibrations and boundary-value problems in mathematical physics. The eigenvalue-eigenfunction problem is formulated in the calculus of variations, including the minimax definition of the eigenvalue and its usefulness in proving general theorems about the behavior of the eigenvalues. Chapter 3 develops the method of **separation of variables** for the solution of **boundary-value problems.** The Sturm-Liouville problem is discussed along with the related problem of expanding functions in series of orthogonal functions. Some special functions, such as Bessel functions, Legendre functions, and spherical harmonics, are discussed. Chapter 4 presents the **Green's function** method of solving **boundary-value problems.** Nonhomogeneous boundary-value problems are discussed, including some which arise in potential theory and diffraction theory. The equivalence between a boundary-value problem and a problem in integral equations is established. Chapter 5 extends the discussion of **integral equations,** including the Hilbert-Schmidt and Fredholm theories. Chapter 6 introduces **transform methods,** with special emphasis on Fourier and

Laplace transforms.   This subject is introduced late so that its applications, not only to ordinary and partial differential equations, but also to integral equations, can be discussed.

I have specifically *not* tried to make the various chapters self-contained, realizing full well that this might limit the book somewhat in its use as a reference.   It seems to me that the interrelations between the various parts of the theory should be emphasized, so that the reader does not get the impression that applied mathematics is a collection of disjointed topics.   There are many recurring themes which thread their way through the whole development.   One of these is the vector space concept, which gives a framework for linear problems in general.   Another is the eigenvalue problem, which is first met in an algebraic context but later reappears in the study of ordinary and partial differential equations and integral equations.   The calculus of variations presents a unified method of handling many problems. The same can be said of transform techniques.   The method of constructing Green's functions is applicable to many types of boundary-value problems, and it allows one to formulate problems in terms of integral equations, thus opening up new possibilities for solution.

There is more than enough material here for an average class to cover in a two-semester course meeting three hours a week.   Since Chap. 6 depends most heavily on the complex variable theory, a course based on Chaps. 1 to 5 might be designed for a group of students without this background.   On the other hand, if the class has had a semester of complex variable analysis and has a greater interest in integral transform techniques, one could go directly from Chap. 4 to Chap. 6.

The exercises which follow every section are generally of three types: (1) those which test the understanding of the material just covered, (2) those which extend the results to new situations, and (3) those which lay the groundwork for new concepts to be introduced later.   Those which fall into the third category will be marked with an asterisk, not necessarily because they are more difficult, but as a guide to the reader.

Most of the material is standard, and so I have not attempted to cite specific references throughout.   Each chapter is followed by a list of some of the standard references on the subject.   I should like to acknowledge the help and encouragement of my colleagues at Case Institute of Technology, especially Profs. Sidney W. McCuskey, Robert A. Clark, and Louis J. Green.   By allowing me to develop the course in methods of mathematical physics as a key course in the mathematics curriculum, they gave me the stimulus to write this book.   I also wish to thank my many classes of students who studied so patiently from the preliminary material, worked the many exercises, and made many helpful suggestions.   Finally, I want to thank Mrs. Francine Schwab and Miss Pauline Tolar for their patience and efficiency in typing the manuscript.

John W. Dettman

Contents

Chapter 1. Algebraic Preliminaries

1.1 Linear Equations. Summation Convention

The problem of solving systems of linear algebraic equations frequently arises in analysis and in its applications to physical problems. Such a system can be written as

$$a_{11}x_1 + a_{12}x_2 + \cdots + a_{1n}x_n = c_1$$
$$a_{21}x_1 + a_{22}x_2 + \cdots + a_{2n}x_n = c_2$$
$$\cdot \cdot \cdot \cdot \cdot \cdot \cdot \cdot \cdot \cdot \cdot \cdot \cdot \cdot \cdot \cdot \cdot$$
$$a_{m1}x_1 + a_{m2}x_2 + \cdots + a_{mn}x_n = c_m$$

The problem is: Given constants a_{11}, a_{12}, ..., a_{mn} and c_1, c_2, ..., c_m, under what conditions will there exist a set x_1, x_2, ..., x_n which simultaneously satisfies the system of equations, and how may this set of unknowns be determined? Before we turn to the solution of this problem, let us first consider some alternative ways of writing the system of linear equations.

By use of the Σ notation for summation, the system can be written as follows:

$$\sum_{j=1}^{n} a_{1j}x_j = c_1$$
$$\sum_{j=1}^{n} a_{2j}x_j = c_2$$
$$\cdot \cdot \cdot \cdot \cdot \cdot \cdot$$
$$\sum_{j=1}^{n} a_{mj}x_j = c_m$$

Realizing that the first subscript on the a's and the subscript on the c's agree in each equation and that in the system this subscript takes on the values 1 to m, successively, we can write

$$\sum_{j=1}^{n} a_{ij}x_j = c_i \qquad i = 1, 2, 3, \ldots, m$$

1

Furthermore, we note that the Σ is really not necessary, since in each equation the summation takes place over the repeated subscript j; i.e., in the left-hand side of each equation j takes on the values 1 through n, and the terms are then summed.   For this reason we now drop the Σ and adopt the following convention, known as the **summation convention.**   *If in a given term in an expression a Latin[1] subscript is repeated, a summation over that subscript is implied. The term is the sum of all possible such terms with the repeated subscript taking on the successive values 1 through n.*   The value of n must be stated, unless it is understood ahead of time and no ambiguity can arise.   By use of the summation convention, the system of linear equations can be written simply as

$$a_{ij}x_j = c_i \qquad i = 1, 2, \ldots, m$$
$$j = 1, 2, \ldots, n$$

The summation convention can be a very useful tool and can produce a great saving in writing.   Skillful use of it will shorten many proofs and clarify one's thinking involving lengthy expressions, where one might get bogged down in details if the expressions are written out in full.   However, until thoroughly familiar with its use, one must be careful to learn exactly what operations involving the summation convention are legitimate.   The following discussion and examples may help to clarify some of these points.

The repeated subscript is often called a **dummy subscript,** because the letter designating it can be changed without changing the expression, provided it is understood that the new letter takes on the same values in the summation as the old.   For example, the system of linear equations can just as well be written as

$$a_{ik}x_k = c_i \qquad i = 1, 2, \ldots, m$$
$$k = 1, 2, \ldots, n$$

i.e., the dummy j has been changed to k without affecting the system of equations, since the same summation takes place because of the repeated k.   Or as another example,

$$a_i b_i = a_j b_j = a_1 b_1 + a_2 b_2 + \cdots + a_n b_n$$

A subscript which is not repeated in the same term of an equation is called a **free subscript.**   For example, in $a_{ij}x_j = c_i$, i is a free subscript.   The range 1 to m of i indicates the number of different equations in the system, while the range 1 to n of j indicates the number of terms in the summation which occurs in each equation.   When i takes on the value 10, it refers to the tenth equation in the system.   In the equation

$$a_i + b_i = c_i$$

---

[1] Here we are anticipating certain cases where we may need a repeated subscript without summation.   In this case, we shall use Greek subscripts, having made the summation convention apply specifically to Latin subscripts.

i is a free subscript. Although it is repeated on the left-hand side of the equation, it is not repeated in a single term. However, in an expression like

$$c_i(a_i + b_i) = c_1(a_1 + b_1) + c_2(a_2 + b_2) + \cdots + c_n(a_n + b_n)$$

it is a dummy, and a summation is implied.

Unless it is otherwise stated, "numbers" like the a's, c's, and x's which appear in expressions like $a_{ij}x_j = c_i$ come from a **field** where the following rules of algebra hold:[1]

1. **Associative law of addition:** $(a + b) + c = a + (b + c)$
2. **Commutative law of addition:** $a + b = b + a$
3. **Associative law of multiplication:** $(ab)c = a(bc)$
4. **Commutative law of multiplication:** $ab = ba$
5. **Distributive law:** $a(b + c) = ab + ac$

Assuming "numbers" from a field, it is not difficult to prove the following statements involving the summation convention:

$$a_i b_i = b_i a_i$$
$$a_i(b_i + c_i) = a_i b_i + a_i c_i$$
$$(a_i b_i)(c_j d_j) = (a_i c_i)(b_i d_i)$$

The proof of the third in the case where i and j take on the value 1, 2, 3 would proceed as follows:

$$
\begin{aligned}
(a_i b_i)(c_j d_j) &= (a_1 b_1 + a_2 b_2 + a_3 b_3)(c_1 d_1 + c_2 d_2 + c_3 d_3) \\
&= a_1 b_1 c_1 d_1 + a_1 b_1 c_2 d_2 + a_1 b_1 c_3 d_3 \\
&\quad + a_2 b_2 c_1 d_1 + a_2 b_2 c_2 d_2 + a_2 b_2 c_3 d_3 \\
&\quad \cdot + a_3 b_3 c_1 d_1 + a_3 b_3 c_2 d_2 + a_3 b_3 c_3 d_3 \\
&= a_1 c_1 b_1 d_1 + a_1 c_2 b_1 d_2 + a_1 c_3 b_1 d_3 \\
&\quad + a_2 c_1 b_2 d_1 + a_2 c_2 b_2 d_2 + a_2 c_3 b_2 d_3 \\
&\quad + a_3 c_1 b_3 d_1 + a_3 c_2 b_3 d_2 + a_3 c_3 b_3 d_3 \\
&= (a_i c_j)(b_i d_j)
\end{aligned}
$$

In this expression there is a summation over i and j, so that both are dummies. A subscript should never be repeated more than once in the same term, or confusion may arise. For example, one might be tempted to write

$$
\begin{aligned}
(a_i b_i)(c_j d_j) &= (a_i b_i)(c_i d_i) \\
&= (a_i c_i)(b_i d_i) \\
&= (a_i c_i)(b_j d_j)
\end{aligned}
$$

---

[1] For the other postulates of a field consult a book on algebra such as G. Birkhoff and S. Maclane, "A Survey of Modern Algebra," The Macmillan Company, New York, 1949. Some examples of a field are the real numbers and the complex numbers. The field of complex numbers includes the field of the real numbers and is called an extension of the real-number field.

This, of course, is incorrect and can be avoided by careful observation of the rule that a *dummy may be repeated only once in a single term*. Upon substitution from one expression into another it may be necessary to change the "name" of a dummy in order to adhere to this rule. For example, if $y_i = a_{ij}x_j$ and $z_i = b_{ij}x_j$, then $y_iz_i = a_{ij}x_jb_{ik}x_k = a_{ij}b_{ik}x_jx_k$. Here, the dummy j is changed to k in one expression in order to avoid the second repetition of j in the final expression. We cannot express something like $a_1b_1c_1 + a_2b_2c_2 + a_3b_3c_3$ using the summation convention, but this does not turn out to be a serious penalty to pay.

The identities illustrated above are true for finite sums but would not necessarily hold for infinite sums. For this reason, we shall not apply the summation convention to infinite sums but shall go back to the notation $\sum\limits_{i=1}^{\infty}$ when we wish to write an infinite sum. *Otherwise the summation convention will be implied, unless the contrary is stated.*

The summation convention can also be used to some advantage in expressions involving partial derivatives. For example, if $w(x_1,x_2,x_3,\ldots,x_n)$ is a function of $x_1, x_2, \ldots, x_n$, which are in turn functions of a parameter t, then

$$\frac{dw}{dt} = \frac{\partial w}{\partial x_i}\frac{dx_i}{dt}$$

Here the summation in the usual "chain rule" is implied by the repetition of the subscript i. As another example, consider a vector $\mathbf{V}$ with components v_1, v_2, v_3 which are functions of three space variables x_1, x_2, x_3. Then the divergence of $\mathbf{V}$, written $\nabla \cdot \mathbf{V}$, is

$$\nabla \cdot \mathbf{V} = \frac{\partial v_1}{\partial x_1} + \frac{\partial v_2}{\partial x_2} + \frac{\partial v_3}{\partial x_3} = \frac{\partial v_i}{\partial x_i}$$

Exercises 1.1

1. Write out and hence verify the identities $a_ib_i = b_ia_i$ and

$$a_i(b_i + c_i) = a_ib_i + a_ic_i$$

*2. If $y_i = b_{ij}x_j$ and $z_i = a_{ij}y_j$, show that $z_i = c_{ij}x_j$ where $c_{ij} = a_{ik}b_{kj}$.

*3. If $a_{ij} = a_{ji}$ and $b_{ij} = -b_{ji}$, show that $a_{ij}b_{ij} = 0$.

*4. We define the **Kronecker delta** δ_{ij} as follows: $\delta_{ij} = 1$ if $i = j$; and $\delta_{ij} = 0$ if $i \neq j$. Show that $a_{ij}\delta_{jk} = a_{ik} = \delta_{ij}a_{jk}$, where i, j, and k take on the values 1, 2, $\ldots$, n.

5. If $x_1, x_2, \ldots, x_n$ are a set of independent variables which are in turn functions of a set of independent variables $y_1, y_2, \ldots, y_n$, i.e., $x_i = x_i(y_1,y_2,\ldots,y_n)$, and the Jacobian of the transformation is not equal to zero, show that

$$\delta_{ij} = \frac{\partial x_i}{\partial x_j} = \frac{\partial x_i}{\partial y_k}\frac{\partial y_k}{\partial x_j}$$

*6. We define e_{ijk} as follows: $e_{ijk} = 0$ if $i = j, j = k$, or $i = k$; $e_{ijk} = 1$ if i, j, k are an even permutation of the numbers 1, 2, 3; and $e_{ijk} = -1$ if i, j, k are an odd permutation of 1, 2, 3. Show that $e_{ijk}a_{1i}a_{2j}a_{3k} = e_{ijk}a_{i1}a_{j2}a_{k3} = $

$$
\begin{vmatrix}
a_{11} & a_{12} & a_{13} \\
a_{21} & a_{22} & a_{23} \\
a_{31} & a_{32} & a_{33}
\end{vmatrix}
$$

7. If $\mathbf{U}$ and $\mathbf{V}$ are vectors with components u_1, u_2, u_3 and v_1, v_2, v_3, and

$$\mathbf{U} \cdot \mathbf{V} = u_i v_i$$

and the components of $\mathbf{U} \times \mathbf{V}$ are $e_{ijk}u_j v_k$, show the following, using subscript notation and summation convention:

$$\mathbf{U} \cdot \mathbf{V} = \mathbf{V} \cdot \mathbf{U}$$
$$\mathbf{U} \times \mathbf{V} = -\mathbf{V} \times \mathbf{U}$$
$$\mathbf{U} \cdot (\mathbf{U} \times \mathbf{V}) = 0$$
$$\mathbf{V} \cdot (\mathbf{U} \times \mathbf{V}) = 0$$

$u_i e_{ijk} u_j v_k$

8. If $\mathbf{U}$ is a vector function of the three space variables x_1, x_2, x_3, show that the components of the curl of $\mathbf{U}$, written $\nabla \times \mathbf{U}$, can be expressed as $e_{ijk}\dfrac{\partial u_k}{\partial x_j}$, where u_1, u_2, u_3 are the components of $\mathbf{U}$.

9. Using subscript notation, prove the following vector identities:

$$
\mathbf{U} \cdot (\mathbf{V} \times \mathbf{W}) =
\begin{vmatrix}
u_1 & u_2 & u_3 \\
v_1 & v_2 & v_3 \\
w_1 & w_2 & w_3
\end{vmatrix}
$$

$$\mathbf{U} \cdot (\mathbf{V} \times \mathbf{W}) = -\mathbf{V} \cdot (\mathbf{U} \times \mathbf{W}) = -\mathbf{W} \cdot (\mathbf{V} \times \mathbf{U})$$
$$\nabla \cdot (\nabla \times \mathbf{U}) = 0$$

1.2   Matrices

Another way of writing a system of linear algebraic equations is in terms of matrices. A **matrix** is an $m \times n$ array of **elements**[1] from a field arranged in rows and columns as follows:

$$
A =
\begin{Vmatrix}
a_{11} & a_{12} & \cdots & a_{1n} \\
a_{21} & a_{22} & \cdots & a_{2n} \\
\multicolumn{4}{c}{\dotfill} \\
a_{m1} & a_{m2} & \cdots & a_{mn}
\end{Vmatrix}
$$

and which obeys certain laws of equality, addition, subtraction, and multiplication, which we shall state presently. If we want to specify the elements of A, we write a_{ij}, $i = 1, 2, \ldots, m$, $j = 1, 2, \ldots, n$. The first subscript designates the row and the second the column from which the element is taken. If $m = n$, then we have a **square matrix of order n.**

---

[1] For our purposes it will be sufficient to assume that the elements are from the field of complex numbers, which of course includes real numbers.

Two matrices are **equal** if and only if their corresponding elements are equal. We may write this as follows:

$$A = B \text{ if and only if } a_{ij} = b_{ij} \qquad i = 1, 2, \ldots, m$$
$$j = 1, 2, \ldots, n$$

The **sum** of two matrices is the matrix formed by adding corresponding elements, or

$$A + B = C \text{ if and only if } a_{ij} + b_{ij} = c_{ij} \qquad i = 1, 2, \ldots, m$$
$$j = 1, 2, \ldots, n$$

The **difference** of two matrices is the matrix formed by subtracting corresponding elements, or

$$A - B = C \text{ if and only if } a_{ij} - b_{ij} = c_{ij} \qquad i = 1, 2, \ldots, m$$
$$j = 1, 2, \ldots, n$$

The **product** of an $m \times n$ and an $n \times p$ matrix is an $m \times p$ matrix, formed as follows:

$$AB = C \text{ if and only if } c_{ij} = a_{ik}b_{kj} \qquad i = 1, 2, \ldots, m$$
$$j = 1, 2, \ldots, p$$
$$k = 1, 2, \ldots, n$$

Clearly we can add and subtract only matrices with the same number of rows and columns, and we can multiply matrices only where the matrix on the left has the same number of columns as the matrix on the right has rows.

If we define an $m \times n$ matrix A, with elements a_{ij}, an $n \times 1$ matrix X, with elements $x_1, x_2, \ldots, x_n$, and an $m \times 1$ matrix C, with elements $c_1, c_2, \ldots, c_m$, and use the definitions for matrix multiplication and equality, we can write the system of equations $a_{ij}x_j = c_i$ as

$$AX = C$$

In terms of linear algebraic equations, we see that the definitions of addition, subtraction, and multiplication do make sense. For example, if $a_{ij}x_j = c_i$ and $b_{ij}x_j = d_i$, then $c_i + d_i = a_{ij}x_j + b_{ij}x_j = (a_{ij} + b_{ij})x_j$ and

$$c_i - d_i = a_{ij}x_j - b_{ij}x_j = (a_{ij} - b_{ij})x_j$$

In matrix notation these statements can be written

$$AX = C, BX = D \text{ implies } (A + B)X = C + D \text{ and } (A - B)X = C - D$$

Also, if $y_i = a_{ij}x_j$ and $z_i = b_{ij}y_j$, then $z_i = b_{ik}a_{kj}x_j = c_{ij}x_j$, where $c_{ij} = b_{ik}a_{kj}$.[1] In matrix notation this can be written

$$Y = AX, Z = BY \text{ implies } Z = B(AX) = (BA)X = CX, \text{ where } BA = C$$

[1] See exercise 2, Sec. 1.1.

By working with elements and their algebraic properties, one can easily show that the matrix operations satisfy the following laws:

1. **Associative law of addition:** $(A + B) + C = A + (B + C)$
2. **Commutative law of addition:** $A + B = B + A$
3. **Associative law of multiplication:** $(AB)C = A(BC)$ $a_{ij}b_{jk}$ c_{kl}
4. **Distributive laws:** $A(B + C) = AB + AC$; $(B + C)A = BA + CA$

Multiplication is not, in general, commutative, since $a_{ij}b_{jk} \neq b_{ij}a_{jk}$, even if the multiplication makes sense both ways. This is the reason why it was necessary to state two distributive laws, i.e., $A(B + C) \neq (B + C)A$.

A **zero matrix** O is a matrix every one of whose elements is 0. It has the following obvious properties:

$$A - A = O$$
$$A + O = A$$
$$OA = AO = O$$

which hold for all matrices A for which these operations make sense.

The **identity matrix** I is the $n \times n$ matrix with elements δ_{ij} (Kronecker delta, defined in Exercises 1.1). It has the property

$$AI = IA = A$$

for all $n \times n$ matrices A (see Exercises 1.1).

The **transpose** A' of a matrix A is the matrix formed by interchanging the rows and columns of A. If A is $m \times n$, then A' is $n \times m$. We can express the elements of A' as follows:

$$a'_{ij} = a_{ji}$$

The following theorem is easily proved. *The transpose of the product of two matrices is the product of their transposes in the opposite order, or* $(AB)' = B'A'$. Let $C = AB$; then $c_{ik} = a_{ij}b_{jk}$; $c'_{ik} = c_{ki} = a_{kj}b_{ji} = b_{ji}a_{kj} = b'_{ij}a'_{jk}$. Therefore, $(AB)' = C' = B'A'$. The multiplications make sense, since, if A is $m \times n$ and B is $n \times p$, then A' is $n \times m$ and B' is $p \times n$, and B' and A' can be multiplied in that order.

Multiplication of a matrix A by a scalar k from the field which contains the elements of A results in a matrix whose elements are the elements of A multiplied by k, i.e., $B = kA$ if and only if $b_{ij} = ka_{ij}$ for $i = 1, 2, \ldots, m$ and $j = 1, 2, \ldots, n$. The negative of a matrix, $-A$, is that matrix formed by multiplying each element by -1, or equivalently, by changing the sign of each element, i.e., $-A$ has elements $-a_{ij}$. We now see that we could have defined subtraction in terms of addition of the negative.

$$A - B = A + (-B)$$

An $n \times n$ matrix A is **symmetric** if and only if it is equal to its transpose, i.e., $A = A'$, or $a_{ij} = a_{ji}$.

An $n \times n$ matrix A is **skew-symmetric** if and only if it is equal to the negative of its transpose, i.e., $A = -A'$, or $a_{ij} = -a_{ji}$.

If a matrix A has complex elements, then we define its **conjugate** A^* as the matrix formed from A by taking the complex conjugate of each element, i.e., A^* has elements a_{ij}^*.   Matrices with complex elements are important in quantum mechanics.   Of particular importance are those called hermitian matrices.   A **hermitian matrix** is a matrix which is equal to the transpose of its conjugate, i.e., $A = (A^*)'$, or $a_{ij} = a_{ji}^*$.   If all the elements happen to be real, then the hermitian property is the same as the symmetry property.

Exercises 1.2

1. Verify the associative and commutative laws for matrix addition, the associative law for matrix multiplication, and the two distributive laws.

2. Construct an example to show that matrix multiplication is not, in general, commutative.

*3. If A and B are $n \times n$ matrices and $AB = O$, does this imply that $A = O$ or $B = O$? Explain.

*4. Show that every square matrix with complex elements can be written as the sum of a symmetric matrix and a skew-symmetric matrix. HINT: Write A as $\frac{1}{2}(A + A') + \frac{1}{2}(A - A')$.

*5. If X is a column matrix (a matrix with one column) with elements x_1, x_2, x_3 being the three rectangular cartesian coordinates of a point in three-dimensional space, A is a 3×3 matrix of real constants, B is a 1×3 row matrix of real constants, and k is a real constant, show that the general equation of a quadric surface is

$$X'AX + BX + k = 0$$

Also show that only the symmetric part of A enters the equation (see exercise 4).

*6. A **diagonal matrix** is an $n \times n$ matrix with zero elements except along the principal diagonal (upper left to lower right).   Show that the elements of a diagonal matrix can be written as $a_{\alpha\beta} = d_\alpha \delta_{\alpha\beta}$, where $d_1, d_2, \ldots, d_n$ are the diagonal elements.   Also show that every diagonal matrix is symmetric and that multiplication of two diagonal matrices is commutative.

7. Prove that if A and B are symmetric and $AB = D$, D diagonal, then $AB = BA$.

8. If A and B are hermitian, show that $-i(AB - BA)$ is hermitian.

1.3   Determinants

Before we return to the problem of solving systems of linear algebraic equations, we must first discuss determinants.

Every $n \times n$ matrix has associated with it a determinant which is a number from the field which contains the elements of the matrix.   The **determinant** of the matrix A, written

$$\begin{vmatrix} a_{11} & a_{12} & \cdots & a_{1n} \\ a_{21} & a_{22} & \cdots & a_{2n} \\ \cdots\cdots\cdots\cdots\cdots\cdots \\ a_{n1} & a_{n2} & \cdots & a_{nn} \end{vmatrix}$$

or more simply $|A|$, is a number given by the following expression:

$$|A| = e_{i_1 i_2 i_3 \cdots i_n} a_{1i_1} a_{2i_2} a_{3i_3} \cdots a_{ni_n}$$

$e_{i_1 i_2 i_3 \cdots i_n} = 0$ if any pair of subscripts are equal

$\quad\quad\quad = 1$ if $i_1, i_2, \ldots, i_n$ is an even permutation[1] of $1, 2, 3, \ldots, n$

$\quad\quad\quad = -1$ if $i_1, i_2, \ldots, i_n$ is an odd permutation of $1, 2, 3, \ldots, n$

Note that the expression for $|A|$ is a single number because of the summations over the repeated subscripts $i_1, i_2, \ldots, i_n$. The definition can be stated as follows: Form all possible products of n elements from A, selecting first an element from the first row, second an element from the second row, and so on until one from each row has been selected for a given product, but being careful that no two elements come from the same column. Then attach a plus or minus sign to each product according to whether the column subscripts of the elements chosen form an even or an odd permutation of the integers 1 to n. Finally, add all such products with their attached signs. The resulting sum is the value of the determinant. Since for each product there are n ways of selecting a factor from the first row, $n - 1$ ways of selecting a factor from the second row, $n - 2$ ways of selecting a factor from the third row, etc., the number of terms in the sum which gives the value of the determinant is $n!$.

It is not hard to show that the above definition can be changed by replacing the word "row" with "column" and the word "column" with "row" throughout. In other words, starting from the definition, we can show that

$$|A| = e_{i_1 i_2 i_3 \cdots i_n} a_{i_1 1} a_{i_2 2} a_{i_3 3} \cdots a_{i_n n}$$

or simply $|A| = |A'|$. Since $e_{i_1 i_2 i_3 \cdots i_n}$ is zero if any pair of subscripts are equal, for the terms which appear in either of the above expansions the set of numbers $i_1, i_2, \ldots, i_n$ must include all the integers from 1 to n. Consider a particular term $e_{i_1 i_2 \cdots i_n} a_{i_1 1} a_{i_2 2} \cdots a_{i_n n}$ (no summations) in the expansion. We do not change the value of this product if we rearrange the factors so that the row subscripts are in normal order, i.e.,

$$a_{i_1 1} a_{i_2 2} a_{i_3 3} \cdots a_{i_n n} = a_{1j_1} a_{2j_2} a_{3j_3} \cdots a_{nj_n}$$

This rearrangement of factors induces the permutation of the column subscripts $j_1, j_2, \ldots, j_n$. The term on the left appears once, and only once, in one expansion, while the term on the right appears once, and only once, in the

---

[1] A **permutation** of n different integers is an arrangement of the integers. There are, for example, six different permutations of the integers 1, 2, 3, i.e., 1, 2, 3; 2, 3, 1; 3, 1, 2; 1, 3, 2; 2, 1, 3; and 3, 2, 1. An **inversion** of the order of a pair of adjacent integers changes the permutation. If it takes an even number of inversions to change a given permutation to the **normal order** $1, 2, 3, \ldots, n$, then the permutation is said to be **even**. If an odd number of inversions is required to restore to normal order, then it is **odd**. Hence, 1, 2, 3; 2, 3, 1; and 3, 1, 2 are even, while 1, 3, 2; 2, 1, 3; and 3, 2, 1 are odd. It can be shown that evenness and oddness are independent of the specific set of inversions used to change the permutation to normal order.

other expansion. Therefore, the expansions will be equal, provided the corresponding terms appear with the same sign, or if $e_{i_1 i_2 \cdots i_n} = e_{j_1 j_2 \cdots j_n}$ for corresponding terms. This will be the case, because $i_1, i_2, \ldots, i_n$ is restored to normal order by an even or an odd number of inversions, the same number of which are applied to the normal order to produce $j_1, j_2, \ldots, j_n$.

This result is extremely important, for it indicates that any property of a determinant which depends on a property of a row or an operation on rows can be stated equally well for columns.

The following properties of determinants are easily proved from the definition:

1. If every element in a given row (or column) of a square matrix is zero, its determinant is zero.

2. If every element in a given row (or column) of a square matrix is multiplied by the same number k, the determinant is multiplied by k.

3. If any pair of rows (or columns) of a square matrix are interchanged, the sign of its determinant is changed.

4. If two rows (or columns) of a square matrix are proportional, its determinant is zero.

5. If each element of a given row (or column) of a square matrix can be written as the sum of two terms, then its determinant can be written as the sum of two determinants, each of which contains one of the terms in the corresponding row (or column).

6. If to each element of a given row (or column) of a square matrix is added k times the corresponding element of another row (or column), the value of its determinant is unchanged.

By way of illustration, we shall prove property 3. We begin by showing that if two adjacent rows are interchanged, the sign of the determinant is changed.

$$|A| = e_{i_1 i_2 \cdots i_k i_{k+1} \cdots i_n} a_{1i_1} a_{2i_2} \cdots a_{ki_k} a_{k+1 i_{k+1}} \cdots a_{ni_n}$$
$$= e_{i_1 i_2 \cdots i_k i_{k+1} \cdots i_n} a_{1i_1} a_{2i_2} \cdots a_{k+1 i_{k+1}} a_{ki_k} \cdots a_{ni_n}$$

This follows because the order of multiplying the a's in each term is unimportant. Now i_k and i_{k+1} are dummy subscripts, so we replace i_k by i_{k+1} and i_{k+1} by i_k.

$$|A| = e_{i_1 i_2 \cdots i_{k+1} i_k \cdots i_n} a_{1i_1} a_{2i_2} \cdots a_{k+1 i_k} a_{ki_{k+1}} \cdots a_{ni_n}$$
$$= -e_{i_1 i_2 \cdots i_k i_{k+1} \cdots i_n} a_{1i_1} a_{2i_2} \cdots a_{k+1 i_k} a_{ki_{k+1}} \cdots a_{ni_n}$$

The minus sign in the last line is necessary because the inversion of i_k and i_{k+1} in $e_{i_1 i_2 \cdots i_{k+1} i_k \cdots i_n}$ causes every even permutation of subscripts to become odd and every odd permutation of subscripts to become even. The last line, except for the minus sign, is the expansion of the determinant of the matrix formed from A by interchanging the kth and the $(k + 1)$st rows. Property 3 now follows by observation that any pair of rows can be interchanged by a succession of an odd number of interchanges of adjacent rows, each of which changes the sign of the preceding determinant. For example, if we wish to interchange the jth and the kth rows, $k > j$, we can accomplish this by interchanging the jth row successively with the $k - j - 1$ intervening rows, by interchanging the jth and the kth rows (now adjacent), and finally by interchanging the kth row with the $k - j - 1$ rows between its present position and the original position of the jth row. This requires a total of $2(k - j - 1) + 1$ interchanges of adjacent rows, which is always an odd number.

An interesting outcome of defining matrix multiplication as we did is that the determinant of the product of two square matrices is the product of their determinants, i.e.,

$$|AB| = |A|\,|B|$$

To prove this, we begin by defining

$$e_{i_1 i_2 \cdots i_n} a_{j_1 i_1} a_{j_2 i_2} \cdots a_{j_n i_n}$$

If $j_1, j_2, \ldots, j_n = 1, 2, \ldots, n$ in normal order, then this expression gives the value of the determinant of A by definition. If any pair of the j's have the same value, then the value of the expression is zero, since it will then represent a determinant with two rows equal. If $j_1, j_2, \ldots, j_n$ is a permutation of $1, 2, \ldots, n$, then the expression gives either plus or minus the determinant of A, depending on whether it takes an even or an odd number of interchanges of rows to arrive at the expression for $|A|$. This can be summarized as follows:

$$e_{i_1 i_2 \cdots i_n} a_{j_1 i_1} a_{j_2 i_2} \cdots a_{j_n i_n} = |A|\, e_{j_1 j_2 \cdots j_n}$$

Similarly, $e_{i_1 i_2 \cdots i_n} a_{i_1 j_1} a_{i_2 j_2} \cdots a_{i_n j_n} = |A|\, e_{j_1 j_2 \cdots j_n}$

The desired result now follows:

$$\begin{aligned}
|A|\,|B| &= |A|\, e_{i_1 i_2 \cdots i_n} b_{i_1 1} b_{i_2 2} \cdots b_{i_n n} \\
&= e_{j_1 j_2 \cdots j_n} a_{j_1 i_1} a_{j_2 i_2} \cdots a_{j_n i_n} b_{i_1 1} b_{i_2 2} \cdots b_{i_n n} \\
&= e_{j_1 j_2 \cdots j_n} (a_{j_1 i_1} b_{i_1 1})(a_{j_2 i_2} b_{i_2 2}) \cdots (a_{j_n i_n} b_{i_n n}) \\
&= |AB|
\end{aligned}$$

Another way of expanding the determinant of a square matrix is the so-called **expansion by cofactors.** Starting from the definition, we can write

$$\begin{aligned}
|A| &= e_{i_1 i_2 \cdots i_n} a_{1 i_1} a_{2 i_2} \cdots a_{n i_n} \\
&= a_{1 i_1} e_{i_1 i_2 \cdots i_n} a_{2 i_2} \cdots a_{n i_n} \\
&= a_{1 i_1} A_{1 i_1}
\end{aligned}$$

where $A_{1 i_1} = e_{i_1 i_2 \cdots i_n} a_{2 i_2} \cdots a_{n i_n}$

are the **cofactors** of the elements in the first row. In general,

$$A_{j i_j} = e_{i_1 \cdots i_{j-1} i_j i_{j+1} \cdots i_n} a_{1 i_1} \cdots a_{j-1 i_{j-1}} a_{j+1 i_{j+1}} \cdots a_{n i_n}$$

is the cofactor of the element in the jth row, i_jth column, and the expansion by cofactors of the jth row is given by

$$|A| = a_{ji_j} A_{ji_j} \qquad \text{(no summation on } j)$$

We also have an expansion by cofactors of column elements, as follows:

$$|A| = a_{i_jj} A_{i_jj} \qquad \text{(no summation on } j)$$

The cofactors themselves are, except possibly for a sign change, determinants of $(n-1) \times (n-1)$ square matrices formed from A by striking out one row and one column. Beginning from the definition of the cofactor, we have the following:

$$A_{ji_j} = (-1)^{j-1} e_{i_j i_1 i_2 \cdots i_{j-1} i_{j+1} \cdots i_n} a_{1i_1} a_{2i_2} \cdots a_{j-1i_{j-1}} a_{j+1i_{j+1}} \cdots a_{ni_n}$$

Here we have moved the subscript i_j ahead of the others by $j-1$ inversions, hence the factor $(-1)^{j-1}$. If it takes p inversions to put $i_1, i_2, \ldots, i_{j-1}, i_{j+1}, \ldots, i_n$ in normal order except for the missing integer i_j, then it takes $p + i_j - 1$ inversions to put $i_j, i_1, i_2, \ldots, i_{j-1}, i_{j+1}, \ldots, i_n$ in normal order. Hence, we can write

$$e_{i_j i_1 i_2 \cdots i_{j-1} i_{j+1} \cdots i_n} = (-1)^{i_j-1} e_{k_1 k_2 \cdots k_{n-1}}$$

where $k_1, k_2, \ldots, k_{n-1}$ is the set of $n-1$ integers obtained from $i_1, i_2, \ldots, i_{j-1}, i_{j+1}, \ldots, i_n$ by repeating an integer if it is less than i_j, and reducing by 1 any integer which is greater than i_j. It now follows that

$$A_{ji_j} = (-1)^{j+i_j} e_{k_1 k_2 \cdots k_{n-1}} b_{1k_1} b_{2k_2} \cdots b_{n-1k_{n-1}}$$

The b's are the elements of an $(n-1) \times (n-1)$ matrix formed from A by striking out the jth row and the i_jth column. The final result is that the cofactor A_{ji_j} is $(-1)^{j+i_j}$ times the determinant of the matrix formed from A by omitting the jth row and i_jth column.[1]

The next question is what happens if we write down a cofactor expansion using the elements of a given row but the cofactors of a different row. In other words, what is the value of

$$a_{ji_k} A_{ki_k}$$

where $j \neq k$? Using the expression for the cofactor, we have

$$a_{ji_k} A_{ki_k} = a_{ji_k} e_{i_1 i_2 \cdots i_n} a_{1i_1} \cdots a_{ji_j} \cdots a_{k-1i_{k-1}} a_{k+1i_{k+1}} \cdots a_{ni_n}$$
$$= e_{i_1 i_2 \cdots i_n} a_{1i_1} \cdots a_{ji_j} \cdots a_{ji_k} \cdots a_{ni_n}$$
$$= 0$$

because the resulting expression is the expansion of a determinant with two rows equal. This result and the cofactor expansion of $|A|$ can be combined together in the single statement

$$a_{ij} A_{kj} = |A|\, \delta_{ik}$$

---

[1] This determinant is called the **minor** of a_{ji_j}.

If $|A| \neq 0$, then we can write

$$a_{ij} \frac{A_{kj}}{|A|} = \delta_{ik}$$

or

$$a_{ij} \frac{A'_{jk}}{|A|} = \delta_{ik}$$

In terms of matrices, what we have just shown is that for every square matrix A for which $|A| \neq 0$ there exists a **right inverse** matrix A^{-1}, with elements

$$a_{ij}^{-1} = \frac{A_{ji}}{|A|}$$

such that $$A A^{-1} = I$$

Starting from the cofactor expansion by column elements, it is not difficult to show that

$$\frac{A'_{ij}}{|A|} a_{jk} = \delta_{ik}$$

or, in other words,

$$A^{-1}A = I$$

Therefore, this right inverse is also a left inverse, and we may refer to it simply as the inverse of A. The inverse is unique, for, if another inverse B existed, then $AB = I$ and

$$A^{-1}AB = IB = B = A^{-1}I = A^{-1}$$

If a matrix A has an inverse, then

$$A A^{-1} = I$$

and $$|A|\,|A^{-1}| = |AA^{-1}| = |I| = 1$$

Therefore, $|A| \neq 0$, and we have the following theorem: *A square matrix A has an inverse if and only if $|A| \neq 0$.* Such a matrix is called **nonsingular.**

We are now partially able to solve systems of linear algebraic equations. Suppose that

$$AX = C$$

is a system of n linear algebraic equations in n unknowns and that $|A| \neq 0$. Since A is nonsingular, it has an inverse, A^{-1}. If the system of equations has a solution, it can be found by multiplication on the left by A^{-1}, i.e.,

$$A^{-1}AX = IX = X = A^{-1}C$$

In terms of elements,

$$x_i = \frac{A'_{ij}c_j}{|A|}$$

The numerators in this expression are determinants of $n \times n$ matrices formed from A by replacing the ith column with the column of c's. We have shown so far that, *if* there is a solution, it is given by $A^{-1}C$. To show that the solution actually satisfies the equations, we substitute as follows:

$$a_{ki} \frac{A'_{ij}}{|A|} c_j = \delta_{kj} c_j = c_k$$

We have arrived at **Cramer's rule:** *If a system of n linear algebraic equations in n unknowns,*

$$a_{ij} x_j = c_i$$

has a nonsingular coefficient matrix A, then the system has a unique solution given by

$$x_i = \frac{A'_{ij} c_j}{|A|}$$

We still have to resolve the question in the case where the coefficient matrix is singular and in the case where the number of unknowns and the number of equations are different. These cases will be taken up in the next section.

We conclude this section with the definition of two special nonsingular matrices, which are defined in terms of their inverses. The first of these is the **orthogonal matrix,** which is a square matrix whose transpose is its inverse, i.e.,

$$A' = A^{-1}$$

When we are dealing with matrices with complex elements, the counterpart of an orthogonal matrix is a **unitary matrix,** which is a square matrix the transpose of whose conjugate is its inverse, i.e.,

$$(A^*)' = A^{-1}$$

Exercises 1.3

1. Prove properties 1, 2, and 5 of determinants, starting from the definition.

2. Assuming properties 3 and 5, prove properties 4 and 6 of determinants.

3. Expand the following determinant, using (*a*) the definition, (*b*) cofactor expansions, and (*c*) properties 1 to 6 to reduce the problem to simpler determinants:

$$\begin{vmatrix} 1 & 3 & -1 & 2 \\ 2 & 1 & 3 & 1 \\ -1 & 2 & -1 & 3 \\ -2 & 1 & 2 & -3 \end{vmatrix}$$

*4. If A is orthogonal, prove that $|A| = \pm 1$.

*5. If A and B are nonsingular $n \times n$ matrices, show that $(AB)^{-1} = B^{-1}A^{-1}$.

6. The **adjoint** of a square matrix A is the transpose of the matrix of the cofactors of A. Show that if A is nonsingular, the determinant of its adjoint is equal to $|A|^{n-1}$.

*7. We define as **elementary row operations** on a matrix the following: (*a*) interchange of two rows; (*b*) multiplication of a row by a number $k \neq 0$; (*c*) addition of two rows.

Show that each of these operations can be performed on an $n \times n$ matrix, A, by multiplying on the left by an **elementary matrix**, E, which is obtained from the identity matrix by the same operation. Show that if A is nonsingular, A can be reduced to the identity matrix by a finite number of elementary row operations and that A^{-1} can be computed by performing the same operations in the same order on the identity matrix.

*8. Rephrase the results of exercise 7 in terms of elementary column operations.

1.4   Systems of Linear Algebraic Equations.   Rank of a Matrix

We now return to the problem of solving a system of linear algebraic equations. Recall that we were able to write this system in the matrix form

$$AX = C$$

where A is the given $m \times n$ **coefficient matrix,** C is a column matrix of given constants, and X is a column matrix representing the solution (if it exists). We define the **augmented matrix** B as the $m \times (n + 1)$ matrix formed from A by adding the column of c's as the last column.

Every matrix contains certain square matrices formed by deleting rows or columns or both. We define the **rank of a matrix** as the order of the highest-order square matrix with a nonvanishing determinant contained in the matrix. It is obvious that the rank of the coefficient matrix is less than or equal to the rank of the augmented matrix, because every square matrix contained in the former is also contained in the latter.

We are now ready to prove the following theorem: *The system of linear algebraic equations has a solution if and only if the rank of the augmented matrix is equal to the rank of the coefficient matrix.*

We begin the proof of this theorem by considering **elementary row operations** and **elementary matrices.** We define an elementary row operation as one of the following operations on a matrix: (1) the interchange of a pair of rows, (2) the multiplication of a row by a nonzero number, or (3) the addition of two rows. It is not difficult to show that any of these operations can be performed on an $m \times n$ matrix by multiplying on the left by an elementary $m \times m$ matrix, obtained from the identity matrix by the corresponding operation.[1] If we multiply both sides of the system of algebraic equations by an elementary matrix E, i.e.,

$$\bar{A}X = EAX = EC = \bar{C}$$

we retain the equality and the general form of the equations. We have a new coefficient matrix $\bar{A}$ and a new augmented matrix $\bar{B}$, with

$$\bar{A} = EA$$
$$\bar{B} = EB$$

[1] See Exercises 1.3.

Multiplication on the left by elementary matrices has the following effects on the system of equations, corresponding to the three row operations listed above: (1) interchanges a pair of equations, (2) multiplies an equation through by a nonzero number, and (3) adds two equations together.   These are the three operations required for the **Gauss-Jordan reduction,** which we shall now outline.   First, arrange the equations so that $a_{11} \neq 0$.   Then multiply the first equation by $1/a_{11}$.   Next, add to the second equation $(-a_{21})$ times the first.   This makes the coefficient of x_1 in the second equation zero.   Repeat the process until the coefficients of x_1 in all equations but the first are zero. The next step is to rearrange the equations so that the coefficient of x_2 in the second equation is nonzero, divide through the second equation by this coefficient, and proceed as before to make the coefficient of x_2 in all equations but the second zero.   After a finite number of steps, the system of equations reduces to

$$x_1 + \bar{a}_{1r+1}x_{r+1} + \cdots + \bar{a}_{1n}x_n = \bar{c}_1$$
$$x_2 + \bar{a}_{2r+1}x_{r+1} + \cdots + \bar{a}_{2n}x_n = \bar{c}_2$$
$$\cdots\cdots\cdots\cdots\cdots\cdots\cdots\cdots\cdots\cdots$$
$$x_r + \bar{a}_{rr+1}x_{r+1} + \cdots + \bar{a}_{rn}x_n = \bar{c}_r$$
$$0 = \bar{c}_{r+1}$$
$$0 = \bar{c}_{r+2}$$
$$\cdots\cdots\cdots$$
$$0 = \bar{c}_m$$

From this reduction, it is clear that if one or more of the $\bar{c}_{r+1}, \ldots, \bar{c}_m$ are not zero, there will be no solution, and we say that the system of equations is **inconsistent.**   If $\bar{c}_{r+1} = \bar{c}_{r+2} = \cdots = \bar{c}_m = 0$, then we can write the solution

$$x_1 = \bar{c}_1 - \bar{a}_{1r+1}x_{r+1} - \cdots - \bar{a}_{1n}x_n$$
$$x_2 = \bar{c}_2 - \bar{a}_{2r+1}x_{r+1} - \cdots - \bar{a}_{2n}x_n$$
$$\cdots\cdots\cdots\cdots\cdots\cdots\cdots\cdots\cdots\cdots$$
$$x_r = \bar{c}_r - \bar{a}_{rr+1}x_{r+1} - \cdots - \bar{a}_{rn}x_n$$

In this case we say that the equations are **consistent.**   If $r = n$, there is a unique solution.   If $r < n, x_1, x_2, \ldots, x_r$ can be written in terms of $x_{r+1}, \ldots, x_n$, which can be assigned arbitrarily.   In this case there is an $(n - r)$-fold infinity of solutions.

If $r = m = n$, the solution is unique and is given by Cramer's rule.   Thus

$$AX = C$$
$$IAX = IC$$
$$E_p \cdots E_2E_1IAX = E_p \cdots E_2E_1IC$$
$$A^{-1}AX = A^{-1}C$$
$$X = A^{-1}C$$

Here $E_1, E_2, \ldots, E_p$ are the elementary row matrices which are involved in the reduction, and [1]

$$E_p \cdots E_2 E_1 I = A^{-1}$$

Finally, we state these results in terms of the ranks of the coefficient and augmented matrices. The reduction was performed by a finite number of row operations, none of which changes the rank of a matrix. Suppose M is a matrix of rank r and $\bar{M}$ is a matrix obtained from M by a row operation. If $\bar{D}$ is an $(r + 1)$st-order determinant from $\bar{M}$, then:

Case 1. $\bar{D} = D$ or $\bar{D} = -D$, where in each case D is an $(r + 1)$st-order determinant from M. But $D = 0$, since M is of rank r.

Case 2. $\bar{D} = D$ or $\bar{D} = kD$, where $k \neq 0$ and D is an $(r + 1)$st-order determinant from M. But $D = 0$, since M is of rank r.

Case 3. $\bar{D} = D$ or $\bar{D} = D + \tilde{D}$, where D and $\tilde{D}$ are $(r + 1)$st-order determinants from M. But $D = \tilde{D} = 0$, since M is of rank r.

Therefore, a row operation cannot increase the rank of a matrix. Likewise, a row operation cannot decrease the rank of a matrix, for in this case M can be obtained from $\bar{M}$ by a row operation which cannot increase the rank.

If we write the reduced form of the system of equations as

$$\bar{A}X = \bar{C}$$

then

$$\bar{A} = \begin{Vmatrix} 1 & 0 & 0 & \cdots & 0 & \bar{a}_{1r+1} & \bar{a}_{1r+2} & \cdots & \bar{a}_{1n} \\ 0 & 1 & 0 & \cdots & 0 & \bar{a}_{2r+1} & \bar{a}_{2r+2} & \cdots & \bar{a}_{2n} \\ \multicolumn{9}{c}{\cdots\cdots\cdots\cdots\cdots\cdots\cdots\cdots} \\ 0 & 0 & 0 & \cdots & 1 & \bar{a}_{rr+1} & \bar{a}_{rr+2} & \cdots & \bar{a}_{rn} \\ 0 & 0 & 0 & \cdots & 0 & 0 & 0 & \cdots & 0 \\ \multicolumn{9}{c}{\cdots\cdots\cdots\cdots\cdots\cdots\cdots\cdots} \\ 0 & 0 & 0 & \cdots & 0 & 0 & 0 & \cdots & 0 \end{Vmatrix}$$

and

$$\bar{B} = \begin{Vmatrix} 1 & 0 & 0 & \cdots & 0 & \bar{a}_{1r+1} & \bar{a}_{1r+2} & \cdots & \bar{a}_{1n} & \bar{c}_1 \\ 0 & 1 & 0 & \cdots & 0 & \bar{a}_{2r+1} & \bar{a}_{2r+2} & \cdots & \bar{a}_{2n} & \bar{c}_2 \\ \multicolumn{10}{c}{\cdots\cdots\cdots\cdots\cdots\cdots\cdots\cdots} \\ 0 & 0 & 0 & \cdots & 1 & \bar{a}_{rr+1} & \bar{a}_{rr+2} & \cdots & \bar{a}_{rn} & \bar{c}_r \\ 0 & 0 & 0 & \cdots & 0 & 0 & 0 & \cdots & 0 & \bar{c}_{r+1} \\ \multicolumn{10}{c}{\cdots\cdots\cdots\cdots\cdots\cdots\cdots\cdots} \\ 0 & 0 & 0 & \cdots & 0 & 0 & 0 & \cdots & 0 & \bar{c}_m \end{Vmatrix}$$

Obviously $\bar{A}$ is of rank r. If $\bar{c}_{r+1} = \bar{c}_{r+2} = \cdots = \bar{c}_m = 0$, then the system of equations has a solution and the rank of $\bar{B}$ is also r. If one or more of the $\bar{c}_{r+1}$ to $\bar{c}_m$ are not zero, then the rank of $\bar{B}$ is greater than r and the system of equations has no solution. This completes the proof of the theorem.

[1] See Exercises 1.3.

A case of particular importance is the case where $c_1 = c_2 = \cdots = c_n = 0$. In this case, we say we have a system of **homogeneous linear equations.** Adding a column of zeros to the coefficient matrix cannot affect its rank; therefore the augmented matrix always has the same rank as the coefficient matrix, and such a system always has a solution.   This is not surprising, since $x_1 = x_2 = \cdots = x_n = 0$ is obviously a solution.   This is called the **trivial solution.**   We are often concerned about whether the system has a **nontrivial solution,** where at least one of the x's is not zero.   From the above discussion follow two important corollaries, the proofs of which will be left for the reader.

A system of m homogeneous linear algebraic equations in n unknowns always has a nontrivial solution if $m < n$.

A system of n homogeneous linear algebraic equations in n unknowns has a nontrivial solution if and only if the determinant of the coefficient matrix is zero.

Exercises 1.4

1. Prove the two corollaries at the end of this section.

2. Prove that multiplication of an $m \times n$ matrix A on the right by an $n \times n$ elementary matrix obtained from the identity by an elementary column operation cannot change the rank of A.

3. Solve the system, if it has a solution:

$$2x + y - z + u = -2$$
$$x - y - z + u = 1$$
$$x - 4y - 2z + 2u = 6$$
$$4x + y - 3z + 3u = -1$$

*4. Determine the values of λ for which the following system has a nontrivial solution:

$$9x - 3y = \lambda x$$
$$-3x + 12y - 3z = \lambda y$$
$$-3y + 9z = \lambda z$$

Find the nontrivial solution in each case.

*5. If $X = X_0$ is a solution of $AX = O$, show that $X = kX_0$ is also a solution for any k.

*6. If X_0 is a solution of $AX = O$ and X_1 is a solution of $AX = C$, show that $kX_0 + X_1$ is also a solution of $AX = C$.   State a criterion for uniqueness of the solution of $AX = C$.

1.5   Vector Spaces

It is assumed that the reader is familiar with three-dimensional vector analysis.   The collection of vectors encountered there follows certain laws of combination which make it an example of an algebraic system called a vector space.   We shall want to define and use the concept of vector space, but first

let us recall some of the familiar notions about vectors from three-dimensional vector analysis.

One of the easiest ways to denote a three-dimensional vector is in terms of its three components. Let $\mathbf{U}$ be a vector with real components (u_1, u_2, u_3) and $\mathbf{V}$ be a vector with real components (v_1, v_2, v_3);[1] then the vector sum $\mathbf{U} + \mathbf{V}$ has components $(u_1 + v_1, u_2 + v_2, u_3 + v_3)$. We note at once that the sum is a vector and has the properties

$$\mathbf{U} + \mathbf{V} = \mathbf{V} + \mathbf{U}$$
$$(\mathbf{U} + \mathbf{V}) + \mathbf{W} = \mathbf{U} + (\mathbf{V} + \mathbf{W})$$

We define the zero vector $\mathbf{0}$ as the vector with all three components 0. Then obviously,

$$\mathbf{U} + \mathbf{0} = \mathbf{U}$$

for all $\mathbf{U}$. The negative vector of the vector $\mathbf{U}$, denoted by $-\mathbf{U}$, is the vector with components $(-u_1, -u_2, -u_3)$. Clearly,

$$\mathbf{U} + (-\mathbf{U}) = \mathbf{0}$$

Multiplication by a real scalar a is defined as follows:

$$a\mathbf{U} = (au_1, au_2, au_3)$$

This operation leads to a vector and has the following properties:

$$a(\mathbf{U} + \mathbf{V}) = a\mathbf{U} + a\mathbf{V}$$
$$(a + b)\mathbf{U} = a\mathbf{U} + b\mathbf{U}$$
$$(ab)\mathbf{U} = a(b\mathbf{U})$$
$$1\mathbf{U} = \mathbf{U}$$

These familiar properties suggest the postulates of a **vector space,** which we now define. *A vector space over a field is a set of vectors together with two operations, addition and multiplication by a scalar from the field, satisfying the following postulates:*

1. **Closure under addition:** For every pair of vectors $\mathbf{U}$ and $\mathbf{V}$ there is a unique sum denoted by $\mathbf{U} + \mathbf{V}$, which is a vector.

2. **Addition is associative:** $(\mathbf{U} + \mathbf{V}) + \mathbf{W} = \mathbf{U} + (\mathbf{V} + \mathbf{W})$.

3. **Addition is commutative:** $\mathbf{U} + \mathbf{V} = \mathbf{V} + \mathbf{U}$.

4. A **zero vector $\mathbf{0}$** exists, such that $\mathbf{U} + \mathbf{0} = \mathbf{U}$ for all $\mathbf{U}$.

5. A **negative vector** $-\mathbf{U}$ exists for all $\mathbf{U}$, such that $\mathbf{U} + (-\mathbf{U}) = \mathbf{0}$.

6. **Closure under multiplication by a scalar:** For every scalar a from the field and every vector $\mathbf{U}$ there is a unique vector $a\mathbf{U}$.

7. $a(\mathbf{U} + \mathbf{V}) = a\mathbf{U} + a\mathbf{V}$.

8. $(a + b)\mathbf{U} = a\mathbf{U} + b\mathbf{U}$.

9. $(ab)\mathbf{U} = a(b\mathbf{U})$.

10. $1\mathbf{U} = \mathbf{U}$.

[1] In terms of the familiar $\mathbf{i}$, $\mathbf{j}$, $\mathbf{k}$ notation,

$$\mathbf{U} = u_1\mathbf{i} + u_2\mathbf{j} + u_3\mathbf{k} \text{ and } \mathbf{V} = v_1\mathbf{i} + v_2\mathbf{j} + v_3\mathbf{k}$$

From these ten postulates many theorems can be proved. For example, the connection between the zero scalar and the zero vector is

$$0\mathbf{U} = \mathbf{0}$$

for all $\mathbf{U}$. This can be proved as follows:

$$(1 + 0)\mathbf{U} = 1\mathbf{U} + 0\mathbf{U}$$
$$1\mathbf{U} = \mathbf{U} + 0\mathbf{U}$$
$$\mathbf{U} = \mathbf{U} + 0\mathbf{U}$$
$$\mathbf{U} + (-\mathbf{U}) = \mathbf{U} + (-\mathbf{U}) + 0\mathbf{U}$$
$$\mathbf{0} = \mathbf{0} + 0\mathbf{U}$$
$$\mathbf{0} = 0\mathbf{U}$$

The negative of the field and the negative vector are connected by the relation

$$(-1)\mathbf{U} = -\mathbf{U}$$

for all $\mathbf{U}$. This is easy to demonstrate.

$$(1 - 1)\mathbf{U} = 1\mathbf{U} + (-1)\mathbf{U}$$
$$0\mathbf{U} = \mathbf{U} + (-1)\mathbf{U}$$
$$\mathbf{0} = \mathbf{U} + (-1)\mathbf{U}$$
$$-\mathbf{U} + \mathbf{0} = -\mathbf{U} + \mathbf{U} + (-1)\mathbf{U}$$
$$-\mathbf{U} = (-1)\mathbf{U}$$

The proofs of some other useful properties will be left for the exercises.

We have already seen that the vectors of three-dimensional vector analysis form a vector space. There are many other examples. Consider, for example, the set of n-tuples of complex numbers. They form a vector space over the field of complex numbers, if we define addition and multiplication by a scalar as follows. If $\mathbf{U} = (u_1, u_2, \ldots, u_n)$ and $\mathbf{V} = (v_1, v_2, \ldots, v_n)$, then

$$\mathbf{U} + \mathbf{V} = (u_1 + v_1, u_2 + v_2, \ldots, u_n + v_n)$$

If a is a complex scalar, then

$$a\mathbf{U} = (au_1, au_2, \ldots, au_n)$$

Obviously, we have closure under addition and multiplication by a scalar. Also, from the properties of complex numbers it is easy to verify postulates 2, 3, 7, 8, 9, and 10. The zero vector is defined as $\mathbf{0} = (0, 0, \ldots, 0)$, and it clearly satisfies postulate 4. The negative of $\mathbf{U}$ is defined as

$$-\mathbf{U} = (-u_1, -u_2, \ldots, -u_n)$$

and it satisfies postulate 5.

As another example, consider the set of continuous real-valued functions of the real variable x defined on the interval $0 \leq x \leq 1$. This is a vector space over the field of real numbers, if we define sum as $\mathbf{f} + \mathbf{g} = f(x) + g(x)$, and multiplication by a scalar as $a\mathbf{f} = af(x)$. The zero vector is the function which is identically zero in the interval, and the negative is defined by $-\mathbf{f} = -f(x)$. It is not difficult to show that the ten postulates of a vector space are satisfied.

A set of vectors $\mathbf{X}_1, \mathbf{X}_2, \ldots, \mathbf{X}_n$ is said to be **linearly dependent** if there exists a set of scalars $c_1, c_2, \ldots, c_n$, not all zero, such that

$$c_i \mathbf{X}_i = \mathbf{0}$$

If a set of vectors is not linearly dependent, then it is said to be **linearly independent**. In other words, if $\mathbf{X}_1, \mathbf{X}_2, \ldots, \mathbf{X}_n$ are independent, then $c_i \mathbf{X}_i = \mathbf{0}$ implies that $c_i = 0$ for all i.

A set of vectors $\mathbf{X}_1, \mathbf{X}_2, \ldots, \mathbf{X}_n$ in a vector space is said to span the space if every vector in the space can be written as a linear combination of the set, i.e., for every $\mathbf{U}$ in the space there exists a set of scalars $c_1, c_2, \ldots, c_n$, such that

$$\mathbf{U} = c_i \mathbf{X}_i$$

A set $\mathbf{X}_1, \mathbf{X}_2, \ldots, \mathbf{X}_n$ may span a vector space and still not be linearly independent. However, if it is dependent we can select from the set a subset which is linearly independent and also spans the space.[1] Suppose $\mathbf{X}_1, \mathbf{X}_2, \ldots, \mathbf{X}_n$ are dependent; then there exists a set of scalars $\gamma_1, \gamma_2, \ldots, \gamma_n$, not all zero, such that

$$\gamma_i \mathbf{X}_i = \mathbf{0}$$

Without loss of generality, we can assume that $\gamma_n \neq 0$, and we can solve for $\mathbf{X}_n$ in terms of $\mathbf{X}_1, \mathbf{X}_2, \ldots, \mathbf{X}_{n-1}$.

$$\mathbf{X}_n = -\frac{\gamma_1}{\gamma_n}\mathbf{X}_1 - \frac{\gamma_2}{\gamma_n}\mathbf{X}_2 - \cdots - \frac{\gamma_{n-1}}{\gamma_n}\mathbf{X}_{n-1}$$

Hence, for any $\mathbf{U}$ in the vector space

$$\mathbf{U} = c_1\mathbf{X}_1 + c_2\mathbf{X}_2 + \cdots + c_{n-1}\mathbf{X}_{n-1}$$
$$+ c_n\left[-\frac{\gamma_1}{\gamma_n}\mathbf{X}_1 - \frac{\gamma_2}{\gamma_n}\mathbf{X}_2 - \cdots - \frac{\gamma_{n-1}}{\gamma_n}\mathbf{X}_{n-1}\right]$$

Therefore, the subset $\mathbf{X}_1, \mathbf{X}_2, \ldots, \mathbf{X}_{n-1}$ spans the space. If this subset is not independent, we can repeat the process again. Eventually we shall arrive at a subset $\mathbf{X}_1, \mathbf{X}_2, \ldots, \mathbf{X}_m$ with $m < n$, which spans the space and is linearly independent.

We define the **dimension** of a vector space as the minimum number of nonzero vectors which span the space.[2] For example, in the vector space of n-tuples of complex numbers we may choose the vectors $\mathbf{X}_1 = (1,0,0,\ldots,0)$, $\mathbf{X}_2 = (0,1,0,\ldots,0), \ldots, \mathbf{X}_n = (0,0,0,\ldots,1)$. They span the space, for

---

[1] Here we must exclude the so-called **null space,** consisting of just the zero vector. The null space is spanned by the zero vector which is dependent.

[2] According to this definition the null space has a dimension of zero.

any vector $\mathbf{U} = (u_1, u_2, u_3, \ldots, u_n)$ can be written as a linear combination of the $\mathbf{X}$'s, i.e.,

$$\mathbf{U} = u_1\mathbf{X}_1 + u_2\mathbf{X}_2 + u_3\mathbf{X}_3 + \cdots + u_n\mathbf{X}_n$$

The $\mathbf{X}$'s are linearly independent, for

$$c_1\mathbf{X}_1 + c_2\mathbf{X}_2 + c_3\mathbf{X}_3 + \cdots + c_n\mathbf{X}_n = (c_1, c_2, c_1, \ldots, c_n) = \mathbf{0}$$

implies that $c_1 = c_2 = c_3 = \cdots = c_n = 0$. As we shall show, this implies that n is the minimum number of vectors which span the space, and therefore the dimension of the space is n.

It may not be possible to find a finite number of vectors which span the space. For example, the vector space of continuous functions on the interval $0 \leq x \leq 1$ is not spanned by a finite number of vectors.[1] We say that a vector space is **finite-dimensional** if and only if it is spanned by a finite number of vectors. Otherwise it is **infinite-dimensional.** At first, we shall confine our attention to finite-dimensional vector spaces. Some things have to be modified in the case of infinite-dimensional vector spaces, and we shall return to this case in a later section.

A **basis** of a vector space is a set of linearly independent vectors which spans the space. We have already shown that from any finite set of vectors which spans the space we can select a linearly independent subset which spans the space. Such a subset forms a basis for the space. There may be many bases for the same vector space. For example, we have already given a basis for the vector space of n-tuples of complex numbers, but another one would consist of the vectors

$$\mathbf{Y}_1 = (1,0,0,\ldots,0) \qquad \mathbf{Y}_2 = (1,1,0,\ldots,0)$$
$$\mathbf{Y}_3 = (1,1,1,0,\ldots,0),\ldots \qquad \mathbf{Y}_n = (1,1,1,\ldots,1)$$

However, it is easily shown that *every basis must contain the same number of vectors*.

Suppose that we have two bases $\mathbf{X}_1, \mathbf{X}_2, \ldots, \mathbf{X}_n$ and $\mathbf{Y}_1, \mathbf{Y}_2, \ldots, \mathbf{Y}_m$. Since the $\mathbf{X}$'s span the space, $\mathbf{Y}_1$ can be expressed as a linear combination of the $\mathbf{X}$'s, i.e.,

$$\mathbf{Y}_1 = c_1\mathbf{X}_1 + c_2\mathbf{X}_2 + \cdots + c_n\mathbf{X}_n$$

where at least one of the c's is not zero. Assume $c_n \neq 0$ (otherwise renumber the $\mathbf{X}$'s so that it is). Then

$$\mathbf{X}_n = \frac{1}{c_n}[\mathbf{Y}_1 - c_1\mathbf{X}_1 - c_2\mathbf{X}_2 - \cdots - c_{n-1}\mathbf{X}_{n-1}]$$

Therefore, the set of vectors $\mathbf{Y}_1, \mathbf{X}_1, \mathbf{X}_2, \ldots, \mathbf{X}_{n-1}$ spans the vector space, and $\mathbf{Y}_2$ can be expressed as a linear combination of this set, i.e.,

$$\mathbf{Y}_2 = b_1\mathbf{Y}_1 + \gamma_1\mathbf{X}_1 + \gamma_2\mathbf{X}_2 + \cdots + \gamma_{n-1}\mathbf{X}_{n-1}$$

[1] The functions $1, x, x^2, \ldots$ are all continuous and independent.

Here at least one of the γ's is not zero. Otherwise $\mathbf{Y}_1$ and $\mathbf{Y}_2$ would not be independent. Solve for one of the $\mathbf{X}$'s whose coefficient is not zero in terms of $\mathbf{Y}_1$, $\mathbf{Y}_2$, and the $n - 2$ other $\mathbf{X}$'s which span the vector space. After repeating this process m times, we arrive at a set of vectors $\mathbf{Y}_1$, $\mathbf{Y}_2$, ..., $\mathbf{Y}_m$ and $n - m$ of the $\mathbf{X}$'s which span the space. From this we conclude that $n \geq m$. The same argument can be applied with the roles of the $\mathbf{X}$'s and $\mathbf{Y}$'s interchanged, leading to the conclusion that $m \geq n$. The final result that $n = m$ follows.

To find the dimension of a finite-dimensional vector space it is sufficient to demonstrate any basis and count the number of vectors in the set. This verifies our conclusion that the space of n-tuples of complex numbers is an n-dimensional space.

The fact that a basis spans a vector space means that every vector in the space has a representation as a linear combination of basis vectors. The fact that the basis is a set of linearly independent vectors implies that *the representation in terms of a given basis is unique.* Suppose that $\mathbf{U}$ has two representations in terms of the basis $\mathbf{X}_1$, $\mathbf{X}_2$, ..., $\mathbf{X}_n$,

$$\mathbf{U} = a_i\mathbf{X}_i = b_i\mathbf{X}_i$$

Then $$\mathbf{0} = \mathbf{U} - \mathbf{U} = (a_i - b_i)\mathbf{X}_i$$

But the $\mathbf{X}$'s are independent, so that $a_i = b_i$ for all i.

Suppose that we have an n-dimensional vector space over the field of complex numbers, with a basis $\mathbf{X}_1$, $\mathbf{X}_2$, ..., $\mathbf{X}_n$. Relative to this basis every vector in the space has a unique representation in terms of n scalars. There is, therefore, a one-to-one correspondence between the vector space and the vector space of n-tuples of complex numbers. Furthermore, if $\mathbf{U} = a_i\mathbf{X}_i$ and $\mathbf{V} = b_i\mathbf{X}_i$, then $\mathbf{U} + \mathbf{V} = (a_i + b_i)\mathbf{X}_i$. If c is a complex scalar, $c\mathbf{U} = (ca_i)\mathbf{X}_i$. Therefore, addition of vectors and multiplication of a vector by a scalar correspond to addition and multiplication by a scalar of the corresponding vectors in the space of n-tuples. Such a relation between two vector spaces is called an **isomorphism.**

A **subspace** of a vector space is the space consisting of all possible linear combinations of a subset $\mathbf{X}_i$ of vectors from the vector space. That every subspace is also a vector space is derived from the fact that every vector in the subspace can be expressed as a linear combination of vectors. For example, if $\mathbf{U} = a_i\mathbf{X}_i$, $\mathbf{V} = b_i\mathbf{X}_i$, and $\mathbf{W} = c_i\mathbf{X}_i$, then

$$\mathbf{U} + \mathbf{V} = (a_i + b_i)\mathbf{X}_i = (b_i + a_i)\mathbf{X}_i = \mathbf{V} + \mathbf{U}$$

$$(\mathbf{U} + \mathbf{V}) + \mathbf{W} = [(a_i + b_i) + c_i]\mathbf{X}_i = [a_i + (b_i + c_i)]\mathbf{X}_i = \mathbf{U} + (\mathbf{V} + \mathbf{W})$$

The subspace always contains the zero vector

$$\mathbf{0} = 0\mathbf{X}_1 + 0\mathbf{X}_2 + \cdots + 0\mathbf{X}_n$$

and a negative for every vector in the subspace, i.e., if $\mathbf{U} = a_i\mathbf{X}_i$, then

$$-\mathbf{U} = (-a_i)\mathbf{X}_i$$

Multiplication of a vector $\mathbf{U}$ by a scalar c is defined by

$$c\mathbf{U} = (ca)_i\mathbf{X}_i$$

and the remaining postulates follow immediately.

If the subset $\mathbf{X}_i$ is a basis of the vector space, then the subspace is the whole space.   If the subset $\mathbf{X}_i$ is linearly independent and not a basis, then the subspace is a **proper subspace.** i.e., is not the whole space.   An example of a subspace would be the space spanned by the vectors $(1,-1,0)$ and $(0,1,-1)$ in three-dimensional euclidean space.   This two-dimensional subspace consists of the plane containing the two given vectors and the origin.

Exercises 1.5

1. Establish the following statements:

a. The collection of complex numbers is a two-dimensional vector space over the field of real scalars.

b. The collection of $n \times 1$ column matrices with complex elements is an n-dimensional vector space over the field of complex scalars.

c. The collection of all polynomials of degree three or less is a four-dimensional subspace of the vector space of continuous real-valued functions of the real variable x defined on the interval $0 \le x \le 1$.

d. The collection of all $m \times n$ matrices with complex elements is an mn-dimensional vector space over the field of complex scalars.

2. Prove the following theorems pertaining to vector spaces:

a. The zero vector is unique.

b. The negative of a vector is unique.

c. $a\mathbf{0} = \mathbf{0}$ for any scalar a.

d. If $a\mathbf{U} = \mathbf{0}$, then either $a = 0$, or $\mathbf{U} = \mathbf{0}$, or both.

3. Are the vectors $(0,-1,0)$, $(0,1,-1)$, $(1,-2,1)$ linearly independent?   Can $(-2,1,-3)$ be expressed as a linear combination of these three?   Express your result both geometrically and in terms of solutions of linear algebraic equations.

4. Prove that two finite-dimensional vector spaces which are isomorphic have the same dimension.

*5. An n-dimensional vector space over the field of complex scalars is isomorphic to the vector space of n-tuples of complex numbers.   If m vectors are given with $m \le n$, state a test for linear dependence in terms of the rank of an $n \times m$ matrix formed by using the m n-tuples as columns.   What happens in the case $m > n$?

*6. Prove that in an n-dimensional vector space any set of $n + 1$ vectors is linearly dependent.

1.6   Scalar Product

In three-dimensional vector analysis we define the scalar product of two vectors as

$$(\mathbf{U},\mathbf{V}) = u_1v_1 + u_2v_2 + u_3v_3$$

This is directly related to the magnitudes of the vectors and the cosine of the angle between the two vectors. It has the following properties, which are easily verified.

$$(\mathbf{U},\mathbf{V}) = (\mathbf{V},\mathbf{U})$$

$$(\mathbf{U},\mathbf{V} + \mathbf{W}) = (\mathbf{U},\mathbf{V}) + (\mathbf{U},\mathbf{W})$$

$$(a\mathbf{U},\mathbf{V}) = a(\mathbf{U},\mathbf{V})$$

$$(\mathbf{U},\mathbf{U}) \geq 0$$

$$(\mathbf{U},\mathbf{U}) = 0, \text{ if and only if } \mathbf{U} = \mathbf{0}$$

The concept of scalar product can be generalized to vector spaces other than the familiar one mentioned above. We shall retain essentially the same properties only slightly modified to include the possibility of the scalar product being a complex number. In the applications we are usually concerned with vector spaces over the field of complex numbers, and in this case we define a **scalar product**[1] $(\mathbf{U},\mathbf{V})$ which has a complex value and satisfies the following postulates:

1. $(\mathbf{U},\mathbf{V}) = (\mathbf{V},\mathbf{U})^*$
2. $(\mathbf{U},\mathbf{V} + \mathbf{W}) = (\mathbf{U},\mathbf{V}) + (\mathbf{U},\mathbf{W})$
3. $(a\mathbf{U},\mathbf{V}) = a^*(\mathbf{U},\mathbf{V})$
4. $(\mathbf{U},\mathbf{U}) \geq 0$
5. $(\mathbf{U},\mathbf{U}) = 0$ if and only if $\mathbf{U} = \mathbf{0}$

Properties 4 and 5 are equivalent to the statement that the *scalar product of a vector with itself is positive-definite.* Recall that, in three-dimensional vector analysis, the scalar product of a vector with itself is the square of the length of the vector. Although "length of a vector" does not have the usual meaning in a generalized vector space, we still define length, or more commonly **norm**, of a vector as

$$\|\mathbf{U}\| = \sqrt{(\mathbf{U},\mathbf{U})}$$

and it turns out that this has most of the properties we usually associate with length or distance.

From the postulates for scalar product, we can prove some additional useful properties. For example,

$$(\mathbf{U},a\mathbf{V}) = a(\mathbf{U},\mathbf{V})$$

This is proved as follows:

$$(\mathbf{U},a\mathbf{V}) = (a\mathbf{V},\mathbf{U})^* = [a^*(\mathbf{V},\mathbf{U})]^* = a(\mathbf{V},\mathbf{U})^* = a(\mathbf{U},\mathbf{V})$$

The proofs of the following two properties will be left for the exercises.

$$(\mathbf{U} + \mathbf{V}, \mathbf{W}) = (\mathbf{U},\mathbf{W}) + (\mathbf{V},\mathbf{W})$$

$$\|a\mathbf{U}\| = |a| \, \|a\mathbf{U}\|$$

[1] Sometimes referred to as an inner product.

A very important property is **Schwarz's inequality**

$$|(\mathbf{U},\mathbf{V})| \le \|\mathbf{U}\| \, \|\mathbf{V}\|$$

This can be proved as follows.   For any scalar a

$$0 \le \|\mathbf{U} + a\mathbf{V}\|^2 = (\mathbf{U} + a\mathbf{V}, \, \mathbf{U} + a\mathbf{V})$$
$$= (\mathbf{U},\mathbf{U}) + (a\mathbf{V},\mathbf{U}) + (\mathbf{U},a\mathbf{V}) + (a\mathbf{V},a\mathbf{V})$$
$$= \|\mathbf{U}\|^2 + a^*(\mathbf{V},\mathbf{U}) + a(\mathbf{U},\mathbf{V}) + |a|^2 \, \|\mathbf{V}\|^2$$

Now let $a = \lambda(\mathbf{U},\mathbf{V})^*/|(\mathbf{U},\mathbf{V})|$, with λ real.   This is possible if $(\mathbf{U},\mathbf{V}) \ne 0$, but if $(\mathbf{U},\mathbf{V}) = 0$, then Schwarz's inequality is trivial.   Making this substitution in the above, we have

$$0 \le \|\mathbf{U}\|^2 + 2\lambda \, |(\mathbf{U},\mathbf{V})| + \lambda^2 \, \|\mathbf{V}\|^2$$

This is a quadratic expression in the real variable λ with real coefficients. Therefore, the discriminant must be less than or equal to zero.   Hence,

$$4 \, |(\mathbf{U},\mathbf{V})|^2 - 4 \, \|\mathbf{U}\|^2 \, \|\mathbf{V}\|^2 \le 0$$

or
$$|(\mathbf{U},\mathbf{V})| \le \|\mathbf{U}\| \, \|\mathbf{V}\|$$

From Schwarz's inequality follows another important inequality, known as the **triangle inequality**,

$$\|\mathbf{U} + \mathbf{V}\| \le \|\mathbf{U}\| + \|\mathbf{V}\|$$

For any pair of vectors

$$\|\mathbf{U} + \mathbf{V}\|^2 = \|\mathbf{U}\|^2 + \|\mathbf{V}\|^2 + (\mathbf{U},\mathbf{V}) + (\mathbf{V},\mathbf{U})$$
$$\le \|\mathbf{U}\|^2 + \|\mathbf{V}\|^2 + 2 \, |(\mathbf{U},\mathbf{V})|$$
$$\le \|\mathbf{U}\|^2 + \|\mathbf{V}\|^2 + 2 \, \|\mathbf{U}\| \, \|\mathbf{V}\|$$
$$\le (\|\mathbf{U}\| + \|\mathbf{V}\|)^2$$

from which it follows that

$$\|\mathbf{U} + \mathbf{V}\| \le \|\mathbf{U}\| + \|\mathbf{V}\|$$

Let us now consider some examples of scalar products.   Consider the vector space of n-tuples of complex numbers.   Here we can define a scalar product as

$$(\mathbf{U}, \, \mathbf{V}) = u_1^* v_1 + u_2^* v_2 + \cdots + u_n^* v_n = u_i^* v_i$$

Then
$$(\mathbf{V},\mathbf{U}) = v_i^* u_i = u_i v_i^* = (u_i^* v_i)^* = (\mathbf{U},\mathbf{V})^*$$
$$(\mathbf{U}, \, \mathbf{V} + \mathbf{W}) = u_i^*(v_i + w_i) = u_i^* v_i + u_i^* w_i$$
$$= (\mathbf{U},\mathbf{V}) + (\mathbf{U},\mathbf{W})$$
$$(a\mathbf{U},\mathbf{V}) = (au_i)^* v_i = a^* u_i^* v_i = a^*(\mathbf{U},\mathbf{V})$$
$$(\mathbf{U},\mathbf{U}) = u_i^* u_i = |u_1|^2 + |u_2|^2 + \cdots + |u_n|^2$$

Since $(\mathbf{U},\mathbf{U})$ is a sum of squares of real numbers, it will be greater than or equal to zero, and it will be zero if and only if $u_1 = u_2 = \cdots = u_n = 0$.   Hence, we have verified that this definition of scalar product satisfies all the postulates and therefore the other properties follow without further proof. For example, Schwarz's inequality says

$$|u_i^* v_i| \leq \sqrt{(u_i^* u_i)(v_j^* v_j)}$$

and the triangle inequality says

$$\sqrt{(u_i + v_i)^*(u_i + v_i)} \leq \sqrt{u_i^* u_i} + \sqrt{v_i^* v_i}$$

As another example, consider the set of complex-valued functions of the real variable x defined on the interval $0 \leq x \leq 1$ which are integrable and square integrable, i.e., for which $\int_0^1 f(x)\,dx$ and $\int_0^1 |f(x)|^2\,dx$ exist.[1] We define addition in the space by

$$\mathbf{f} + \mathbf{g} = f(x) + g(x) \qquad 0 \leq x \leq 1$$

At every point in the interval

$$\begin{aligned}
|f + g|^2 &= (f^* + g^*)(f + g) \\
&= |f|^2 + |g|^2 + f^*g + g^*f \\
&\leq |f|^2 + |g|^2 + 2\,|f^*g| \\
&\leq |f|^2 + |g|^2 + 2\,|f|\,|g|
\end{aligned}$$

Also $\qquad\qquad (|f| - |g|)^2 = |f|^2 + |g|^2 - 2\,|f|\,|g| \geq 0$

Therefore, $\qquad\qquad 2\,|f|\,|g| \leq |f|^2 + |g|^2$

and hence $\qquad\qquad |f + g|^2 \leq 2\,(|f|^2 + |g|^2)$

at every point in the interval. Therefore,

$$\int_0^1 |f + g|^2\,dx \leq 2\int_0^1 |f|^2\,dx + 2\int_0^1 |g|^2\,dx$$

This shows that if $\mathbf{f}$ and $\mathbf{g}$ are square integrable, then $\mathbf{f} + \mathbf{g}$ is as well, for the only way that these integrals can diverge is for the defining limits to be infinity. But if $|f|^2$ and $|g|^2$ are integrable

$$\int_0^1 |f|^2\,dx < \infty$$

$$\int_0^1 |g|^2\,dx < \infty$$

and therefore, $\qquad\qquad \int_0^1 |f + g|^2\,dx < \infty$

[1] In more advanced treatises this integral is usually taken to be the Lebesgue integral, and this class of functions is referred to as the class $L_2(0,1)$. For our purposes we shall consider only integration in the Riemann sense. A sufficient condition for integrability in the Riemann sense is that the function be piecewise continuous, i.e., the interval $0 \leq x \leq 1$ can be divided up into a finite number of subintervals in each of which the function is continuous and has limits as x approaches the end points of all the subintervals.

This proves the closure property for addition.

Multiplication by a complex scalar is defined as

$$a\mathbf{f} = af(x) \qquad 0 \leq x \leq 1$$

Closure under multiplication by a scalar is easily demonstrated.

$$\int_0^1 |af|^2 \, dx = \int_0^1 |a|^2 \, |f|^2 \, dx = |a|^2 \int_0^1 |f|^2 \, dx < \infty$$

The other postulates of a vector space are easily verified.

For scalar product in this space,[1] we define

$$(\mathbf{f},\mathbf{g}) = \int_0^1 f^* g \, dx$$

This quantity exists for every pair of square integrable functions, for

$$|f^*g| = |f| \, |g| \leq \tfrac{1}{2}(|f|^2 + |g|^2)$$

and

$$\int_0^1 |f^*g| \, dx \leq \frac{1}{2} \int_0^1 (|f|^2 + |g|^2) \, dx < \infty$$

and a function which is absolutely integrable is integrable.

This scalar product satisfies the postulates since

$$(\mathbf{g},\mathbf{f})^* = \left[\int_0^1 g^* f \, dx\right]^* = \int_0^1 (g^* f)^* \, dx$$

$$= \int_0^1 f^* g \, dx = (\mathbf{f},\mathbf{g})$$

$$(\mathbf{f}, \, \mathbf{g} + \mathbf{h}) = \int_0^1 f^*(g + h) \, dx$$

$$= \int_0^1 f^* g \, dx + \int_0^1 f^* h \, dx$$

$$= (\mathbf{f},\mathbf{g}) + (\mathbf{f},\mathbf{h})$$

$$(\mathbf{f},\mathbf{f}) = \int_0^1 f^* f \, dx = \int_0^1 |f|^2 \, dx \geq 0$$

If $(\mathbf{f},\mathbf{f}) = 0$, then $f(x) = 0$ **almost everywhere.** By this we mean that $f(x) = 0$ except on a set of points which do not contribute to the integral. For example, suppose $f(x) = 0$ except at the points $0, \tfrac{1}{4}, \tfrac{1}{2}, \tfrac{3}{4}, 1$ where $f(x) = 1$; then

$$\int_0^1 |f|^2 \, dx = 0$$

---

[1] We have to assume integrability to ensure the existence of $(\mathbf{1},\mathbf{f}) = \int_0^1 f(x) \, dx$.

even though $f(x) \neq 0$ everywhere.   This is by no means the most general set of points on which the function can differ from zero and still not change the value of the integral.   However, if f is piecewise continuous, there are at most a finite number of points on which it differs from zero if $\int_0^1 |f|^2 \, dx = 0$.

Schwarz's inequality for this space takes the form

$$\left| \int_0^1 f^*g \, dx \right| \leq \sqrt{\int_0^1 |f|^2 \, dx} \sqrt{\int_0^1 |g|^2 \, dx}$$

and the triangle inequality is

$$\left[\int_0^1 |f + g|^2 \, dx \right]^{\frac{1}{2}} \leq \left[\int_0^1 |f|^2 \, dx \right]^{\frac{1}{2}} + \left[\int_0^1 |g|^2 \, dx \right]^{\frac{1}{2}}$$

In a vector space we sometimes refer to a vector as a **point.** We then define the **distance between two points** as the norm of the difference of the two vectors, i.e.,

$$d(\mathbf{U},\mathbf{V}) = \| \mathbf{U} - \mathbf{V} \|$$

We see that this definition of distance satisfies all the usual properties which we associate with a distance, i.e.,

1. The distance is positive unless the two points coincide.

$$\| \mathbf{U} - \mathbf{V} \| \geq 0$$
$$\| \mathbf{U} - \mathbf{V} \| = 0 \text{ if and only if } \mathbf{U} = \mathbf{V}$$

2. The distance is symmetric.

$$\| \mathbf{U} - \mathbf{V} \| = \| \mathbf{V} - \mathbf{U} \|$$

3. The triangle inequality is satisfied.

$$\| \mathbf{U} - \mathbf{V} \| \leq \| \mathbf{U} - \mathbf{W} \| + \| \mathbf{W} - \mathbf{V} \|$$

A vector space in which distance between points is defined with these three properties is called a **metric space.**[1]   A vector space may be a metric space without having a scalar product (see exercises 5 and 6).

In the case of the vector space of n-tuples of complex numbers, the distance formula is

$$d(\mathbf{U},\mathbf{V}) = \sqrt{(u_i - v_i)^*(u_i - v_i)} = \| \mathbf{U} - \mathbf{V} \|$$

In the case of the vector space of square integrable functions,

$$d(\mathbf{f},\mathbf{g}) = \sqrt{\int_0^1 |f - g|^2 \, dx} = \| \mathbf{f} - \mathbf{g} \|$$

[1] $d(\mathbf{U},\mathbf{V})$ is called the **metric** for the space.

In this case $d = 0$ implies $f = g$ almost everywhere. Here two functions are considered equal even though they may differ on a set of points which does not contribute to the integral.

Exercises 1.6

1. Prove the following properties of scalar product from the postulates:

a. $(U + V, W) = (U,W) + (V,W)$

b. $\|aU\| = |a|\ \|U\|$

2. Prove the following statements for a vector space with a scalar product:

a. The parallelogram rule

$$\|U + V\|^2 + \|U - V\|^2 = 2\ \|U\|^2 + 2\ \|V\|^2$$

b. The Pythagorean theorem

$$\|U + V\|^2 = \|U\|^2 + \|V\|^2 \text{ if } (U,V) = 0$$

c. $\|U - V\| \geq |\ \|U\| - \|V\|\ |$

3. Show that Schwarz's inequality is an equality if and only if the two vectors are proportional.

4. Show that the triangle inequality is an equality if and only if the two vectors are proportional and the constant of proportionality is a nonnegative real number.

*5. Suppose that in a vector space over the field of real numbers a positive-definite norm is defined for each vector which satisfies the triangle inequality and $\|aU\| = |a|\ \|U\|$. Show that a real-valued scalar product can be defined as follows:

$$(U,V) = \tfrac{1}{2}\{\|U + V\|^2 - \|U\|^2 - \|V\|^2\}$$

which satisfies the postulates, if the following identity is satisfied by the norms:

$$\|U + V\|^2 + \|U - V\|^2 = 2\ \|U\|^2 + 2\ \|V\|^2$$

*6. Consider the vector space of n-tuples of real numbers with norm defined by $\|U\| = |u_1| + |u_2| + \cdots + |u_n|$. Show that this has the desired properties of a norm, i.e., positive-definiteness, $\|aU\| = |a|\ \|U\|$, and triangle inequality, but that one cannot define from it a scalar product as in exercise 5.

1.7   Orthonormal Basis.   Linear Transformations

We have already seen that in an n-dimensional vector space there are many bases, all of which are sets of n linearly independent vectors which span the space. If in the space we can define a scalar product, we can select certain bases with special properties. The most important of these is known as an **orthonormal basis.**

Two vectors are **orthogonal** if and only if their scalar product is zero. A vector is said to be **normalized** if its norm is one. A set of vectors X_i is **orthonormal** if

$$(X_i, X_j) = \delta_{ij}$$

Suppose in an n-dimensional vector space we have a set of n orthonormal vectors which span the space; then they must be linearly independent, for

$$a_i \mathbf{X}_i = \mathbf{0}$$

implies that $a_i = 0$ for all i, since

$$0 = (\mathbf{X}_j, \mathbf{0}) = (\mathbf{X}_j, a_i \mathbf{X}_i) = a_i \delta_{ji} = a_j$$

Therefore, the set of vectors $\mathbf{X}_i$ is a basis. Having such a basis is very convenient, because the representation of any vector in the space is very easy to find in terms of an orthonormal basis.

Suppose $\mathbf{U}$ is a vector with a representation

$$\mathbf{U} = u_i \mathbf{X}_i$$

in terms of the orthonormal basis $\mathbf{X}_i$. Then

$$(\mathbf{X}_j, \mathbf{U}) = u_i(\mathbf{X}_j, \mathbf{X}_i)$$
$$= u_i \delta_{ji}$$
$$= u_j$$

We call the u_i the **components** of $\mathbf{U}$ relative to the orthonormal basis $\mathbf{X}_i$. If we have another vector $\mathbf{V}$ with representation

$$\mathbf{V} = v_i \mathbf{X}_i$$

then
$$(\mathbf{U}, \mathbf{V}) = (u_i \mathbf{X}_i, v_j \mathbf{X}_j)$$
$$= u_i^* v_j (\mathbf{X}_i, \mathbf{X}_j)$$
$$= u_i^* v_j \delta_{ij}$$
$$= u_i^* v_i$$

Recall that we have an isomorphism between the n-dimensional vector space and the space of n-tuples of complex numbers and that the scalar product in the space of n-tuples for a pair of vectors $(u_1, u_2, \ldots, u_n)$ and $(v_1, v_2, \ldots, v_n)$ is $u_i^* v_i$. We now see that under this isomorphism scalar product is preserved, i.e.,

$$(\mathbf{U}, \mathbf{V}) = u_i^* v_i$$

We now show that from any linearly independent set of vectors which span the vector space we can construct an orthonormal basis. This process is known as the **Schmidt process.** Let $\mathbf{Y}_i$ be a set of linearly independent vectors not orthonormal. Then compute

$$\mathbf{X}_1 = \frac{\mathbf{Y}_1}{\|\mathbf{Y}_1\|}$$

$\mathbf{X}_1$ is then normalized, for

$$\|\mathbf{X}_1\|^2 = \frac{(\mathbf{Y}_1, \mathbf{Y}_1)}{\|\mathbf{Y}_1\|^2} = 1$$

Next compute
$$\mathbf{X}_2 = \frac{\mathbf{Y}_2 - c_1\mathbf{X}_1}{\|\mathbf{Y}_2 - c_1\mathbf{X}_1\|}$$

where c_1 is determined so that $(\mathbf{X}_1,\mathbf{X}_2) = 0$, i.e.,

$$(\mathbf{X}_1,\mathbf{X}_2) = \frac{(\mathbf{X}_1,\mathbf{Y}_2) - c_1}{\|\mathbf{Y}_2 - c_1\mathbf{X}_1\|} = 0$$

$$c_1 = (\mathbf{X}_1,\mathbf{Y}_2)$$

Next compute
$$\mathbf{X}_3 = \frac{\mathbf{Y}_3 - c_2\mathbf{X}_1 - c_3\mathbf{X}_2}{\|\mathbf{Y}_3 - c_2\mathbf{X}_1 - c_3\mathbf{X}_2\|}$$

with
$$c_2 = (\mathbf{X}_1,\mathbf{Y}_3)$$

$$c_3 = (\mathbf{X}_2,\mathbf{Y}_3)$$

This process is continued until all the **Y**'s are used up and as many **X**'s are computed as there are **Y**'s. None of the **X**'s can be the zero vector, because that would imply that a linear combination of the **Y**'s gives the zero vector, contradicting the linear independence of the **Y**'s.

Let us now consider the possibility of changing the representation of a vector space by a change of basis. Let $\mathbf{X}_i$ and $\mathbf{Y}_i$ be two bases for the same vector space; then any vector **U** has a representation in terms of each basis.

$$\mathbf{U} = u_i\mathbf{X}_i$$

$$\mathbf{U} = \bar{u}_i\mathbf{Y}_i$$

Also the **X**'s have representations in terms of the **Y**'s.

$$\mathbf{X}_i = a_{ji}\mathbf{Y}_j$$

Substituting, we have

$$\mathbf{U} = \bar{u}_i\mathbf{Y}_i = u_j\mathbf{X}_j = u_ja_{ij}\mathbf{Y}_i = a_{ij}u_j\mathbf{Y}_i$$

Since the representation of a vector in terms of a given basis is unique, we have

$$\bar{u}_i = a_{ij}u_j$$

Let U be a column matrix with elements u_i, $\bar{U}$ be a column matrix with elements $\bar{u}_i$, and A be a square matrix with elements a_{ij}; then the change of representation can be written in terms of matrices as

$$\bar{U} = AU$$

If α is any scalar, then

$$\alpha\mathbf{U} = \alpha u_i\mathbf{X}_i = \alpha\bar{u}_i\mathbf{Y}_i$$

and the change of representation can be written as

$$A(\alpha U) = \alpha(AU) = \alpha\bar{U}$$

If we have two vectors **U** and **V**, then

$$\mathbf{U} + \mathbf{V} = (u_i + v_i)\mathbf{X}_i = (\bar{u}_i + \bar{v}_i)\mathbf{Y}_i$$

and
$$A(U + V) = AU + AV = \bar{U} + \bar{V}$$

Putting the last two statements together, we have

$$A(\alpha U + \beta V) = \alpha A U + \beta A V = \alpha \bar{U} + \beta \bar{V}$$

In summary, we can say that the change of representation, which can be characterized by the square matrix A, is a **linear transformation** of the vector space.

Operators which have the property

$$\mathcal{O}(\alpha p + \beta q) = \alpha \mathcal{O}(p) + \beta \mathcal{O}(q)$$

are called **linear operators**.   Beside the one considered above, some familiar examples are the derivative and the integral, i.e.,

$$\frac{d}{dx}[\alpha f(x) + \beta q(x)] = \alpha \frac{d}{dx} f(x) + \beta \frac{d}{dx} q(x)$$

$$\int [\alpha f(x) + \beta q(x)]\, dx = \alpha \int f(x)\, dx + \beta \int q(x)\, dx$$

Now let us specialize to the case where we change from one orthonormal basis $\mathbf{X}_i$ to another orthonormal basis $\mathbf{Y}_i$.   We have the relation

$$\mathbf{X}_i = a_{ji}\mathbf{Y}_j$$

and
$$\begin{aligned}
\delta_{ik} = (\mathbf{X}_i, \mathbf{X}_k) &= (a_{ji}\mathbf{Y}_j, a_{mk}\mathbf{Y}_m) \\
&= a_{ji}^* a_{mk}(\mathbf{Y}_j, \mathbf{Y}_m) \\
&= a_{ji}^* a_{mk}\delta_{jm} \\
&= a_{ji}^* a_{jk} \\
&= (a_{ij}^*)' a_{jk}
\end{aligned}$$

or
$$(A^*)'A = I$$

This says that A is a **unitary matrix**.   If we are working with a vector space over the field of real numbers, the matrix A will be real and A will be **orthogonal**.   A transformation of a vector space

$$\bar{U} = A U$$

where A is unitary is called a **unitary transformation**.

One of the important properties of a unitary transformation is that it leaves the scalar product invariant, i.e.,

$$\begin{aligned}
\bar{u}_i^* \bar{v}_i = (\bar{U}^*)'\bar{V} &= (A^*U^*)'A V \\
&= (U^*)'(A^*)'A V \\
&= (U^*)'I V \\
&= (U^*)'V
\end{aligned}$$

Since the length or norm of a vector can be expressed in terms of the scalar product, we sometimes say that a *unitary transformation is a norm preserving transformation.*

Exercises 1.7

1. Test the following set of vectors for linear independence and construct from it an orthonormal basis: $(1,0,1,0)$, $(1,-1,0,1)$, $(0,1,-1,1)$, $(1,-1,1,-1)$.

*2. Consider two sets of rectangular cartesian-coordinate systems for euclidean three space, with a common origin. Unit vectors in the direction of the three coordinate axes for the two coordinate systems serve as two different orthonormal bases. In terms of the cosines of the angles between the two sets of axes, find the matrix A relating the two coordinate systems

$$\bar{X} = AX$$

and show that A is orthogonal.

3. Given two bases $\mathbf{X}_i$ and $\mathbf{Y}_i$ such that $\mathbf{X}_i = a_{ji}\mathbf{Y}_j$. Prove that the matrix A with elements a_{ij} is nonsingular. Hence, find the inverse transformation.

4. Consider the set of all linear transformations of a finite-dimensional vector space, corresponding to change of bases. Define the product of two transformations as follows. If $\bar{U} = AU$ and $\bar{\bar{U}} = B\bar{U}$, then $\bar{\bar{U}} = BAU = CU$, where $C = BA$. Prove the following:

a. The product of three transformations is associative.

b. There exists an identity transformation such that $AI = IA = A$ for every A.

c. For every transformation A there exists an inverse A^{-1}, such that

$$A^{-1}A = AA^{-1} = I$$

Hence, the set of transformations is a **group**.

*5. A set of functions $f_n(x)$ is said to be orthonormal on the interval $a \leq x \leq b$, if

$$\int_a^b f_n^*(x) f_m(x)\, dx = \delta_{nm}$$

Show that $f_n(x) = (1/\sqrt{\pi}) \sin nx$ is orthonormal on the interval $0 \leq x \leq 2\pi$.

*6. The set of functions 1, x, x^2, ..., x^n, ... is linearly independent. It is not, however, orthonormal. Construct the first four of a set of polynomials from these which are orthonormal on the interval $-1 \leq x \leq 1$. These polynomials are proportional to the **Legendre polynomials** (see Sec. 3.3).

7. Given an m-dimensional subspace in an n-dimensional vector space, show that any vector in the vector space can be uniquely represented as the sum of a vector in the subspace and a vector orthogonal to every vector in the subspace.

*8. Find c_i, $i = 1, 2, \ldots, m$, which minimize $\|\mathbf{U} - c_i\mathbf{X}_i\|^2$, where $\mathbf{U}$ is a given vector in n-dimensional vector space, and $\mathbf{X}_i$ is a set of m orthonormal vectors. Also prove **Bessel's inequality**

$$\|\mathbf{U}\|^2 \geq \sum_{i=1}^m |(\mathbf{X}_i,\mathbf{U})|^2$$

When does Bessel's inequality become an equality?

*9. Prove **Parseval's equation** for a finite-dimensional vector space with scalar product

$$(\mathbf{U},\mathbf{V}) = (\mathbf{X}_i,\mathbf{U})^*(\mathbf{X}_i,\mathbf{V})$$

where $\mathbf{X}_i$ is an orthonormal basis.

*10. A matrix A represents a **self-adjoint** linear transformation if, for every vector pair $\mathbf{X}$ and $\mathbf{Y}$ on which it may act, $(Y,AX) = (AY,X)$. Prove that A is hermitian if and only if it is self-adjoint in the whole space.

1.8 Infinite-dimensional Vector Spaces. Function Space

Except for the space of continuous functions mentioned in Sec. 1.5 and the space of square integrable functions mentioned in Sec. 1.6, we have considered only finite-dimensional vector spaces so far. The easiest way to construct an infinite-dimensional vector space is to generalize the space of n-tuples of complex numbers to the space of infinite sequences of complex numbers. We shall define a vector in this space as follows:

$$\mathbf{U} = (u_1, u_2, u_3, \ldots)$$

If we try to define a norm in this space as a direct extension of the definition in the space of n-tuples, we have

$$\|\mathbf{U}\|^2 = \sum_{i=1}^{\infty} |u_i|^2$$

Since this involves an infinite-sum, not all sequences will define vectors with finite norms. Therefore, we shall include in our space only those sequences for which

$$\sum_{i=1}^{\infty} |u_i|^2 < \infty$$

We still must define addition and multiplication by a scalar and show that the postulates of a vector space are satisfied. If $\mathbf{U} = (u_1, u_2, u_3, \ldots)$ and $\mathbf{V} = (v_1, v_2, v_3, \ldots)$ are vectors such that $\sum_{i=1}^{\infty} |u_i|^2 < \infty$ and $\sum_{i=1}^{\infty} |v_i|^2 < \infty$, then the vector sum is $\mathbf{U} + \mathbf{V} = (u_1 + v_1, u_2 + v_2, u_3 + v_3, \ldots)$. To prove closure, we have to show that $\sum_{i=1}^{\infty} |u_i + v_i|^2 < \infty$. The proof follows.

For every i

$$\begin{aligned}
|u_i + v_i|^2 &= (u_i^* + v_i^*)(u_i + v_i) \\
&= |u_i|^2 + |v_i|^2 + u_i^* v_i + u_i v_i^* \\
&\leq |u_i|^2 + |v_i|^2 + 2\,|u_i^* v_i| \\
&\leq |u_i|^2 + |v_i|^2 + 2\,|u_i|\,|v_i|
\end{aligned}$$

We also have

$$(|u_i| - |v_i|)^2 = |u_i|^2 + |v_i|^2 - 2\,|u_i|\,|v_i| \geq 0$$

so that

$$|u_i|^2 + |v_i|^2 \geq 2\,|u_i|\,|v_i|$$

Therefore,

$$|u_i + v_i|^2 \leq 2\{|u_i|^2 + |v_i|^2\}$$

and

$$\sum_{i=1}^{\infty} |u_i + v_i|^2 < 2\sum_{i=1}^{\infty} |u_i|^2 + 2\sum_{i=1}^{\infty} |v_i|^2 < \infty$$

Multiplication by a complex scalar a is defined as

$$a\mathbf{U} = (au_1, au_2, au_3, \ldots)$$

Closure under this operation is easily verified.

$$\sum_{i=1}^{\infty} |au_i|^2 = \sum_{i=1}^{\infty} |a|^2 |u_i|^2$$

$$= |a|^2 \sum_{i=1}^{\infty} |u_i|^2 < \infty$$

The zero vector is defined as

$$\mathbf{0} = (0,0,0, \ldots)$$

and the negative

$$-\mathbf{U} = (-u_1, -u_2, -u_3, \ldots)$$

The other eight postulates are easily verified. Obviously one cannot find a finite number of vectors which span the space, and therefore it is infinite-dimensional.

A scalar product can be defined in this space as follows:

$$(\mathbf{U},\mathbf{V}) = \sum_{i=1}^{\infty} u_i^* v_i$$

We can show that for every pair of vectors in the space this scalar product exists. For every i

$$|u_i^* v_i| = |u_i|\, |v_i| \le \tfrac{1}{2}\{|u_i|^2 + |v_i|^2\}$$

Therefore, $\sum_{i=1}^{\infty} |u_i^* v_i|$ converges, since absolute convergence implies convergence.

The set of vectors $\mathbf{X}_1 = (1,0,0, \ldots), \mathbf{X}_2 = (0,1,0, \ldots), \mathbf{X}_3 = (0,0,1, \ldots), \ldots$ is orthonormal, and it spans the space in the following sense. If

$$\mathbf{U}_n = \sum_{i=1}^{n} u_i \mathbf{X}_i$$

then

$$\|\mathbf{U}_n - \mathbf{U}\|^2 = \sum_{i=n+1}^{\infty} |u_i|^2 \to 0$$

as $n \to \infty$. We write

$$\mathbf{U} = \sum_{i=1}^{\infty} u_i \mathbf{X}_i$$

and say that u_i is the component of $\mathbf{U}$ relative to the orthonormal basis $\mathbf{X}_i$, i.e., $u_i = (\mathbf{X}_i, \mathbf{U})$.

A sequence of vectors $\{\mathbf{X}^n\}$ in a metric space is said to be a **Cauchy sequence** if for every $\epsilon > 0$ there exists an $N(\epsilon)$ such that

$$d(\mathbf{X}^n, \mathbf{X}^m) < \epsilon$$

whenever $n > N$ and $m > N$. A sequence $\{\mathbf{X}^n\}$ has a **limit** in the space if there exists a vector $\mathbf{X}$ in the space such that for every $\epsilon > 0$ there exists an $N(\epsilon)$ such that

$$d(\mathbf{X},\mathbf{X}^n) < \epsilon$$

whenever $n > N$. If a sequence has a limit, then it is a Cauchy sequence, for given $\epsilon/2$ there exists an $N(\epsilon)$ such that

$$d(\mathbf{X},\mathbf{X}^n) < \frac{\epsilon}{2} \qquad d(\mathbf{X},\mathbf{X}^m) < \frac{\epsilon}{2}$$

whenever $n > N$ and $m > N$. Then by the triangle inequality we have

$$d(\mathbf{X}^n,\mathbf{X}^m) \le d(\mathbf{X},\mathbf{X}^n) + d(\mathbf{X},\mathbf{X}^m) < \epsilon$$

whenever $n > N$ and $m > N$. However, the converse may not be true, i.e., a Cauchy sequence may not have a limit, unless the space is complete.

A metric space is said to be **complete** if every Cauchy sequence has a limit in the space. As is well known from analysis, the space of real numbers is complete where the metric is $d(x,y) = |x - y|$. With this fact it is not difficult to show that the k-tuples of complex numbers is a complete metric space under the metric

$$d(\mathbf{X},\mathbf{Y}) = \sqrt{(x_i^* - y_i^*)(x_i - y_i)} \qquad i = 1, 2, \ldots, k$$

We now show that the space of infinite sequences of complex numbers is a complete metric space.

Let $\{\mathbf{X}^n\}$ be a Cauchy sequence. Then for every $\epsilon > 0$ there exists an $N(\epsilon)$ such that

$$d(\mathbf{X}^n,\mathbf{X}^m) = \left[\sum_{i=1}^{\infty} |x_i^n - x_i^m|^2 \right]^{\frac{1}{2}} < \epsilon$$

whenever $n > N$ and $m > N$. This implies that for each i

$$|x_i^n - x_i^m| < \epsilon$$

or that each sequence of components is a Cauchy sequence. Hence for every i there exists an x_i such that

$$\lim_{n \to \infty} x_i^n = x_i$$

Now define
$$\mathbf{X} = (x_1, x_2, \ldots)$$

It remains to show that $d(\mathbf{X},\mathbf{X}^n) \to 0$ as $n \to \infty$ and that $\mathbf{X}$ is in the space, i.e., $\sum_{i=1}^{\infty} |x_i|^2 < \infty$.

For some fixed M consider $\sum_{i=1}^{M} |x_i - x_i^n|^2$.   Now

$$\sum_{i=1}^{M} |x_i - x_i^n|^2 = \sum_{i=1}^{M} |x_i - x_i^m + x_i^m - x_i^n|^2$$

$$\leq 2 \sum_{i=1}^{M} |x_i - x_i^m|^2 + 2 \sum_{i=1}^{M} |x_i^m - x_i^n|^2$$

We can determine an $N(\epsilon)$ such that

$$\sum_{i=1}^{M} |x_i^m - x_i^n|^2 < \frac{\epsilon^2}{4}$$

$$|x_i - x_i^m|^2 < \frac{\epsilon^2}{4M}$$

when $n > N$ and $m > N$.   Then

$$\sum_{i=1}^{M} |x_i - x_i^n|^2 < \epsilon^2$$

This is possible for arbitrary M.   Therefore we can let $M \to \infty$, and we have

$$d(\mathbf{X}, \mathbf{X}^n) = \left[\sum_{i=1}^{\infty} |x_i - x_i^n|^2 \right]^{\frac{1}{2}} < \epsilon$$

when $n > N$.   Finally

$$\sum_{i=1}^{\infty} |x_i|^2 \leq 2 \sum_{i=1}^{\infty} |x_i - x_i^n|^2 + 2 \sum_{i=1}^{\infty} |x_i^n|^2 < \infty$$

so that $\mathbf{X}$ is in the space.

We have seen that the space of infinite sequences of complex numbers described above is a complete metric space with a scalar product.   Such a space is known as a **Hilbert space** and is of basic importance in applied mathematics, particularly in the study of quantum mechanics.   We have seen that normed spaces do not necessarily have scalar products (see Exercises 1.6). However, if a norm is defined, we can define Cauchy sequences and discuss completeness.   A complete normed vector space is called a **Banach space.**

Now let us turn our attention to another infinite-dimensional vector space, the space of square integrable functions defined in Sec. 1.6.   We have already seen that this is a vector space.   That it is infinite-dimensional will become apparent as we proceed.   We say that a set of functions $\phi_1, \phi_2, \phi_3, \ldots$ is orthonormal on the interval $a \leq x \leq b$ if

$$(\boldsymbol{\phi}_i, \boldsymbol{\phi}_j) = \int_a^b \phi_i^* \phi_j \, dx = \delta_{ij}$$

Consider the problem of approximating by the method of least squares a square integrable function $f(x)$ by a linear combination of the functions from the orthonormal set, i.e., we wish to choose $c_1, c_2, \ldots, c_n$ to minimize

$$\int_a^b \left| f - \sum_{i=1}^n c_i \phi_i \right|^2 dx$$

Expanding this quantity, we have

$$\int_a^b |f|^2 \, dx + \sum_{i=1}^n |c_i|^2 - \sum_{i=1}^n c_i \int_a^b f^* \phi_i \, dx - \sum_{i=1}^n c_i^* \int_a^b \phi_i^* f \, dx$$

The minimum occurs when

$$\int_a^b |f|^2 \, dx + \sum_{i=1}^n |c_i|^2 - \sum_{i=1}^n c_i \int_a^b f^* \phi_i \, dx - \sum_{i=1}^n c_i^* \int_a^b f \phi_i^* \, dx$$

$$+ \sum_{i=1}^n \int_a^b f^* \phi_i \, dx \int_a^b f \phi_i^* \, dx = \int_a^b |f|^2 \, dx + \sum_{i=1}^n \left| c_i - \int_a^b f \phi_i^* \, dx \right|^2$$

is minimum.   Clearly this can be minimized by choosing

$$c_i = \int_a^b \phi_i^* f \, dx = (\boldsymbol{\phi}_i, \mathbf{f})$$

The actual minimum value is then

$$\int_a^b |f|^2 \, dx - \sum_{i=1}^n |c_i|^2 \geq 0$$

The quantity on the left is a positive nonincreasing function of n.   This does not imply, however, that, as n increases without bound, this quantity necessarily goes to zero.   In any case, we do have **Bessel's inequality**

$$\int_a^b |f|^2 \, dx \geq \sum_{i=1}^\infty |c_i|^2$$

so that the series $\sum_{i=1}^\infty |c_i|^2$ always converges.   Therefore, corresponding to every square integrable function $f(x)$ there is a vector in the space of infinite sequences.

Bessel's inequality becomes an equality if and only if, for every square integrable function,

$$\lim_{n \to \infty} \int_a^b \left| f - \sum_{i=1}^n c_i \phi_i \right|^2 dx = 0$$

In this case we say that $\phi_1, \phi_2, \phi_3, \ldots$ is a **complete set of functions** and $\sum_{i=1}^\infty c_i \phi_i$ **converges in mean** to $f(x)$.   Convergence in mean does not imply convergence at each point of the interval.   Consider, for example, a square integrable function $g(x)$ which differs from $f(x)$ on a set of points which does not contribute to the integral.   Then

$$c_i = \int_a^b \phi_i^* f\, dx = \int_a^b \phi_i^* g\, dx$$

and the series which converge in mean to the two functions are indistinguishable.   In general, it will require stronger conditions on $f(x)$ than merely square integrability to prove pointwise convergence.   For example, if $f(x)$ and $\phi_i(x)$ are continuous and $\sum_{i=1}^{\infty} c_i \phi_i$ converges uniformly, then

$$\lim_{n \to \infty} \int_a^b \left| f - \sum_{i=1}^{n} c_i \phi_i \right|^2 dx$$

$$= \int_a^b \left| f - \sum_{i=1}^{\infty} c_i \phi_i \right|^2 dx$$

$$= \int_a^b |f - g|^2\, dx = 0$$

where $g = \sum_{i=1}^{\infty} c_i \phi_i$ and g is continuous.   But $f - g$ is continuous, and therefore

$$f = g = \sum_{i=1}^{\infty} c_i \phi_i$$

everywhere in the interval $a \le x \le b$.

Unfortunately, $f(x)$ will not always be continuous, and $\sum_{i=1}^{\infty} c_i \phi_i$ will not necessarily converge uniformly.   Therefore, the problem of finding expansions of arbitrary square integrable functions in terms of orthogonal sets of functions needs further discussion.   We shall return to this problem in the next section and in Chaps. 2, 3, and 5.

If the orthonormal set of functions $\phi_1, \phi_2, \phi_3, \ldots$ is complete, then Bessel's inequality becomes an equality:

$$\int_a^b |f|^2\, dx = \sum_{i=1}^{\infty} |c_i|^2$$

This is called the **completeness relation.**   It can be stated more generally, i.e., if

$$b_i = \int_a^b \phi_i^* f\, dx = (\boldsymbol{\phi}_i, \mathbf{f})$$

$$c_i = \int_a^b \phi_i^* g\, dx = (\boldsymbol{\phi}_i, \mathbf{g})$$

then

$$\int_a^b |f|^2\, dx = \sum_{i=1}^{\infty} |b_i|^2$$

$$\int_a^b |g|^2\, dx = \sum_{i=1}^{\infty} |c_i|^2$$

We also have

$$\|\mathbf{f} + \mathbf{g}\|^2 = \|\mathbf{f}\|^2 + \|\mathbf{g}\|^2 + 2 \text{ Re } (\mathbf{f},\mathbf{g})$$

$$\|\mathbf{f} + i\mathbf{g}\|^2 = \|\mathbf{f}\|^2 + \|\mathbf{g}\|^2 - 2 \text{ Im } (\mathbf{f},\mathbf{g})$$

Therefore, $(\mathbf{f},\mathbf{g}) = \text{Re } (\mathbf{f},\mathbf{g}) + i \text{ Im } (\mathbf{f},\mathbf{g})$

$$= \tfrac{1}{2}\{\|\mathbf{f} + \mathbf{g}\|^2 - \|\mathbf{f}\|^2 - \|\mathbf{g}\|^2\}$$

$$- \tfrac{1}{2}i\{\|\mathbf{f} + i\mathbf{g}\|^2 - \|\mathbf{f}\|^2 - \|\mathbf{g}\|^2\}$$

$$= \frac{1}{2}\left\{\sum_{j=1}^{\infty} |b_j + c_j|^2 - \sum_{j=1}^{\infty} |b_j|^2 - \sum_{j=1}^{\infty} |c_j|^2\right\}$$

$$- \frac{1}{2} i \left\{\sum_{j=1}^{\infty} |b_j + ic_j|^2 - \sum_{j=1}^{\infty} |b_j|^2 - \sum_{j=1}^{\infty} |c_j|^2\right\}$$

$$= \sum_{j=1}^{\infty} [\tfrac{1}{2}(b_j^* c_j + c_j^* b_j) - \tfrac{1}{2}i(ib_j^* c_j - ic_j^* b_j)]$$

$$= \sum_{j=1}^{\infty} b_j^* c_j$$

or

$$\int_a^b f^* g \, dx = \sum_{i=1}^{\infty} b_i^* c_i = \sum_{i=1}^{\infty} \int_a^b f^* \phi_i \, dx \int_a^b g \phi_i^* \, dx$$

This is **Parseval's equation.**[1]

We have already seen that the space of functions integrable and square integrable on the interval $a \leq x \leq b$ is a metric space. If the set of orthonormal functions ϕ_1, ϕ_2, ϕ_3, . . . is complete, and we define

$$f_n(x) = \sum_{i=1}^n c_i \phi_i$$

where

$$c_i = (\boldsymbol{\phi}_i, \mathbf{f})$$

then

$$\|\mathbf{f} - \mathbf{f}_n\|^2 = \int_a^b |\mathbf{f} - \mathbf{f}_n|^2 \, dx \to 0$$

as $n \to \infty$. Therefore, the sequence of functions $\{f_n(x)\}$ has a limit $f(x)$ in the space and is therefore a Cauchy sequence. The content of the **Riesz-Fischer theorem,**[2] formulated in terms of the Lebesgue integral, is that the space $L_2(a,b)$ is complete, i.e., that every Cauchy sequence has a limit in the space and is therefore a Hilbert space. Now suppose ϕ_1, ϕ_2, ϕ_3, . . . is an

---

[1] Compare with exercise 9, Sec. 1.7.

[2] See E. C. Titchmarsh, "The Theory of Functions," Oxford University Press, New York, 1939, pp. 386–388.

arbitrary set of orthonormal functions in $L_2(a,b)$ and c_1, c_2, c_3, ... is any sequence of complex numbers such that

$$\sum_{i=1}^{\infty} |c_i|^2 < \infty$$

Let

$$f_n(x) = \sum_{i=1}^{n} c_i \phi_i$$

Then f_n is in $L_2(a,b)$ for any n.   Furthermore,

$$\|\mathbf{f}_n - \mathbf{f}_m\|^2 = \sum_{i=m+1}^{n} |c_i|^2 \to 0$$

as m and $n \to \infty$.   Hence $\{f_n\}$ is a Cauchy sequence.   Therefore there exists a function $f(x)$ in $L_2(a,b)$ such that

$$\lim_{n \to \infty} \|\mathbf{f}_n - \mathbf{f}\|^2 = \lim_{n \to \infty} \int_a^b |f - f_n|^2 \, dx = 0$$

Furthermore, by Schwarz's inequality

$$|(\mathbf{f} - \mathbf{f}_n, \boldsymbol{\phi}_k)| \leq \|\mathbf{f} - \mathbf{f}_n\| \to 0$$

as $n \to \infty$, so that

$$c_k = \lim_{n \to \infty} (\boldsymbol{\phi}_k, \mathbf{f}_n) = (\boldsymbol{\phi}_k, \mathbf{f})$$

This is not to say that the set of functions ϕ_1, ϕ_2, ϕ_3, ... is complete, for although there is a limit function associated with every sequence $c_1, c_2, c_3, \ldots$, some functions in $L_2(a,b)$ may not be producible in this way.   There is, however, an equivalent definition to completeness for a set of orthonormal functions which we shall now state.

A set of orthonormal functions ϕ_1, ϕ_2, ϕ_3, ... is said to be **closed** if no normalized function is orthogonal to every function in the set.   *If a set of functions is complete, then it is closed.*   If it is not closed, then there exists a normalized function $f(x)$ such that

$$c_i = \int_a^b \phi_i^* f \, dx = 0$$

for all i.   Furthermore,

$$\lim_{n \to \infty} \int_a^b \left| f - \sum_{i=1}^{n} c_i \phi_i \right|^2 dx = \int_a^b |f|^2 \, dx = 1$$

which contradicts the completeness assumption.   Therefore, the set must be closed.   The converse is also true, i.e., *if a set is closed, it is complete.*   For if it is not complete, there exists a function $f(x)$ such that

$$\int_a^b |f|^2 \, dx - \sum_{i=1}^{\infty} |c_i|^2 > 0$$

where

$$c_i = (\boldsymbol{\phi}_i, \mathbf{f})$$

However, the function $g_n = \sum\limits_{i=1}^{n} c_i \phi_i$ converges in mean to a $g(x)$ such that

$$c_i = (\boldsymbol{\phi}_i, \mathbf{g}) = (\boldsymbol{\phi}_i, \mathbf{f})$$

Therefore, the function $h = g - f$ is orthogonal to all the ϕ_i and

$$\|\mathbf{h}\| = \|\mathbf{g} - \mathbf{f}\| \geq \big| \|\mathbf{g} - \mathbf{g}_n\| - \|\mathbf{f} - \mathbf{g}_n\| \big| > 0$$

and h is a normalizable function.   Hence, the set cannot be closed.

Suppose we have two complete sets of orthonormal functions, $\phi_1, \phi_2, \phi_3, \ldots$ and $\Psi_1, \Psi_2, \Psi_3, \ldots$.   The expansion coefficients of $f(x)$ relative to ϕ_i are $c_i = \int_a^b \phi_i^* f\, dx$, and the expansion coefficients relative to Ψ_i are $d_i = \int_a^b \Psi_i^* f\, dx$. If we apply Parseval's equation to ϕ_i and f, we have

$$c_i = (\boldsymbol{\phi}_i, \mathbf{f}) = \sum_{j=1}^{\infty} (\boldsymbol{\phi}_i, \boldsymbol{\Psi}_j)(\boldsymbol{\Psi}_j, \mathbf{f}) = \sum_{j=1}^{\infty} a_{ij}\, d_j$$

where

$$a_{ij} = (\boldsymbol{\phi}_i, \boldsymbol{\Psi}_j)$$

By applying the Parseval relation to Ψ_i and f, we also have

$$d_i = (\boldsymbol{\Psi}_i, \mathbf{f}) = \sum_{j=1}^{\infty} (\boldsymbol{\phi}_j, \boldsymbol{\Psi}_i)^* (\boldsymbol{\phi}_j, \mathbf{f}) = \sum_{j=1}^{\infty} a_{ji}^*\, c_j = \sum_{j=1}^{\infty} (a^*)'_{ij} c_j$$

Furthermore, $$\delta_{ij} = (\boldsymbol{\phi}_i, \boldsymbol{\phi}_j) = \sum_{k=1}^{\infty} (\boldsymbol{\phi}_i, \boldsymbol{\Psi}_k)^* (\boldsymbol{\Psi}_k, \boldsymbol{\phi}_j) = \sum_{k=1}^{\infty} (\boldsymbol{\phi}_i, \boldsymbol{\Psi}_k)(\boldsymbol{\phi}_j, \boldsymbol{\Psi}_k)^*$$

$$= \sum_{k=1}^{\infty} a_{ik} a_{jk}^* = \sum_{k=1}^{\infty} a_{ik} (a^*)'_{kj}$$

Summarizing in terms of infinite matrices,

$$C = AD$$

$$D = (A^*)'C$$

$$A(A^*)' = I$$

which is to say that the change of representation going from one complete orthonormal set of functions to another corresponds to a unitary transformation of the vector space of infinite sequences of complex numbers.   It is this fundamental fact that makes unitary transformations of basic importance in quantum mechanics.

Exercises 1.8

*1. Show that the set of functions $\phi_n = (1/\sqrt{\pi}) \sin nx$ is not a complete set on the interval $0 \leq x \leq 2\pi$.

*2. Let $f(x)$ be continuous on the interval $0 \leq x \leq 2\pi$, and $f(0) = f(2\pi)$, and have a piecewise continuous derivative $f'(x)$. Show that series $\sum_{n=1}^{\infty} n^2(a_n^2 + b_n^2)$, where

$$a_n = \frac{1}{\pi} \int_0^{2\pi} f(x) \cos nx \, dx$$

$$b_n = \frac{1}{\pi} \int_0^{2\pi} f(x) \sin nx \, dx$$

converges.   HINT: Apply Bessel's inequality to the function $f'(x)$.

*3. Show that the set of functions $\phi_n = (1/\sqrt{2\pi})e^{inx}$, $n = 0, \pm 1, \pm 2, \ldots$, is an orthonormal set on the interval $0 \leq x \leq 2\pi$.

*4. If the functions of exercise 3 are a complete set, show that a series representation of a square integrable function $f(x)$ is

$$\frac{a_0}{2} + \sum_{n=1}^{\infty} (a_n \cos nx + b_n \sin nx)$$

where $a_n = \frac{1}{\pi} \int_0^{2\pi} f(x) \cos nx \, dx$ and $b_n = \frac{1}{\pi} \int_0^{2\pi} f(x) \sin nx \, dx$.

5. If $f(z)$ is an analytic function of the complex variable z in the region $R_1 < |z| < R_2$, show that $f(re^{i\theta}) = \sum_{n=-\infty}^{\infty} c_n e^{in\theta}$ where

$$c_n = \frac{1}{2\pi} \int_0^{2\pi} f(re^{i\theta})e^{-in\theta} \, d\theta \qquad R_1 < r < R_2$$

HINT: Start with the Laurent expansion for $f(z)$.

6. Consider the space of continuous functions on the interval $a \leq x \leq b$. Let $\phi_1, \phi_2, \phi_3, \ldots$ be a complete set of orthonormal functions. Let $c_i = \int_a^b \phi_i^* f \, dx$, and assume that $\sum_{i=1}^{\infty} c_i \phi_i$ converges uniformly. Prove that the correspondence $f \sim (c_1, c_2, c_3, \ldots)$ is an isomorphism between the space of continuous functions and the space of infinite sequences, which preserves scalar product.

7. Prove that the space of infinite sequences of complex numbers with

$$\|\mathbf{U}\| = \sum_{i=1}^{\infty} |u_i| < \infty$$

is a Banach space.

1.9   Fourier Series

Perhaps the best known example of a complete set of orthonormal functions is that afforded by the trigonometric functions $\dfrac{1}{\sqrt{2\pi}}$, $\dfrac{1}{\sqrt{\pi}} \cos x$, $\dfrac{1}{\sqrt{\pi}} \sin x$, $\dfrac{1}{\sqrt{\pi}} \cos 2x$, $\dfrac{1}{\sqrt{\pi}} \sin 2x, \ldots$. We shall show in two steps that this set is complete with respect to real-valued functions defined on the interval $0 \leq x \leq 2\pi$

which are piecewise continuous and have a piecewise continuous derivative. Our first theorem will handle the completeness for the subspace of functions which are continuous and for which $f(0) = f(2\pi)$. The second theorem will extend the result to piecewise continuous functions. In the process of proving completeness we shall obtain the conventional pointwise convergence theorems of Fourier analysis.

We first must show that the set of functions is orthonormal. This is easily established as follows:

$$\frac{1}{2\pi} \int_0^{2\pi} dx = 1$$

$$\frac{1}{\pi} \int_0^{2\pi} \cos^2 kx \, dx = \frac{1}{2\pi} \int_0^{2\pi} (1 + \cos 2kx) \, dx = 1 + \left[\frac{\sin 2kx}{4k\pi} \right]_0^{2\pi} = 1$$

$$\frac{1}{\pi} \int_0^{2\pi} \sin^2 kx \, dx = \frac{1}{2\pi} \int_0^{2\pi} (1 - \cos 2kx) \, dx = 1 - \left[\frac{\sin 2kx}{4k\pi} \right]_0^{2\pi} = 1$$

If $m \neq n$,

$$\frac{1}{\pi} \int_0^{2\pi} \cos mx \cos nx \, dx = \frac{1}{2\pi} \int_0^{2\pi} [\cos (m + n)x + \cos (m - n)x] \, dx$$

$$= \frac{1}{2\pi} \left[\frac{\sin (m + n)x}{m + n} + \frac{\sin (m - n)x}{m - n} \right]_0^{2\pi} = 0$$

$$\frac{1}{\pi} \int_0^{2\pi} \sin mx \sin nx \, dx = \frac{1}{2\pi} \int_0^{2\pi} [\cos (m - n)x - \cos (m + n)x] \, dx$$

$$= \frac{1}{2\pi} \left[\frac{\sin (m - n)x}{m - n} - \frac{\sin (m + n)x}{m + n} \right]_0^{2\pi} = 0$$

$$\frac{1}{\pi} \int_0^{2\pi} \sin mx \cos nx \, dx = \frac{1}{2\pi} \int_0^{2\pi} [\sin (m + n)x + \sin (m - n)x] \, dx$$

$$= -\frac{1}{2\pi} \left[\frac{\cos (m + n)x}{m + n} + \frac{\cos (m - n)x}{m - n} \right]_0^{2\pi} = 0$$

$$\frac{1}{\pi} \int_0^{2\pi} \sin mx \cos mx \, dx = \frac{1}{2\pi} \int_0^{2\pi} \sin 2 mx \, dx$$

$$= -\left[\frac{1}{4\pi m} \cos 2 mx \right]_0^{2\pi} = 0$$

Theorem 1. The set of functions $\dfrac{1}{\sqrt{2\pi}}, \dfrac{1}{\sqrt{\pi}} \cos kx, \dfrac{1}{\sqrt{\pi}} \sin kx, k = 1, 2, 3,$

... is a complete set with respect to functions $f(x)$, $0 \leq x \leq 2\pi$, which are continuous and have a piecewise continuous first derivative, and for which $f(0) = f(2\pi)$.

Proof. We first note that $f'(x)$ is integrable and square integrable. Hence, by Bessel's inequality

$$\sum_{k=1}^{\infty} (\alpha_k^2 + \beta_k^2) \leq \frac{1}{\pi} \int_0^{2\pi} |f'(x)|^2 \, dx$$

where

$$\alpha_k = \frac{1}{\pi} \int_0^{2\pi} f'(x) \cos kx \, dx$$

$$= \frac{1}{\pi} \left[f(x) \cos kx \right]_0^{2\pi} + \frac{k}{\pi} \int_0^{2\pi} f(x) \sin kx \, dx$$

$$= kb_k$$

$$\beta_k = \frac{1}{\pi} \int_0^{2\pi} f'(x) \sin kx \, dx$$

$$= \frac{1}{\pi} \left[f(x) \sin kx \right]_0^{2\pi} - \frac{k}{\pi} \int_0^{2\pi} f(x) \cos kx \, dx$$

$$= -ka_k$$

where a_k and b_k are the **Fourier coefficients** of $f(x)$, i.e.,

$$a_k = \frac{1}{\pi} \int_0^{2\pi} f(x) \cos kx \, dx$$

$$b_k = \frac{1}{\pi} \int_0^{2\pi} f(x) \sin kx \, dx$$

Therefore

$$\sum_{k=1}^{\infty} (k^2 a_k^2 + k^2 b_k^2) \leq \frac{1}{\pi} \int_0^{2\pi} |f'(x)|^2 \, dx$$

We can show that $\dfrac{a_0}{2} + \sum_{k=1}^{\infty} (a_k \cos kx + b_k \sin kx)$ converges uniformly.

Consider $|S_n - S_m|^2$ where $S_n = \dfrac{a_0}{2} + \sum_{k=1}^{n} (a_k \cos kx + b_k \sin kx)$. Then

$$|S_n - S_m|^2 = \left| \sum_{k=m+1}^{n} (a_k \cos kx + b_k \sin kx) \right|^2$$

$$= \left| \sum_{k=m+1}^{n} \left[(ka_k) \frac{\cos kx}{k} + (kb_k) \frac{\sin kx}{k} \right] \right|^2$$

$$\leq \sum_{k=m+1}^{n} (k^2 a_k^2 + k^2 b_k^2) \sum_{k=m+1}^{n} \frac{1}{k^2} \leq \frac{1}{\pi} \int_0^{2\pi} |f'(x)|^2 \, dx \sum_{k=m+1}^{n} \frac{1}{k^2}$$

The series $\sum_{k=1}^{\infty} \dfrac{1}{k^2}$ converges.   Hence, $\sum_{k=m+1}^{n} \dfrac{1}{k^2} \to 0$ as m and $n \to \infty$.   There-
fore, $|S_n - S_m|^2 \to 0$ as m and $n \to \infty$ uniformly in x, and we have the Cauchy criterion for uniform convergence of the series.   Next we show that the series converges to $f(x)$.

$$S_n = \frac{a_0}{2} + \sum_{k=1}^{n} (a_k \cos kx + b_k \sin kx)$$

$$= \frac{1}{\pi} \int_0^{2\pi} f(t)[\tfrac{1}{2} + \cos (x - t) + \cos 2 (x - t) + \cdots + \cos n(x - t)]\, dt$$

$$= \frac{1}{\pi} \int_0^{2\pi} f(t) \operatorname{Re} [1 + e^{i(x-t)} + e^{2i(x-t)} + \cdots + e^{ni(x-t)} - \tfrac{1}{2}]\, dt$$

$$= \frac{1}{\pi} \int_0^{2\pi} f(t) \operatorname{Re} \left[\frac{e^{i(n+1)(x-t)} - 1}{e^{i(x-t)} - 1} - \frac{1}{2} \right] dt$$

$$= \frac{1}{\pi} \int_0^{2\pi} f(t) \operatorname{Re} \left[\frac{e^{i(n+1/2)(x-t)} - e^{-i(x-t)/2}}{e^{i(x-t)/2} - e^{-i(x-t)/2}} - \frac{1}{2} \right] dt$$

$$= \frac{1}{2\pi} \int_0^{2\pi} f(t) \frac{\sin (n + 1/2)(x - t)}{\sin [(x - t)/2]}\, dt$$

$$= \frac{1}{2\pi} \int_{-x}^{2\pi - x} f(u + x) \frac{\sin (n + 1/2)u}{\sin u/2}\, du$$

In the last integral we have made the change of variable $u = t - x$.   At this point we must extend the definition of $f(x)$ outside the interval $0 \le x \le 2\pi$. We do this by the periodic extension, i.e., for any $-\infty < x < \infty$ we define $f(x) = f(x + 2\pi p)$ where p is the appropriate integer chosen so that $0 \le x + 2p\pi < 2\pi$.   We note that by the condition $f(0) = f(2\pi)$ the periodic extension is continuous and also that the derivative is piecewise continuous in any finite interval.   We can now write

$$S_n = \frac{1}{2\pi} \int_0^{2\pi} f(u + x) \frac{\sin (n + 1/2)u}{\sin u/2}\, du$$

since the integrand is periodic with period 2π.   We also note that

$$\frac{1}{2\pi} \int_0^{2\pi} f(x) \frac{\sin (n + 1/2)u}{\sin u/2}\, du$$

$$= f(x) \left[\frac{1}{\pi} \int_0^{2\pi} (\tfrac{1}{2} + \cos u + \cos 2u + \cdots + \cos nu)\, du \right]$$

$$= f(x)$$

Hence,
$$S_n - f(x) = \frac{1}{2\pi} \int_0^{2\pi} \left[\frac{f(x + u) - f(x)}{\sin u/2} \right] \sin (n + \tfrac{1}{2})u \, du$$

$$= \frac{1}{2\pi} \int_0^{2\pi} \left[\frac{f(x + u) - f(x)}{\sin u/2} \cos \frac{u}{2} \right] \sin nu \, du$$

$$+ \frac{1}{2\pi} \int_0^{2\pi} [f(x + u) - f(x)] \cos nu \, du$$

Now $f(x + u) - f(x)$ is continuous in u and $\dfrac{f(x + u) - f(x)}{\sin u/2} \cos \dfrac{u}{2}$ is piecewise continuous. The latter follows from

$$\lim_{u \to 0+} 2 \frac{f(x + u) - f(x)}{u} \cos \frac{u}{2} \frac{u/2}{2 \sin u/2} = 2f'(x+)$$

$$\lim_{u \to 0-} 2 \frac{f(x + u) - f(x)}{u} \cos \frac{u}{2} \frac{u/2}{2 \sin u/2} = 2f'(x-)$$

Therefore, $S_n - f(x)$ can be expressed as the sum of Fourier coefficients of a continuous and a piecewise continuous function. Hence, by Bessel's inequality

$$\lim_{n \to \infty} [S_n - f(x)] = \lim_{n \to \infty} \frac{1}{2\pi} \int_0^{2\pi} \left[\frac{f(x + u) - f(x)}{\sin u/2} \right] \cos \frac{u}{2} \sin nu \, dx$$

$$+ \lim_{n \to \infty} \frac{1}{2\pi} \int_0^{2\pi} [f(x + u) - f(x)] \cos nu \, du$$

$$= 0$$

and we have

$$f(x) = \frac{a_0}{2} + \sum_{k=1}^{\infty} (a_k \cos kx + b_k \sin kx)$$

and the convergence is uniform. We can multiply the series by $(1/\pi)f(x)$ and integrate term by term, thus obtaining the completeness relation

$$\frac{1}{\pi} \int_0^{2\pi} |f(x)|^2 \, dx = \frac{a_0^2}{2} + \sum_{k=1}^{\infty} (a_k^2 + b_k^2)$$

We note that in proving theorem 1, we have obtained the following corollary.

Corollary 1.1.   If $f(x)$ is a continuous periodic function with period 2π, with a piecewise continuous derivative, it can be expanded in a uniformly convergent series

$$f(x) = \frac{a_0}{2} + \sum_{k=1}^{\infty} (a_k \cos kx + b_k \sin kx)$$

where
$$a_k = \frac{1}{\pi} \int_0^{2\pi} f(x) \cos kx \, dx$$

$$b_k = \frac{1}{\pi} \int_0^{2\pi} f(x) \sin kx \, dx$$

Next we show that the same orthonormal set of trigonometric functions is complete with respect to a larger class of functions.

Theorem 2.   The set of functions $\dfrac{1}{\sqrt{2\pi}}, \dfrac{1}{\sqrt{\pi}} \cos kx, \dfrac{1}{\sqrt{\pi}} \sin kx, k = 1, 2, 3,$

... is a complete orthonormal set with respect to functions $f(x), 0 \le x \le 2\pi$, which are piecewise continuous and have a piecewise continuous derivative. The Fourier series converges pointwise as follows:

$$\tfrac{1}{2}[f(x+) + f(x-)] = \frac{a_0}{2} + \sum_{k=1}^{\infty} (a_k \cos kx + b_k \sin kx)$$

where $f(0-) = f(2\pi-)$ and $f(2\pi+) = f(0+)$.   The convergence is uniform in any closed interval not containing a discontinuity of the function.

Proof.   We shall prove the pointwise convergence part of the theorem first. To this end we again extend the function by periodicity, i.e., $f(x) = f(x + 2\pi p)$ where p is the appropriate integer chosen so that $0 \le x + 2\pi p < 2\pi$.   With this extension we have $f(x)$ defined as a periodic function with period 2π which has but a finite number of discontinuities in each period.   Suppose that $f(x)$ has but one discontinuity in each period.   Let $f(x)$ have discontinuities at $\xi \pm 2m\pi$, $m = 0, 1, 2, \ldots$ with $0 \le \xi \le 2\pi$.   Then $\lim_{x \to \xi+} f(x) = f(\xi+)$, $\lim_{x \to \xi-} f(x) = f(\xi-)$, and $f(\xi+) \ne f(\xi-)$.

We can put the discontinuity at the origin by translating the x axis, i.e., $t = x - \xi$.   This will not affect the Fourier coefficients of $f(x)$ since it is periodic.   Let $F(t) = f(t + \xi)$ and

$$g(t) = F(t) - \frac{1}{2}[f(\xi+) - f(\xi-)]h(t)$$

where $h(t) = (1/\pi)(\pi - t)$ for $0 \le t < 2\pi$ and is extended periodically for other values of t. $h(t)$ is continuous except at $0, \pm 2\pi, \pm 4\pi, \ldots$, and therefore $g(t)$ is continuous except possibly at these points.   Actually $g(t)$ is continuous everywhere, since

$$\lim_{t \to 0+} g(t) = F(0+) - \tfrac{1}{2}[f(\xi+) - f(\xi-)]$$
$$= f(\xi+) - \tfrac{1}{2}[f(\xi+) - f(\xi-)]$$
$$= \tfrac{1}{2}[f(\xi+) + f(\xi-)]$$
$$\lim_{t \to 0-} g(t) = F(0-) + \tfrac{1}{2}[f(\xi+) - f(\xi-)]$$
$$= f(\xi-) + \tfrac{1}{2}[f(\xi+) - f(\xi-)]$$
$$= \tfrac{1}{2}[f(\xi+) + f(\xi-)]$$

By periodicity $g(t)$ is continuous at $t = \pm 2\pi$, $\pm 4\pi$, ... Therefore, the Fourier series representation for $g(t)$ converges uniformly. It remains to show that the Fourier series for $h(t)$ converges and hence that the series for $F(t)$ and $f(x)$ converge. We shall show that the series for $h(t)$ converges to zero at $t = 0$, which will show that the series for $f(x)$ converges to

$$g(0) = \tfrac{1}{2}[f(\xi+) + f(\xi-)]$$

at $x = \xi$.

The function $h(t)$ is odd and, therefore,

$$c_k = \frac{1}{\pi} \int_0^{2\pi} h(t) \cos kt \, dt$$

$$= \frac{1}{\pi} \int_{-\pi}^{\pi} h(t) \cos kt \, dt = 0$$

Its other Fourier coefficients are

$$d_k = \frac{1}{\pi^2} \int_0^{2\pi} (\pi - t) \sin kt \, dt$$

$$= \frac{1}{\pi^2} \left[-\frac{\pi}{k} \cos kt + \frac{t}{k} \cos kt - \frac{\sin kt}{k^2} \right]_0^{2\pi}$$

$$= \frac{2}{k\pi}$$

Now consider the function $H(t) = (1 - \cos t) h(t)$. This function is continuous, odd, and periodic. Therefore, it has a uniformly convergent Fourier series with coefficients

$$\gamma_k = \frac{1}{\pi} \int_0^{2\pi} H(t) \cos kt \, dt$$

$$= \frac{1}{\pi} \int_{-\pi}^{\pi} H(t) \cos kt \, dt = 0$$

$$\delta_k = \frac{1}{\pi} \int_0^{2\pi} (1 - \cos t) h(t) \sin kt \, dt$$

$$= d_k - \frac{1}{\pi} \int_0^{2\pi} h(t) \cos t \sin kt \, dt$$

$$= d_k - \frac{1}{2\pi} \int_0^{2\pi} h(t) \sin (k + 1)t \, dt - \frac{1}{2\pi} \int_0^{2\pi} h(t) \sin (k - 1)t \, dt$$

$$= d_k - \tfrac{1}{2}[d_{k+1} + d_{k-1}] \qquad k = 2, 3, 4, \ldots$$

For $k = 1$, $\delta_1 = d_1 - \frac{1}{2}d_2$.   Let

$$S_n = \sum_{k=1}^{n} \delta_k \sin kt = (d_1 - \frac{1}{2}d_2)\sin t + [d_2 - \frac{1}{2}(d_3 + d_1)] \sin 2t$$

$$+ \cdots + [d_{n-1} - \frac{1}{2}(d_n + d_{n-2})] \sin (n-1)t$$

$$+ [d_n - \frac{1}{2}(d_{n+1} + d_{n-1})] \sin nt$$

and $\qquad \sigma_n = \sum_{k=1}^{n} d_k \sin kt = d_1 \sin t + d_2 \sin 2t + \cdots + d_n \sin nt$

Then

$$(1 - \cos t)\sigma_n = (d_1 - \frac{1}{2}d_2) \sin t + [d_2 - \frac{1}{2}(d_3 + d_1)] \sin 2t$$

$$+ \cdots + [d_n - \frac{1}{2}(d_{n+1} + d_{n-1})] \sin nt + \frac{1}{2}d_{n+1} \sin nt - \frac{1}{2}d_n \sin (n+1)t$$

$$= S_n + \frac{1}{(n+1)\pi} \sin nt - \frac{1}{n\pi} \sin (n+1)t$$

We know that $\lim\limits_{n \to \infty} S_n = H(t) = (1 - \cos t) \, h(t)$, uniformly in t. Furthermore,

$$|1 - \cos t| \, |\sigma_n - h(t)| = |S_n - H(t) + \frac{1}{(n+1)\pi} \sin nt - \frac{1}{n\pi} \sin (n+1)t|$$

Therefore, $\qquad\qquad |\sigma_n - h(t)| \le \dfrac{|S_n - H(t)| + 2/n\pi}{|1 - \cos t|}$

Suppose t lies in some closed interval not containing $t = 0, \pm 2\pi, \pm 4\pi, \ldots$; then $|1 - \cos t| \ge M > 0$.   Therefore, in such an interval $|\sigma_n - h(t)| \to 0$ as $n \to \infty$, uniformly in t.   Hence, the Fourier series for $h(t)$ converges uniformly to the function in every closed interval not containing $t = 0; \pm 2\pi; \pm 4\pi, \ldots$. At the exceptional points the series converges to zero, since it contains only terms in $\sin kt$.   This completes the proof for one discontinuity.   It can clearly be extended to include the possibility of a finite number of discontinuities in a given period.

In the present case we do not have uniform convergence in the interval $0 \le x \le 2\pi$.   Therefore, we cannot make use of the termwise integration of the series to obtain the completeness relation.   However, we can show that the space is closed with respect to the set of trigonometric functions, and if the space is closed, it is complete.

Let $f(x)$ be a function in the space which is orthogonal to all the functions in the given set, i.e.,

$$a_k = \frac{1}{\pi} \int_0^{2\pi} f(x) \cos kx \, dx = 0$$

$$b_k = \frac{1}{\pi} \int_0^{2\pi} f(x) \sin kx \, dx = 0$$

Hence, the Fourier series $\dfrac{a_0}{2} + \sum\limits_{k=1}^{\infty} (a_k \cos kx + b_k \sin kx)$ converges everywhere to zero.   Therefore, $f(x)$ is equal to zero almost everywhere.   For the space of piecewise continuous functions, "almost everywhere" means everywhere except at a finite number of points.   Hence, $\dfrac{1}{\pi} \displaystyle\int_0^{2\pi} |f(x)|^2 \, dx = 0$.   This shows that the space is closed, since there are no normalizable functions in the space which are orthogonal to every member of the given set of orthonormal functions.

Exercises 1.9

1. Obtain the Fourier series for $f(x) = x/2\pi$, $0 \le x \le 2\pi$.   What does the series converge to at $x = 0$ and $x = 2\pi$?

2. Show that, if $f(x)$ is an even periodic function with period 2π satisfying the conditions of theorem 2, its Fourier series contains no terms in $\sin kx$.   Also show that, if it is odd, its Fourier series contains no $\cos kx$ terms.

3. Obtain a Fourier series for $f(x) = x/2\pi$, $0 \le x \le \pi$, which contains no terms in $\sin kx$.   Obtain a Fourier series for the same function which contains no terms in $\cos kx$.

4. If $f(x)$ satisfies the conditions of theorem 1, show that $f(x) = \sum\limits_{k=-\infty}^{\infty} c_k e^{-ikx}$ in which $c_k = \dfrac{1}{2\pi} \displaystyle\int_0^{2\pi} f(x) e^{ikx} \, dx$ and the convergence is uniform in x.

5. Show that, if $f(x)$ is periodic with period $2L$, is continuous, and has a piecewise continuous derivative in any period,

$$f(x) = \frac{a_0}{2} + \sum_{k=1}^{\infty} \left(a_k \cos \frac{k\pi}{L} x + b_k \sin \frac{k\pi x}{L} \right)$$

where

$$a_k = \frac{1}{L} \int_0^{2L} f(x) \cos \frac{k\pi x}{L} \, dx$$

$$b_k = \frac{1}{L} \int_0^{2L} f(x) \sin \frac{k\pi x}{L} \, dx$$

HINT: Make the change of variables $x = Lt/\pi$.

6. Prove that, if $f(x)$ is periodic with period 2π and has continuous derivatives up to the $(n-1)$st and a piecewise continuous nth derivative, then its Fourier coefficients have the property

$$\lim_{k \to \infty} k^n a_k = 0$$

$$\lim_{k \to \infty} k^n b_k = 0$$

7. Prove that, if $f(x)$ is periodic and continuous and has piecewise continuous first and second derivatives, then except at points of discontinuity of $f'(x)$ its derivative can be computed by termwise differentiation of its Fourier series.

1.10.   Quadratic Forms.   Hermitian Forms

In terms of three-dimensional rectangular cartesian coordinates x_1, x_2, x_3, we can write the equation of the most general quadric surface as[1]

$$X'AX + BX + k = 0$$

where

$$X = \begin{Vmatrix} x_1 \\ x_2 \\ x_3 \end{Vmatrix}$$

is a column matrix representing the vector from the origin to a point with coordinates x_1, x_2, x_3 on the surface. A is a 3×3 symmetric matrix of real constants; B is a 1×3 row matrix of real constants; and k is a real constant. The first term in this equation,

$$Q = X'AX = a_{11}x_1^2 + a_{22}x_2^2 + a_{33}x_3^2 + 2a_{12}x_1x_2 + 2a_{13}x_1x_3 + 2a_{23}x_2x_3$$

is a quadratic form in the three variables.   A standard problem in analytic geometry is to determine an orthogonal transformation of coordinates (rotation of axes)

$$X = T\bar{X}$$

which will reduce Q to the diagonal form

$$Q = \bar{X}'T'AT\bar{X} = \bar{X}'D\bar{X} = \lambda_1\bar{x}_1^2 + \lambda_2\bar{x}_2^2 + \lambda_3\bar{x}^2$$

This problem occurs frequently in other applications, so we shall study it in its more general form in n-dimensional vector space.

Let

$$X = \begin{Vmatrix} x_1 \\ x_2 \\ . \\ . \\ . \\ x_n \end{Vmatrix}$$

be a column matrix representing the n-dimensional vector $(x_1, x_2, \ldots, x_n)$ with real components.

$$Q = X'AX$$

is a quadratic form in $x_1, x_2', \ldots, x_n$, where A is an $n \times n$ real matrix.   Without loss of generality, we can assume that A is symmetric, for

$$Q = X'[\tfrac{1}{2}(A + A') + \tfrac{1}{2}(A - A')]X$$
$$= X'[\tfrac{1}{2}(A + A')]X$$

---

[1] See exercise 5, Sec. 1.2.

and $\frac{1}{2}(A + A')$ is symmetric. The problem is to find an orthogonal transformation

$$X = T\bar{X}$$

which will reduce the quadratic form Q to the diagonal form

$$Q = X'AX = \bar{X}'T'AT\bar{X} = \bar{X}'D\bar{X} = \lambda_1\bar{x}_1^2 + \lambda_2\bar{x}_2^2 + \cdots + \lambda_n\bar{x}_n^2$$

In other words, the problem reduces to finding a matrix T such that $T'AT = D$, where D is diagonal. This can always be done for a real symmetric matrix A. The proof follows.

Since we are assuming that T is orthogonal, we have[1]

$$TT'AT = AT = TD$$

$$a_{ij}t_{j\alpha} = t_{ij}d_{j\alpha} = \lambda_\alpha t_{i\alpha}$$

Let the αth column of T be Y_α, a column matrix; then the last equation becomes

$$AY_\alpha = \lambda_\alpha Y_\alpha$$

Dropping the subscript α, we are seeking vectors Y such that

$$AY = \lambda Y$$

This equation can also be written

$$(A - \lambda I)Y = O$$

This equation will have a nontrivial solution if and only if

$$|A - \lambda I| = 0$$

This is called the **characteristic equation.** It is an nth degree polynomial equation in λ, which has exactly n roots, $\lambda_1, \lambda_2, \ldots, \lambda_n$. These are called the **characteristic roots** or **eigenvalues** of the matrix A.

We first show that all eigenvalues are real. For each eigenvalue λ there is a nontrivial **eigenvector** Y such that

$$AY = \lambda Y$$

Taking the conjugate of both sides of the equation, we have

$$AY^* = \lambda^*Y^*$$

Taking the transpose,

$$(Y^*)'A = \lambda^*(Y^*)'$$

Then $$(Y^*)'AY = \lambda^*(Y^*)'Y = \lambda^* \|\mathbf{Y}\|^2$$

---

[1] Recall that the summation convention applies only to Latin subscripts. Therefore, there is no summation on α.

Also $$(Y^*)'AY = \lambda(Y^*)'Y = \lambda \|\mathbf{Y}\|^2$$

Subtracting, $$(\lambda^* - \lambda) \|\mathbf{Y}\|^2 = 0$$

from which we conclude that λ is real.

Next we show that for two different eigenvalues the corresponding eigenvectors are orthogonal. Assuming $\lambda_\alpha \neq \lambda_\beta$, then

$$AY_\alpha = \lambda_\alpha Y_\alpha$$

$$AY_\beta = \lambda_\beta Y_\beta$$

$$Y_\alpha'A = \lambda_\alpha Y_\alpha'$$

$$Y_\alpha'AY_\beta = \lambda_\alpha Y_\alpha'Y_\beta = \lambda_\alpha(\mathbf{Y}_\alpha,\mathbf{Y}_\beta)$$

$$Y_\alpha'AY_\beta = \lambda_\beta Y_\alpha'Y_\beta = \lambda_\beta(\mathbf{Y}_\alpha,\mathbf{Y}_\beta)$$

Subtracting, $$(\lambda_\alpha - \lambda_\beta)(\mathbf{Y}_\alpha,\mathbf{Y}_\beta) = 0$$

Therefore, $$(\mathbf{Y}_\alpha,\mathbf{Y}_\beta) = 0$$

If all eignevalues are different, then the columns of T, treated as n-dimensional vectors, are orthogonal to one another. They can also be normalized, since, if

$$AY = \lambda Y$$

then $$A\frac{Y}{\|\mathbf{Y}\|} = \lambda \frac{Y}{\|\mathbf{Y}\|}$$

Therefore, $$T'T = I$$

and in this case our problem is solved. The diagonal elements of D are the n different eigenvalues of A.

If some of the eigenvalues are equal, then we have to proceed differently. In this case, we can select a subset of eigenvalues $\lambda_1, \lambda_2, \ldots, \lambda_m$, with $1 \leq m < n$, which are all different. The corresponding eigenvectors $\mathbf{Y}_1, \mathbf{Y}_2, \ldots, \mathbf{Y}_m$ are an orthonormal set. Now we define an orthogonal matrix

$$S = \| Y_1 Y_2 \cdots Y_m Z_1 Z_2 \cdots Z_{n-m}\|$$

where the Z's are column matrices obtained by solving the equations

$$(\mathbf{Y}_i,\mathbf{Z}_j) = 0 \qquad i = 1, 2, \ldots, m$$

$$(\mathbf{Z}_k,\mathbf{Z}_j) = 0 \qquad k = 1, 2, \ldots, j-1$$

These equations always have a nontrivial solution, since they are a set of $m + k$ homogeneous linear equations in n unknowns with $m + k < n$. We also assume that the $\mathbf{Z}$'s have been normalized.   If we perform the multiplication $S'AS$, we have

$$
S'AS = \begin{Vmatrix}
\lambda_1 & 0 & 0 & \cdots & 0 & 0 & 0 & \cdots & 0 \\
0 & \lambda_2 & 0 & \cdots & 0 & 0 & 0 & \cdots & 0 \\
0 & 0 & \lambda_3 & \cdots & 0 & 0 & 0 & \cdots & 0 \\
\cdots & \cdots & \cdots & \cdots & \cdots & \cdots & \cdots & \cdots & \cdots \\
0 & 0 & 0 & \cdots & \lambda_m & 0 & 0 & \cdots & 0 \\
0 & 0 & 0 & \cdots & 0 & c_{11} & c_{12} & \cdots & c_{1\,n-m} \\
0 & 0 & 0 & \cdots & 0 & c_{21} & c_{22} & \cdots & c_{2\,n-m} \\
\cdots & \cdots & \cdots & \cdots & \cdots & \cdots & \cdots & \cdots & \cdots \\
0 & 0 & 0 & \cdots & 0 & c_{n-m1} & c_{n-m2} & \cdots & c_{n-m\ n-m}
\end{Vmatrix}
$$

The matrix C is a real symmetric $(n - m) \times (n - m)$ matrix.   It is not diagonal, because the $\mathbf{Z}$'s do not satisfy the eigenvector equation.   Under the orthogonal transformation $X = S\bar{X}$ the quadratic form becomes

$$Q = \bar{X}'S'AS\bar{X} = \lambda_1 \bar{x}_1^2 + \lambda_2 \bar{x}_2^2 + \cdots + \lambda_m \bar{x}_m^2 + \bar{Q}$$

where

$$\bar{Q} = U'CU \qquad U = \begin{Vmatrix} \bar{x}_{m+1} \\ \bar{x}_{m+2} \\ \cdot \\ \cdot \\ \cdot \\ \bar{x}_n \end{Vmatrix}$$

The eigenvalues of C are also eigenvalues of A, since

$$|S'AS - \lambda I| = |S'AS - \lambda S'IS|$$

$$= |S'|\,|S|\,|A - \lambda I|$$

$$= (\lambda_1 - \lambda)(\lambda_2 - \lambda) \cdots (\lambda_m - \lambda)\,|C - \lambda I|$$

Therefore, the eigenvalues of C are the repeated eigenvalues of A.

The next step is to reduce $\bar{Q}$ to diagonal form by finding an orthogonal matrix R such that $R'CR = D$, a diagonal matrix.   This is just the problem we had before, only in an $(n - m)$-dimensional space.   For simplicity, let us assume that the eigenvalues of C are distinct.   If not we can repeat the above process again.   The eigenvalues of C and corresponding eigenvectors satisfy

$$CV_\alpha = \lambda_\alpha V_\alpha \qquad \alpha = m + 1, m + 2, \ldots, n$$

Consider the matrix

$$\bar{R} = \begin{Vmatrix} 1 & 0 & 0 & \cdots & 0 & 0 & 0 & \cdots & 0 \\ 0 & 1 & 0 & \cdots & 0 & 0 & 0 & \cdots & 0 \\ 0 & 0 & 1 & \cdots & 0 & 0 & 0 & \cdots & 0 \\ & & & \cdots & & & & & \\ 0 & 0 & 0 & \cdots & 1 & 0 & 0 & \cdots & 0 \\ 0 & 0 & 0 & \cdots & 0 & r_{11} & r_{12} & \cdots & r_{1\,n-m} \\ 0 & 0 & 0 & \cdots & 0 & r_{21} & r_{22} & \cdots & r_{2\,n-m} \\ & & & \cdots & & & & & \\ 0 & 0 & 0 & \cdots & 0 & r_{n-m1} & r_{n-m2} & \cdots & r_{n-m\,n-m} \end{Vmatrix}$$

Since R is orthogonal, it is easily shown that $\bar{R}$ is orthogonal. If the orthogonal transformation $\bar{R}'$ is applied to $\bar{X}$, it does not affect the part of the quadratic form already diagonalized, but it does diagonalize $\bar{Q}$. Therefore, we have

$$X = S\bar{X} = S\bar{R}\bar{\bar{X}} = T\bar{\bar{X}}$$

a transformation which reduces Q to diagonal form. T is orthogonal, since

$$T^{-1} = (S\bar{R})^{-1} = \bar{R}^{-1}S^{-1} = \bar{R}'S' = (S\bar{R})' = T'$$

Therefore, T is the desired orthogonal transformation.   The columns of T are the complete set of eigenvectors.   Since orthonormal vectors are linearly independent, the eigenvalue problem leads to precisely n linearly independent vectors, whether there are repeated eigenvalues or not.   If a certain eigenvalue is a multiple root of the characteristic equation, we say that the eigenvalue is **degenerate.**   If it occurs as a root m times, we say that it is m-**fold degenerate.**   Nevertheless, there are still m linearly independent eigenvectors, each satisfying the eigenvector equation for the same value of λ, and these vectors span an m-dimensional subspace.

Since the eigenvectors associated with a given real symmetric $n \times n$ matrix are a set of n linearly independent vectors, they form a basis for the n-dimensional space.   Therefore, any vector in the space can be expanded as a linear combination of the eigenvectors.   This fact allows us to solve certain systems of equations in terms of the eigenvectors of a matrix appearing in the equations. Consider, for example, the nonhomogeneous system of equations

$$AX - \lambda X = C$$

where X is an $n \times 1$ column matrix representing the n unknowns, A is a given $n \times n$ real symmetric matrix, λ is a given constant, and C is a given $n \times 1$

column matrix of real constants. Since X is an n-dimensional vector, it can be written as a linear combination of the eigenvectors Y_α of A, i.e.,

$$X = \sum_{\alpha=1}^{n} \gamma_\alpha Y_\alpha$$

Then the system of equations becomes

$$A \sum_{\alpha=1}^{n} \gamma_\alpha Y_\alpha - \lambda \sum_{\alpha=1}^{n} \gamma_\alpha Y_\alpha = C$$

$$\sum_{\alpha=1}^{n} \lambda_\alpha \gamma_\alpha Y_\alpha - \lambda \sum_{\alpha=1}^{n} \gamma_\alpha Y_\alpha = C$$

$$\sum_{\alpha=1}^{n} \lambda_\alpha \gamma_\alpha (\mathbf{Y}_\alpha, \mathbf{Y}_\beta) - \lambda \sum_{\alpha=1}^{n} \gamma_\alpha (\mathbf{Y}_\alpha, \mathbf{Y}_\beta) = (\mathbf{C}, \mathbf{Y}_\beta)$$

$$\lambda_\beta \gamma_\beta - \lambda \gamma_\beta = (\mathbf{C}, \mathbf{Y}_\beta)$$

$$\gamma_\beta = \frac{(\mathbf{C}, \mathbf{Y}_\beta)}{\lambda_\beta - \lambda}$$

Thus the problem is solved, provided $\lambda \neq \lambda_\beta$ for any β. If $\lambda = \lambda_\beta$ for some β, then there is no solution to the problem unless $(\mathbf{Y}_\beta, \mathbf{C}) = 0$. In this case, γ_β is arbitrary, and there are infinitely many solutions.

A real quadratic form is said to be **positive-definite** if $Q = X'AX > 0$ unless $X = 0$. Obviously, if Q is in the diagonal form

$$Q = \lambda_1 x_1^2 + \lambda_2 x_2^2 + \cdots + \lambda_n x_n^2$$

and all the λ's are positive, then $Q = 0$ implies $x_1 = x_2 = \cdots = x_n = 0$, or $X = 0$. Otherwise $Q > 0$, and therefore Q is positive-definite. If Q is not in diagonal form, it can nevertheless be reduced to diagonal form by an orthogonal transformation $X = T\bar{X}$. Under this transformation

$$Q = X'AX = \bar{X}'D\bar{X} = \lambda_1 \bar{x}_1^2 + \lambda_2 \bar{x}_2^2 + \cdots + \lambda_n \bar{x}_n^2$$

where $\lambda_1, \lambda_2, \ldots, \lambda_n$ are the eigenvalues of A. If all the λ's are positive, then $Q > 0$ unless $\bar{X} = 0$. But under the transformation, $X = TO = 0$, so that Q is positive-definite if all the eigenvalues of A are positive. On the other hand, if any one eigenvalue $\lambda_k \leq 0$, then there exists a nonzero vector $\bar{X}$ which will make $Q \leq 0$. The corresponding $X = T\bar{X}$ is also nonzero, and therefore Q is not positive-definite. The conclusion is that *a quadratic form $Q = X'AX$ is positive-definite if and only if all the eigenvalues of A are positive.*

A pair of quadratic forms $Q_1 = X'AX$ and $Q_2 = X'BX$ can be simultaneously reduced to diagonal form if one of them is positive-definite. Let

Q_1 be positive-definite; then there exists an orthogonal transformation $X = T\bar{X}$ which reduces it to the diagonal form

$$Q_1 = \lambda_1 \bar{x}_1^2 + \lambda_2 \bar{x}_2^2 + \cdots + \lambda_n \bar{x}_n^2$$

with all the λ's positive. The transformation $\bar{X} = SY$, with

$$S = \begin{Vmatrix} \lambda_1^{-\frac{1}{2}} & 0 & 0 & \cdots & \cdots & 0 \\ 0 & \lambda_2^{-\frac{1}{2}} & 0 & \cdots & \cdots & 0 \\ 0 & 0 & \cdots & \cdots & \cdots & \cdots \\ \cdots\cdots\cdots\cdots\cdots\cdots\cdots\cdots \\ \cdots & \cdots & \cdots & \cdots & \cdots & 0 \\ 0 & 0 & \cdots & \cdots & 0 & \lambda_n^{-\frac{1}{2}} \end{Vmatrix}$$

reduces Q_1 to

$$Q_1 = y_1^2 + y_2^2 + \cdots + y_n^2 = Y'Y$$

The same transformation $X = TSY$ changes Q_2 to

$$Q_2 = Y'S'T'BTSY = Y'CY$$

C is real and symmetric since

$$C' = S'T'B'T''S'' = S'T'BTS = C$$

so that Q_2 is a quadratic form in Y which can be reduced to diagonal form by an orthogonal transformation $Y = R\bar{Y}$, giving

$$Q_2 = \mu_1 \bar{y}_1^2 + \mu_2 \bar{y}_2^2 + \cdots + \mu_n \bar{y}_n^2$$

The transformation $Y = R\bar{Y}$ does not affect the form of Q_1, since

$$Q_1 = Y'Y = \bar{Y}'R'R\bar{Y} = \bar{Y}'\bar{Y}$$

Hence, the total transformation $X = TSR\bar{Y}$ reduces Q_1 and Q_2 simultaneously to diagonal form. The transformation is not, in general, orthogonal.

The problem corresponding to reduction of quadratic forms in the space of vectors with complex components is the problem of reducing hermitian forms to diagonal form. A **hermitian form** is an expression of the form

$$H = (X*)'AX$$

where A is hermitian, i.e., $(A*)' = A$. The value of H is always real, for

$$H* = (H*)' = (X'A*X*)' = (X*)'(A*)'X = (X*)'AX = H$$

The main theorem dealing with hermitian forms is that *a hermitian form can always be reduced to diagonal form by a unitary transformation*. The proof follows.

We seek a unitary transformation $X = T\bar{X}$, such that $(T^*)' = T^{-1}$, which will reduce H to diagonal form, i.e.,

$$H = (X^*)'AX = (\bar{X}^*)'(T^*)'AT\bar{X} = (\bar{X}^*)'D\bar{X}$$

$$= \lambda_1 |\bar{x}_1|^2 + \lambda_2 |\bar{x}_2|^2 + \cdots + \lambda_n |\bar{x}_n|^2$$

In other words, we wish to find a unitary matrix, such that $(T^*)'AT = D$ or $AT = TD$. In subscript notation this is $a_{ij}t_{j\alpha} = \lambda_\alpha t_{i\alpha}$. Let Y_α be the αth column of T; then

$$AY_\alpha = \lambda_\alpha Y_\alpha$$

Thus we are led to the eigenvalue problem $AY = \lambda Y$ and the characteristic equation $|A - \lambda I| = 0$. The characteristic equation has n solutions $\lambda_1, \lambda_2,$ $\ldots, \lambda_n$, not necessarily distinct.

Since A has complex elements, the eigenvectors Y_α have complex components. However, because A is hermitian, the eigenvalues are real.

$$A^*Y^* = \lambda^*Y^*$$

$$(Y^*)'(A^*)' = (Y^*)'A = \lambda^*(Y^*)'$$

$$(Y^*)'AY = \lambda^*(Y^*)'Y = \lambda^* \|\mathbf{Y}\|^2$$

$$(Y^*)'AY = \lambda(Y^*)'Y = \lambda \|\mathbf{Y}\|^2$$

Subtracting, $(\lambda^* - \lambda) \|\mathbf{Y}\|^2 = 0$, and since $\|\mathbf{Y}\|^2 > 0$, λ is real. Also, for two different eigenvalues the eigenvectors are orthogonal. If $\lambda_\alpha \neq \lambda_\beta$,

$$AY_\alpha = \lambda_\alpha Y_\alpha$$

$$AY_\beta = \lambda_\beta Y_\beta$$

$$(Y^*_\alpha)'(A^*)' = (Y^*_\alpha)'A = \lambda_\alpha(Y^*_\alpha)'$$

$$(Y^*_\alpha)'AY_\beta = \lambda_\alpha(Y^*_\alpha)'Y_\beta = \lambda_\alpha(\mathbf{Y}_\alpha,\mathbf{Y}_\beta)$$

$$(Y^*_\alpha)'AY_\beta = \lambda_\beta(Y^*_\alpha)'Y_\beta = \lambda_\beta(\mathbf{Y}_\alpha,\mathbf{Y}_\beta)$$

Subtracting, $(\lambda_\alpha - \lambda_\beta)(\mathbf{Y}_\alpha,\mathbf{Y}_\beta) = 0$, and therefore $(\mathbf{Y}_\alpha,\mathbf{Y}_\beta) = 0$.

If all the eigenvalues are distinct, we have a set of n orthogonal eigenvectors. The eigenvectors can also be normalized, and therefore they constitute an orthonormal set of vectors. The matrix

$$T = \| Y_1 \, Y_2 \cdots Y_n \|$$

is therefore unitary, and this is the matrix which reduces H to diagonal form. If some of the eigenvalues are equal, we have the degenerate case, and we proceed in a manner quite similar to that used in the case of the quadratic form. The details will not be given.

Exercises 1.10

1. Show that the general equation of a quadric surface in three-dimensional euclidean space,

$$X'AX + BX + k = 0$$

can be reduced to the form $Y'AY = c$ if A is nonsingular.

2. On the basis of the eigenvalues of A, classify the quadric surfaces

$$X'AX + BX + k = 0$$

into ellipsoids, hyperboloids, paraboloids, and cylinders.

3. Find an orthogonal transformation which will reduce

$$Q = 2x_1^2 + 2x_2^2 + 2x_3^2 - x_1x_2 - x_2x_3$$

to diagonal form.

4. Find a transformation which will simultaneously reduce

$$Q_1 = 3x_1^2 - 2x_1x_2 + 3x_2^2$$

and $Q_2 = x_1x_2$ to diagonal form.

5. Show that a pair of hermitian forms can be simultaneously reduced to diagonal form if one of them is positive-definite.

6. The $n \times n$ matrix A is said to be **equivalent** to the $n \times n$ matrix B, written $A \sim B$, if there exist nonsingular matrices S and T such that $SAT = B$. Show that this equivalence relation satisfies the three required properties:

a. Reflexive: for all A, $A \sim A$.

b. Symmetric: if $A \sim B$, then $B \sim A$.

c. Transitive: if $A \sim B$ and $B \sim C$, then $A \sim C$.

7. If T is nonsingular, $T^{-1}AT$ is called a **similarity transformation.** Show that if A and B are equivalent to diagonal matrices under the same similarity transformation, then A and B commute.

8. If $\lambda_1, \lambda_2, \ldots, \lambda_n$ are the eigenvalues of a real symmetric matrix A with corresponding normalized eigenvectors $Y_1, Y_2, \ldots, Y_n$, show that the following equations are satisfied:

a. $(A - \lambda_1 I)a_1 Y_1 = O$

b. $(A - \lambda_2 I)(A - \lambda_1 I)(a_1 Y_1 + a_2 Y_2) = O$

c. $(A - \lambda_n I)(A - \lambda_{n-1}I) \cdots (A - \lambda_1 I)(a_1 Y_1 + a_2 Y_2 + \cdots + a_n Y_n) = O$

for arbitrary $a_1, a_2, \ldots, a_n$. Hence show that $F(A) = O$, where

$$F(\lambda) = (\lambda - \lambda_n)(\lambda - \lambda_{n-1}) \cdots (\lambda - \lambda_1) = 0$$

is the characteristic equation of A. This is a special case of the **Cayley-Hamilton theorem.**

*9. Let A be an $m \times n$ matrix with elements $a_{ij}(t)$ which are differentiable functions of t. If we define the derivative of A by

$$\frac{dA}{dt} = \lim_{\Delta t \to 0} \frac{A(t + \Delta t) - A(t)}{\Delta t}$$

show that $\dfrac{dA}{dt}$ has elements $\dfrac{d}{dt}a_{ij}$.

*10. Let $H(X) = (X^*)'AX$ be a positive-definite hermitian form. Define the **associated bilinear form** $H(X,Y) = (X^*)'AY$. Show that $H(X,Y)$ satisfies the postulates for a scalar product.

1.11. Systems of Ordinary Differential Equations. Vibrations Problems

As an application of some of the ideas developed in the previous sections, we now consider the problem of solving certain systems of ordinary differential equations.   The system of differential equations

$$\alpha_m \frac{d^m x_1}{dt^m} + \alpha_{m-1} \frac{d^{m-1} x_1}{dt^{m-1}} + \cdots + \alpha_1 \frac{dx_1}{dt} = a_{11}x_1 + a_{12}x_2 + \cdots + a_{1n}x_n$$

$$\alpha_m \frac{d^m x_2}{dt^m} + \alpha_{m-1} \frac{d^{m-1} x_2}{dt^{m-1}} + \cdots + \alpha_1 \frac{dx_2}{dt} = a_{21}x_1 + a_{22}x_2 + \cdots + a_{2n}x_n$$

$$\cdots\cdots\cdots\cdots\cdots\cdots\cdots\cdots\cdots$$

$$\alpha_m \frac{d^m x_n}{dt^m} + \alpha_{m-1} \frac{d^{m-1} x_n}{dt^{m-1}} + \cdots + \alpha_1 \frac{dx_n}{dt} = a_{n1}x_1 + a_{n2}x_2 + \cdots a_{nn}x_n$$

where $\alpha_1, \alpha_2, \ldots, \alpha_m$ and a_{ij} are real constants, is a system of n linear ordinary differential equations in n unknowns.   This system can be written in matrix notation as

$$\mathscr{D}X = AX$$

where

$$\mathscr{D} = \alpha_m \frac{d^m}{dt^m} + \alpha_{m-1} \frac{d^{m-1}}{dt^{m-1}} + \cdots + \alpha_1 \frac{d}{dt}$$

is an mth-order linear differential operator.   If A is symmetric, we know that there exists an orthogonal matrix T such that $T'AT = D$, where D is diagonal. This fact leads to a solution of the system.

Let $X = T\bar{X}$; then $\mathscr{D}X = T\mathscr{D}\bar{X} = AT\bar{X}$.   Multiplying on the left by T' gives $\mathscr{D}\bar{X} = T'AT\bar{X} = D\bar{X}$.   In terms of the components of $\bar{X}$, $\mathscr{D}\bar{x}_\beta = \lambda_\beta \bar{x}_\beta$, where the λ's are the eigenvalues of A.   In terms of $\bar{X}$ the variables are separated, so the problem reduces to solving n mth-order ordinary differential equations.   Each $\bar{x}_\beta$ contains m arbitrary constants, so that the general solution of the system has mn arbitrary constants.

Problems of this type occur frequently in the theory of small vibrations. The general theory of small vibrations will be treated in Chap. 2, but we can consider some examples here.   In the case of undamped vibrations, the operator $\mathscr{D}$ is just the second derivative, and the system of differential equations can be written as

$$\ddot{X} = \frac{d^2 X}{dt^2} = AX$$

Under the orthogonal transformation $X = T\bar{X}$, the system becomes

$$\frac{d^2 \bar{x}_\beta}{dt^2} = \lambda_\beta \bar{x}_\beta$$

which has the solution

$$\bar{x}_\beta = c_\beta \sin\left(\sqrt{-\lambda_\beta}\, t + \phi_\beta\right)$$

where c_β and ϕ_β are arbitrary constants. The solution of the original system is $X = T\bar{X}$, and the $2n$ constants c_β and ϕ_β are evaluated in terms of the initial conditions on the x's.

If the initial conditions are properly chosen, it is possible to make $c_\beta = 1$ and $c_i = 0$ for $i \neq \beta$. For such a choice of initial conditions we have the particular solution

$$x_{i\beta} = t_{ij}\bar{x}_{j\beta} = t_{i\beta} \sin (\sqrt{-\lambda_\beta}t + \phi_\beta)$$
$$= y_{i\beta} \sin (\sqrt{-\lambda_\beta}t + \phi_\beta)$$

where the $y_{i\beta}$ is the ith component of the βth eigenvector of A, which satisfies the eigenvalue problem $AY_\beta = \lambda_\beta Y_\beta$. We notice that this particular solution is one in which every component of the solution has the same circular frequency $\omega_\beta = \sqrt{-\lambda_\beta}$. Such a solution is called a **normal mode** of the system, with a **natural frequency** ω_β. The normal modes are directly related to the eigenvalues and eigenvectors of A by the equation

$$\mathbf{X}_\beta = \mathbf{Y}_\beta \sin (\omega_\beta t + \phi_\beta)$$

When we substitute $\mathbf{X}_\beta$ into the system of differential equations, we have

$$\frac{d^2}{dt^2} X_\beta = -\omega_\beta^2 Y_\beta \sin (\omega_\beta t + \phi_\beta) = A Y_\beta \sin (\omega_\beta t + \phi_\beta)$$

or
$$A Y_\beta = \lambda_\beta Y_\beta$$

the eigenvalue problem. Anticipating this result, we could have started out by seeking those particular solutions all of whose components have the same frequency. This would have led to the eigenvalue problem $AY = \lambda Y$ and characteristic equation $|A - \lambda I| = 0$, the roots of which give the natural frequencies. The general solution is then a linear combination of the normal modes $\mathbf{X} = c_k\mathbf{X}_k$. The normal modes are orthogonal, i.e., for $\alpha \neq \beta$

$$(\mathbf{X}_\alpha, \mathbf{X}_\beta) = (\mathbf{Y}_\alpha, \mathbf{Y}_\beta) \sin (\omega_\alpha t + \phi_\alpha) \sin (\omega_\beta t + \phi_\beta) = 0$$

because the eigenvectors are orthogonal. This makes it easy to evaluate the unknown constants in terms of the initial conditions:[1]

$$\mathbf{X}(0) = \sum_{\alpha=1}^{n} c_\alpha \mathbf{Y}_\alpha \sin \phi_\alpha$$

$$[\mathbf{X}(0), \mathbf{Y}_\beta] = c_\beta \sin \phi_\beta$$

$$\dot{\mathbf{X}}(0) = \left(\frac{dX}{dt}\right)_{t=0} = \sum_{\alpha=1}^{n} \omega_\alpha c_\alpha \mathbf{Y}_\alpha \cos \phi_\alpha$$

$$[\dot{\mathbf{X}}(0), \mathbf{Y}_\beta] = \omega_\beta c_\beta \cos \phi_\beta$$

$$c_\beta = \left\{[\mathbf{X}(0), \mathbf{Y}_\beta]^2 - \frac{[\dot{\mathbf{X}}(0), \mathbf{Y}_\beta]^2}{\lambda_\beta}\right\}^{\frac{1}{2}}$$

$$\phi_\beta = \tan^{-1} \frac{\omega_\beta[\mathbf{X}(0), \mathbf{Y}_\beta]}{[\dot{\mathbf{X}}(0), \mathbf{Y}_\beta]}$$

[1] The value of $\tan^{-1}$ is chosen to give $\cos \phi\beta$ and $\sin \phi_\beta$ the correct sign.

As an example of the foregoing discussion, let us consider the small vibrations of the following system of masses and springs:

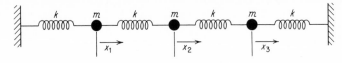

FIGURE 1

The differential equations governing the motion are

$$m\ddot{x}_1 = -kx_1 + k(x_2 - x_1)$$
$$m\ddot{x}_2 = -k(x_2 - x_1) + k(x_3 - x_2)$$
$$m\ddot{x}_3 = k(x_2 - x_3) - kx_3$$

In matrix form they are $\ddot{X} = AX$, where

$$A = \left\|\begin{array}{ccc} -2\alpha & \alpha & 0 \\ \alpha & -2\alpha & \alpha \\ 0 & \alpha & -2\alpha \end{array}\right\|$$

$\alpha = k/m$. The characteristic equation is

$$-(\lambda + 2\alpha)^3 + 2\alpha^2(\lambda + 2\alpha) = 0$$

and it has roots $\lambda_1 = -2\alpha$, $\lambda_2 = (-2 + \sqrt{2})\alpha$, $\lambda_3 = (-2 - \sqrt{2})\alpha$, giving the natural frequencies $\omega_1 = \sqrt{2k/m}$, $\omega_2 = \sqrt{(2 - \sqrt{2})k/m}$, $\omega_3 = \sqrt{(2 + \sqrt{2})k/m}$. The corresponding normal modes are

$$\mathbf{X}_1 = \left\|\begin{array}{c} \dfrac{1}{\sqrt{2}} \\ 0 \\ -\dfrac{1}{\sqrt{2}} \end{array}\right\| \sin(\omega_1 t + \phi_1)$$

$$\mathbf{X}_2 = \left\|\begin{array}{c} \frac{1}{2} \\ \dfrac{1}{\sqrt{2}} \\ \frac{1}{2} \end{array}\right\| \sin(\omega_2 t + \phi_2)$$

$$\mathbf{X}_3 = \left\|\begin{array}{c} \frac{1}{2} \\ -\dfrac{1}{\sqrt{2}} \\ \frac{1}{2} \end{array}\right\| \sin(\omega_3 t + \phi_3)$$

The first mode represents a motion in which the center mass remains fixed and the masses on the sides move in opposite directions with equal amplitude.   In the second mode all masses move in the same direction, the side masses moving with equal amplitude, and the center mass moving with an amplitude $\sqrt{2}$ times the amplitude of the others. The third mode is like the second, except that the center mass moves in the opposite direction from the side masses. Any other possible motion of the system is a linear combination of these normal modes.

The case of forced vibrations with periodic forcing functions can also be handled very readily. Suppose in the above example each mass has an external periodic force acting on it, i.e.,

$$f_1 = b_1 \sin(\mu_1 t + \theta_1)$$
$$f_2 = b_2 \sin(\mu_2 t + \theta_2)$$
$$f_3 = b_3 \sin(\mu_3 t + \theta_3)$$

are the forces acting on masses with displacements x_1, x_2, x_3, respectively. The differential equations can now be written

$$\ddot{X} = AX + F_1 + F_2 + F_3$$

where

$$F_1 = \left\| \begin{matrix} \dfrac{b_1}{m} \\ 0 \\ 0 \end{matrix} \right\| \sin(\mu_1 t + \theta_1) \qquad F_2 = \left\| \begin{matrix} 0 \\ \dfrac{b_2}{m} \\ 0 \end{matrix} \right\| \sin(\mu_2 t + \theta_2)$$

and

$$F_3 = \left\| \begin{matrix} 0 \\ 0 \\ \dfrac{b_3}{m} \end{matrix} \right\| \sin(\mu_3 t + \theta_3)$$

We have the system of nonhomogeneous differential equations

$$\ddot{X} - AX = F_1 + F_2 + F_3$$

There is a complementary solution X_0 which satisfies the homogeneous differential equations $\ddot{X}_0 - AX_0 = 0$ and contains six arbitrary constants. Furthermore, there are three particular solutions Z_1, Z_2, Z_3 which satisfy the equations $\ddot{Z}_i - AZ_i = F_i, i = 1, 2, 3$. Since the equations are linear,

$$X = X_0 + Z_1 + Z_2 + Z_3$$

satisfies the differential equations $\ddot{X} - AX = F_1 + F_2 + F_3$ and has the required number of arbitrary constants, and it is, therefore, the general solution. Our problem is thus one of solving for a particular solution

$$\ddot{Z} - AZ = F = C \sin(\mu t + \theta)$$

Let $Z = B \sin{(\mu t + \theta)}$; then $\ddot{Z} = -\mu^2 B \sin{(\mu t + \theta)}$, and $-\mu^2 B - AB = C$.[1]
B can be written as a linear combination of the eigenvectors of A, i.e.,

$$B = \sum_{\alpha=1}^{n} \gamma_\alpha Y_\alpha$$

Substituting for B,

$$-\mu^2 \sum_{\alpha=1}^{n} \gamma_\alpha Y_\alpha - A \sum_{\alpha=1}^{n} \gamma_\alpha Y_\alpha = C$$

$$-\mu^2 \sum_{\alpha=1}^{n} \gamma_\alpha Y_\alpha - \sum_{\alpha=1}^{n} \lambda_\alpha \gamma_\alpha Y_\alpha = C$$

$$-\mu^2 \sum_{\alpha=1}^{n} \gamma_\alpha (\mathbf{Y}_\alpha, \mathbf{Y}_\beta) - \sum_{\alpha=1}^{n} \lambda_\alpha \gamma_\alpha (\mathbf{Y}_\alpha, \mathbf{Y}_\beta) = (\mathbf{C}, \mathbf{Y}_\beta)$$

$$-\mu^2 \gamma_\beta - \lambda_\beta \gamma_\beta = (\mathbf{C}, \mathbf{Y}_\beta)$$

$$\gamma_\beta = \frac{(\mathbf{C}, \mathbf{Y}_\beta)}{-\mu^2 - \lambda_\beta}$$

provided $\lambda_\beta \neq -\mu^2$. If $-\mu^2 = \lambda_\beta$ for some β, then we have the case of **resonance** where the amplitude of vibration builds up with time, and this must be handled in a different way.

In the case of resonance, $-\mu^2 = \lambda_\beta$ for some β, the problem can still be solved by diagonalizing the matrix A, assuming A is real and symmetric. There exists an orthogonal transformation $Z = T\bar{Z}$ which reduces the equations to

$$\ddot{\bar{z}}_\alpha - \lambda_\alpha \bar{z}_\alpha = \bar{c}_\alpha \sin{(\mu t + \theta)}$$

Particular solutions for these equations are

$$\bar{z}_\alpha = \frac{\bar{c}_\alpha}{-\mu^2 - \lambda_\alpha} \sin{(\mu t + \theta)}$$

except for $\alpha = \beta$, where the method of undetermined coefficients gives the particular solution

$$\bar{z}_\beta = \frac{\bar{c}_\beta}{-2\mu} t \cos{(\mu t + \theta)}$$

The particular solution $Z = T\bar{Z}$ is a linear combination of the particular solutions one of which builds up in amplitude with the factor t. This is typical of resonance without damping.

If the applied forces are not sinusoidal but are periodic, then they can be expanded in Fourier series. Then the response to each component can be calculated by the methods just described. Since the problem is linear, the total response can be calculated by adding the responses of all the components, provided the resulting Fourier series can be shown to converge.

---

[1] Compare with the nonhomogeneous linear equations in Sec. 1.10.

Exercises 1.11

1. Three equal masses are attached to a string at equal distances from one another and from the ends, which are fastened to supports so that there is a tension T in the string. Compute the normal modes and natural frequencies of small transverse vibrations about equilibrium. Describe the normal modes. HINT: Assume the tension constant, neglect gravity, and assume the string weightless.

2. In the example of the three masses mounted on springs given in the text, assume that the system is started from rest in the equilibrium position by a force $mg \sin 2 \sqrt{k/m} \, t$ acting on the center mass. Find the complete solution for the motion.

3. Assuming damping forces $-\beta^2 \dot{x}_1$, $-\beta^2 \dot{x}_2$, and $-\beta^2 \dot{x}_3$ acting on the three masses in exercise 2, find the transient solution for arbitrary initial conditions.

4. Do exercise 2 with damping forces as in exercise 3 and with force $mg \sin \sqrt{2k/m} \, t$ acting on the center mass.

References

Birkhoff, Garrett, and Saunders MacLane: "A Survey of Modern Algebra," The Macmillan Company, New York, 1949.

Churchill, Ruel V.: "Fourier Series and Boundary Value Problems," McGraw-Hill Book Company, Inc., New York, 1941.

Courant, Richard, and David Hilbert: "Methods of Mathematical Physics," Interscience Publishers, Inc., New York, 1953, vol. I.

Halmos, Paul R.: "Finite-dimensional Vector Spaces," D. Van Nostrand Company, Inc., Princeton, N.J., 1958.

Macduffee, Cyrus C.: "Theory of Equations," John Wiley & Sons, Inc., New York, 1954.

Thrall, Robert M., and Leonard Thornheim: "Vector Spaces and Matrices," John Wiley & Sons, Inc., New York, 1957.

Chapter 2. Calculus of Variations

2.1 Maxima and Minima of Functions. Lagrange Multipliers

One of the fundamental theorems of analysis tells us that *a continuous function defined over a bounded closed region takes on a maximum and minimum value somewhere in the region.* This maximum and minimum may occur on the boundary of the region or at an interior point. At an interior point we may have a **relative maximum** or a **relative minimum.** The condition for a relative maximum of the function $f(x_1, x_2, \ldots, x_n)$ at a point with coordinates $(x_1, x_2, \ldots, x_n)$ is that there exist some neighborhood of the point for which

$$f(x_1 + \Delta x_1, x_2 + \Delta x_2, \ldots, x_n + \Delta x_n) - f(x_1, x_2, \ldots, x_n) \leq 0$$

for arbitrary $\Delta x_1, \Delta x_2, \ldots, \Delta x_n$. For a relative minimum there must exist some neighborhood of the point throughout which

$$f(x_1 + \Delta x_1, x_2 + \Delta x_2, \ldots, x_n + \Delta x_n) - f(x_1, x_2, \ldots, x_n) \geq 0$$

If the function $f(x_1, x_2, \ldots, x_n)$ has first partial derivatives at a relative maximum or relative minimum, then it is easy to find necessary conditions for such a point. For example, in some neighborhood of a relative maximum

$$\frac{f(x_1, x_2, \ldots, x_k + \Delta x_k, \ldots, x_n) - f(x_1, x_2, \ldots, x_k, \ldots, x_n)}{\Delta x_k} \leq 0$$

for positive Δx_k. Also

$$\frac{f(x_1, x_2, \ldots, x_k + \Delta x_k, \ldots, x_n) - f(x_1, x_2, \ldots, x_k, \ldots, x_n)}{\Delta x_k} \geq 0$$

for Δx_k negative. But the existence of $\dfrac{\partial f}{\partial x_k}$ at the point $(x_1, x_2, \ldots, x_n)$ implies that

$$\lim_{\Delta x_k \to 0} \frac{f(x_1, x_2, \ldots, x_k + \Delta x_k, \ldots, x_n) - f(x_1, x_2, \ldots, x_k, \ldots, x_n)}{\Delta x_k}$$

68

exists and is independent of whether Δx_k approaches zero through positive or through negative values. Therefore, $\dfrac{\partial f}{\partial x_k} = 0$ at a relative maximum point, and this is true for all k. The necessary condition for a relative minimum point is the same, and the proof is quite similar.

The fact that $\dfrac{\partial f}{\partial x_k} = 0$ for all k is not a sufficient condition for a relative maximum or minimum, as is seen by the example $f(x_1,x_2) = x_1 x_2$.

$$\frac{\partial f}{\partial x_1} = \frac{\partial f}{\partial x_2} = 0 \qquad \text{at } x_1 = x_2 = 0$$

but $f(x_1,x_2)$ takes on positive values in the first and third quadrants and negative values in the second and fourth quadrants. Hence the origin can be neither a maximum nor a minimum point. In this case, the origin is called a **saddle point.** In any case, we say that $\dfrac{\partial f}{\partial x_k} = 0$ is a necessary condition for a **stationary value** of the function. The sufficient conditions for relative maxima and minima involve, in addition to the first partial derivatives' being zero, inequalities containing higher-order derivatives.[1]

The necessary conditions for a relative maximum or minimum can be phrased in another way. Assuming that $f(x_1,x_2, \ldots ,x_n)$ has continuous first partial derivatives in a neighborhood of the extremum point, we can write

$$\Delta f = f(x_1 + \Delta x_1, x_2 + \Delta x_2, \ldots, x_n + \Delta x_n) - f(x_1,x_2, \ldots ,x_n)$$

$$= \frac{\partial f}{\partial x_1}\Delta x_1 + \frac{\partial f}{\partial x_2}\Delta x_2 + \cdots + \frac{\partial f}{\partial x_n}\Delta x_n + \xi_1 \Delta x_1 + \xi_2 \Delta x_2 + \cdots + \xi_n \Delta x_n$$

$$= \frac{\partial f}{\partial x_i}\Delta x_i + \xi_i \Delta x_i$$

where $\xi_i \to 0$ as $\Delta x_i \to 0$. The first-order change, or more simply, the **first variation** of f is $df = \dfrac{\partial f}{\partial x_i}\,dx_i$, where we have replaced Δx_i by the differentials dx_i. *The necessary condition for a relative maximum or minimum of a function with continuous first partial derivatives is that the first variation df vanish for arbitrary changes dx_i in the independent variables x_i.*

If the variables $x_1, x_2, \ldots , x_n$ are not independent but satisfy some condition or conditions of constraint, the extremum points can usually be found by a straightforward procedure of differentiation and solution of simultaneous equations, or by the method of **Lagrange multipliers.** To illustrate the equivalence of these two methods, we consider first the problem of extremizing

[1] See R. Creighton Buck, "Advanced Calculus," McGraw-Hill Book Company, Inc., New York, 1956.

a function of two variables subject to one constraint.   We shall then generalize to the case of a function of n variables subject to k constraints.

Suppose we are asked to locate a relative maximum or minimum of $f(x_1,x_2)$ subject to the constraining condition $g(x_1,x_2) = 0$.   In principle we can solve $g(x_1,x_2) = 0$ for x_2 in terms of x_1, i.e., $x_2 = G(x_1)$.   Substituting in $f(x_1,x_2)$, we have

$$f[x_1,G(x_1)] = F(x_1)$$

a function of the single variable x_1 to be maximized or minimized, a necessary condition for which is $F'(x_1) = 0$.   Hence, we can locate the stationary value by solving simultaneously

$$F'(x_1) = \frac{\partial f}{\partial x_1} + \frac{\partial f}{\partial x_2}\, G'(x_1) = 0$$

$$g(x_1,x_2) = 0$$

From the constraint we have

$$\frac{\partial g}{\partial x_1}\, dx_1 + \frac{\partial g}{\partial x_2}\, dx_2 = 0$$

from which we have

$$G'(x_1) = \frac{dx_2}{dx_1} = -\,\frac{\partial g/\partial x_1}{\partial g/\partial x_2}$$

provided $\dfrac{\partial g}{\partial x_2} \neq 0$.   Hence the equations we are left to solve are

$$\frac{\partial f}{\partial x_1}\frac{\partial g}{\partial x_2} - \frac{\partial f}{\partial x_2}\frac{\partial g}{\partial x_1} = 0$$

$$g(x_1,x_2) = 0$$

Consider the problem of maximizing or minimizing the function

$$H(x_1,x_2,\lambda) = f(x_1,x_2) + \lambda g(x_1,x_2)$$

as a function of the three variables x_1, x_2, λ subject to no constraint.   The necessary conditions for a stationary value are

$$\frac{\partial H}{\partial x_1} = \frac{\partial f}{\partial x_1} + \lambda \frac{\partial g}{\partial x_1} = 0$$

$$\frac{\partial H}{\partial x_2} = \frac{\partial f}{\partial x_2} + \lambda \frac{\partial g}{\partial x_2} = 0$$

$$\frac{\partial H}{\partial \lambda} = g(x_1,x_2) = 0$$

Eliminating λ, we arrive back at the system of equations

$$\frac{\partial f}{\partial x_1}\frac{\partial g}{\partial x_2} - \frac{\partial f}{\partial x_2}\frac{\partial g}{\partial x_1} = 0$$

$$g(x_1,x_2) = 0$$

Thus the two methods are equivalent. The second is called the method of Lagrange multipliers, and the λ is called the **Lagrange multiplier.**

More generally we can consider the problem of maximizing or minimizing a function $f(x_1,x_2, \ldots ,x_n)$ subject to constraints

$$g_1(x_1,x_2, \ldots ,x_n) = 0$$
$$g_2(x_1,x_2, \ldots ,x_n) = 0$$
$$\cdots\cdots\cdots\cdots\cdots$$
$$g_k(x_1,x_2, \ldots ,x_n) = 0$$

with $k < n$. In principle we could solve the constraints for k of the variables in terms of the other $n - k$, substitute into $f(x_1,x_2, \ldots ,x_n)$, and arrive at a function of $n - k$ independent variables to be extremized. Alternatively, we can proceed as follows. The first variation $df = \dfrac{\partial f}{\partial x_i} \, dx_i$ must vanish, but now, because of the k constraints, only $n - k$ of the differentials dx_i are independent. The differentials must satisfy k conditions of constraint, i.e.,

$$\frac{\partial g_j}{\partial x_i} \, dx_i = 0 \qquad i = 1, 2, \ldots , n$$
$$j = 1, 2, \ldots , k$$

Multiplying these equations by λ_j and summing, we have

$$\left(\frac{\partial f}{\partial x_i} + \lambda_j \frac{\partial g_j}{\partial x_i} \right) dx_i = 0$$

which is true for arbitrary λ's and arbitrary values of $n - k$ of the differentials. We pick the λ's so that k of the expressions in the parentheses vanish. The remaining expressions in parentheses must also vanish, since the $n - k$ remaining differentials are arbitrary. We arrive at the following necessary conditions for a relative maximum or minimum:

$$\frac{\partial f}{\partial x_i} + \lambda_j \frac{\partial g_j}{\partial x_i} = 0 \qquad i = 1, 2, \ldots , n$$
$$g_j(x_1,x_2, \ldots ,x_n) = 0 \qquad j = 1, 2, \ldots , k$$

This gives $n + k$ equations to solve for $x_1, x_2, \ldots , x_n$ and $\lambda_1, \lambda_2, \ldots , \lambda_k$. These equations are the necessary conditions for a relative maximum or minimum of

$$H(x_1,x_2, \ldots ,x_n,\lambda_1,\lambda_2, \ldots ,\lambda_k) = f(x_1,x_2, \ldots ,x_n) + \lambda_j g_j(x_1,x_2, \ldots ,x_n)$$

To illustrate the use of Lagrange multipliers, consider the problem of finding the minimum distance from the plane $ax_1 + bx_2 + cx_3 + d = 0$ to the origin. Geometrically it is clear that such a minimum exists. The problem is to minimize $f(x_1,x_2,x_3) = x_1^2 + x_2^2 + x_3^2$ subject to the constraint

$$g(x_1,x_2,x_3) = ax_1 + bx_2 + cx_3 + d = 0$$

In the method of Lagrange multipliers, we minimize

$$H(x_1,x_2,x_3,\lambda) = x_1^2 + x_2^2 + x_3^2 + \lambda(ax_1 + bx_2 + cx_3 + d)$$

The necessary conditions for the minimum are

$$\frac{\partial H}{\partial x_1} = 2x_1 + a\lambda = 0$$

$$\frac{\partial H}{\partial x_2} = 2x_2 + b\lambda = 0$$

$$\frac{\partial H}{\partial x_3} = 2x_3 + c\lambda = 0$$

$$\frac{\partial H}{\partial \lambda} = ax_1 + bx_2 + cx_3 + d = 0$$

Solving for λ, we have

$$\lambda = \frac{2d}{a^2 + b^2 + c^2}$$

The minimum occurs at the point

$$x_1 = -ad/(a^2 + b^2 + c^2) \qquad x_2 = -bd/(a^2 + b^2 + c^2)$$

$$x_3 = -cd/(a^2 + b^2 + c^2)$$

and the actual minimum is equal to $|d|/(a^2 + b^2 + c^2)^{\frac{1}{2}}$.

As another example, consider the real quadratic form

$$Q(x_1,x_2, \ldots ,x_n) = X'AX$$

where A is real and symmetric. If we divide Q by $X'X$, which is positive unless $X = O$, we have a function

$$f(X) = f(x_1,x_2, \ldots ,x_n) = \frac{a_{ij}x_i x_j}{x_k x_k} = \frac{X'AX}{X'X}$$

If $\mathbf{Y}$ is an eigenvector of A corresponding to an eigenvalue λ, then

$$f(Y) = \frac{Y'AY}{Y'Y} = \frac{\lambda Y'Y}{Y'Y} = \lambda$$

and, furthermore, f is stationary with respect to small changes of $\mathbf{X}$ about $\mathbf{Y}$, i.e.,

$$df = \left[\frac{(y_k y_k)(2a_{ij}y_j) - (a_{kj}y_k y_j)(2y_i)}{(y_m y_m)^2} \right] dx_i$$

$$= \left[\frac{(y_k y_k)(2\lambda y_i) - (\lambda y_j y_j)(2y_i)}{(y_m y_m)^2} \right] dx_i$$

$$= 0$$

This suggests that the eigenvalues of A can be found by finding the stationary values of f.

Recall that the eigenvalues of A are all real and that there are a finite number of them. Hence they can be ordered as follows:

$$\lambda_1 \le \lambda_2 \le \lambda_3 \le \cdots \le \lambda_n$$

assuming A is $n \times n$. Any vector $\mathbf{X}$ can be expressed as a linear combination of the normalized eigenvectors $\mathbf{Y}_i$, i.e., $\mathbf{X} = c_i \mathbf{Y}_i$, so that

$$f(X) = \frac{(c_i Y_i')A(c_j Y_j)}{(c_k Y_k')(c_m Y_m)} = \frac{\displaystyle\sum_{i=1}^{n}\sum_{j=1}^{n} (c_i Y_i')c_j(\lambda_j Y_j)}{c_k c_m Y_k' Y_m}$$

$$= \frac{\displaystyle\sum_{i=1}^{n}\sum_{j=1}^{n} \lambda_j c_i c_j \delta_{ij}}{c_k c_m \delta_{km}} = \frac{\displaystyle\sum_{i=1}^{n} \lambda_i c_i^2}{\displaystyle\sum_{k=1}^{n} c_k^2}$$

Now

$$\lambda_1 = \frac{\displaystyle\sum_{i=1}^{n} \lambda_1 c_i^2}{\displaystyle\sum_{k=1}^{n} c_k^2} \quad \text{and} \quad \lambda_n = \frac{\displaystyle\sum_{i=1}^{n} \lambda_n c_i^2}{\displaystyle\sum_{k=1}^{n} c_k^2}$$

so that

$$\lambda_1 - f(X) = \frac{\displaystyle\sum_{i=1}^{n} (\lambda_1 - \lambda_i)c_i^2}{\displaystyle\sum_{k=1}^{n} c_k^2} \le 0$$

$$\lambda_n - f(X) = \frac{\displaystyle\sum_{i=1}^{n} (\lambda_n - \lambda_i)c_i^2}{\displaystyle\sum_{k=1}^{n} c_k^2} \ge 0$$

or

$$\lambda_1 \le f(X) \le \lambda_n$$

for an arbitrary vector $\mathbf{X}$. This inequality allows one very quickly to obtain an upper bound for λ_1 and a lower bound for λ_n, and also indicates that one can find λ_1 by minimizing $f(X)$ and λ_n by maximizing $f(X)$. If we wish to find λ_2, we can proceed as follows. Minimize $f(X)$ over the subspace of vectors orthogonal to $\mathbf{Y}_1$. In this case $\mathbf{X}$ can be expressed as a linear combination of $\mathbf{Y}_2, \mathbf{Y}_3, \ldots, \mathbf{Y}_n$, and we have

$$f(X) = \frac{\displaystyle\sum_{i=2}^{n} \lambda_i c_i^2}{\displaystyle\sum_{k=2}^{n} c_k^2}$$

and the inequality

$$\lambda_2 \le f(X) \le \lambda_n$$

Therefore, the minimum of the function over the subspace yields λ_2 and the corresponding eigenvector $\mathbf{Y}_2$. The next eigenvalue λ_3 can be found by minimizing $f(X)$ over the subspace orthogonal to $\mathbf{Y}_1$ and $\mathbf{Y}_2$. This iterative procedure yields all the eigenvalues and eigenvectors as solutions to problems in the calculus of variations.

The method of Lagrange multipliers yields all the eigenvalues and eigenvectors in one step. We attempt to find the stationary values of $Q(X)$ subject to the constraint $g(X) = X'X - 1 = 0$. The problem is to extremize

$$H(X) = Q(X) - \lambda g(X)$$

The necessary conditions are

$$2a_{ij}x_j - 2\lambda x_i = 0 \qquad x_i x_i = 1$$

The first of these is the eigenvalue problem

$$AX = \lambda X$$

which leads to the characteristic equation

$$|A - \lambda I| = 0$$

which yields the n eigenvalues $\lambda_1, \lambda_2, \ldots, \lambda_n$. The eigenvectors $\mathbf{Y}_1, \mathbf{Y}_2, \ldots, \mathbf{Y}_n$ are determined by solving

$$AY_\alpha = \lambda_\alpha Y_\alpha$$

subject to $(\mathbf{Y}_\alpha, \mathbf{Y}_\alpha) = 1$. That the eigenvectors are orthogonal follows as in Sec. 1.10.

There is still another way to characterize the eigenvalues of A as a variational problem. Let λ_k be the kth eigenvalue from the sequence of ordered eigenvalues; then

$$\lambda_k - f(X) = \frac{\sum_{i=1}^{n}(\lambda_k - \lambda_i)c_i^2}{\sum_{j=1}^{n}c_j^2}$$

This expression can be made nonnegative by choosing

$$c_{k+1} = c_{k+2} = \cdots = c_n = 0$$

We choose the remaining c's to satisfy the $k - 1$ conditions

$$(\mathbf{X}, \mathbf{V}_1) = (\mathbf{X}, \mathbf{V}_2) = \cdots = (\mathbf{X}, \mathbf{V}_{k-1}) = 0$$

where $\mathbf{V}_1, \mathbf{V}_2, \ldots, \mathbf{V}_{k-1}$ is any set of linearly independent vectors. These are $k - 1$ homogeneous linear algebraic equations in k unknowns. These equations always have a nontrivial solution, which is determined to within a constant of proportionality. This constant does not affect $\lambda_k - f(X)$, since it appears as a common factor in both the numerator and the denominator of the above expression. Alternatively one could require that

$$\|\mathbf{X}\|^2 = x_i x_i = \sum_{i=1}^{k} c_i^2 = 1$$

which would determine $c_1, c_2, \ldots, c_k$ exactly. Since $c_1, c_2, \ldots, c_k$ are determined for a given set of vectors $\mathbf{V}_1, \mathbf{V}_2, \ldots, \mathbf{V}_{k-1}$, and since choosing $c_{k+1}, c_{k+2}, \ldots, c_n$ different from zero cannot increase $\lambda_k - f(X)$, we have

$$\min f(X) \leq \lambda_k$$

where $\mathbf{X}$ is orthogonal to $\mathbf{V}_1, \mathbf{V}_2, \ldots, \mathbf{V}_{k-1}$. Now we know from previous considerations that, if $\mathbf{V}_1 = \mathbf{Y}_1, \mathbf{V}_2 = \mathbf{Y}_2, \ldots, \mathbf{V}_{k-1} = \mathbf{Y}_{k-1}$, then $\min f(X) = \lambda_k$. Therefore,

$$\lambda_k = \max\,[\min f(X)]$$

as the set $\mathbf{V}_1, \mathbf{V}_2, \ldots, \mathbf{V}_{k-1}$ is allowed to change. This is called the **minimax** definition of the eigenvalue. The vector which defines the kth eigenvalue is the kth eigenvector, for then

$$(\mathbf{X}, \mathbf{Y}_j) = \left(\sum_{i=1}^{k} c_i \mathbf{Y}_i, \mathbf{Y}_j \right) = c_j = 0 \qquad \text{for } j < k$$
$$= c_j = 1 \qquad \text{for } j = k$$

The advantage of this definition is that we can define the kth eigenvalue conceptually without first knowing the $k - 1$ preceding ones.

Exercises 2.1

1. Using the method of Lagrange multipliers, find the points on the surface of the ellipsoid

$$9x_1^2 + 12x_2^2 + 9x_3^2 - 6x_1x_2 - 6x_2x_3 - 25 = 0$$

which make the distance from the origin stationary. Show that these points are on mutually orthogonal axes through the origin.

2. Let $Q(X) = X'AX$ be a positive-definite quadratic form with A real and symmetric, and $N(X) = X'X$. We have already shown that the eigenvalues of A are the stationary values of $Q(X)$ subject to $N(X) = 1$. Show that the eigenvalues of A can be found by finding the stationary values of $N(X)$ subject to $Q(X) = 1$. What is the relation between the stationary values of N and the eigenvalues of A? $N(X)$ is just the square of the distance from the origin to the surface $Q(X) = 1$.

*3. Let $Q(X) = X'AX$ be a real quadratic form and $E(X) = X'BX$ be a positive-definite real quadratic form. A and B are both $n \times n$ real symmetric matrices. Show that the stationary values of $Q(X)$ subject to $E(X) = 1$ are the solutions of the characteristic equation $|A - \lambda B| = 0$. How is this problem related to the problem of simultaneous reduction of E and Q to diagonal form discussed in Sec. 1.10?

*4. If $Q(X) = X'AX$ is a real quadratic form, $Q(X,Y) = X'AY$ is called the **associated bilinear form.** Show the following:

a. $Q(X,Y) = Q(Y,X)$.

b. $Q(X,Y) = \frac{1}{4}[Q(X + Y) - Q(X - Y)]$.

c. If λ is an eigenvalue of A and Y is the corresponding eigenvector,

$$Q(X,Y) - \lambda N(X,Y) = 0$$

for arbitrary X. Here $N(X,Y)$ refers to the bilinear form $N(X,Y) = X'Y$ associated with $N(X) = X'X$.

d. $N(U,V) = N(U,Y_i)N(V,Y_i)$ where $\mathbf{Y}_i$, $i = 1, 2, 3, \ldots, n$, are the n eigenvectors and $\mathbf{U}$ and $\mathbf{V}$ are any vectors in the n-dimensional vector space.

5. Let $H(Z) = (Z^*)'AZ$ be a hermitian form, with A a hermitian matrix with eigenvalues $\lambda_1 \leq \lambda_2 \leq \lambda_3 \leq \cdots \leq \lambda_n$. Show that

$$\lambda_1 \leq f(Z) \leq \lambda_n$$

where $f(Z) = H(Z)/(Z^*)'Z$, and that the stationary values of $H(Z)$ subject to $(Z^*)'Z = 1$ are the eigenvalues of A. HINT: In the second part let

$$a_{kj} = \alpha_{kj} + i\beta_{kj} \quad \text{and} \quad z_j = x_j + iy_j.$$

2.2 Maxima and Minima of Functionals. Euler's Equation

The types of problems considered in Sec. 2.1 can be handled by the ordinary calculus. The subject matter of the calculus of variations deals, on the other hand, with the problem of maximizing or minimizing **functionals** (usually integrals) which depend on the definition of some function or functions. In Sec. 2.1, we extremized functions in some finite-dimensional vector space. In this section, we shall treat the problem of extremizing functionals in an infinite-dimensional function space. Some examples of this kind of problem are the following:

1. Find the shortest curve $y = y(x)$ in the xy plane connecting the points $(0,0)$ and (a,b). To solve this we must minimize

$$s = \int_{(0,0)}^{(a,b)} ds = \int_0^a \left[1 + \left(\frac{dy}{dx} \right)^2 \right]^{\frac{1}{2}} dx$$

subject to the conditions $y(0) = 0$ and $y(a) = b$.

2. Find the shortest curve lying in the surface $z = z(x,y)$ and connecting the points (x_1,y_1,z_1) and (x_2,y_2,z_2) on the surface. Here we must minimize

$$s = \int_{(x_1,y_1,z_1)}^{(x_2,y_2,z_2)} ds = \int_{(x_1,y_1,z_1)}^{(x_2,y_2,z_2)} [(dx)^2 + (dy)^2 + (dz)^2]^{\frac{1}{2}}$$

$$= \int_{(x_1,y_1)}^{(x_2,y_2)} \left[(dx)^2 + (dy)^2 + \left(\frac{\partial z}{\partial x} dx + \frac{\partial z}{\partial y} dy \right)^2 \right]^{\frac{1}{2}}$$

Suppose we seek parametric equations of the curve

$$x = x(t) \qquad y = y(t) \qquad z = z[x(t),y(t)] \qquad 0 \leq t \leq 1$$

such that

$$x(0) = x_1 \qquad y(0) = y_1 \qquad z(x_1,y_1) = z_1$$

and

$$x(1) = x_2 \qquad y(1) = y_2 \qquad z(x_2,y_2) = z_2$$

Then the problem is to minimize

$$\int_0^1 \left\{ \left[1 + \left(\frac{\partial z}{\partial x}\right)^2\right] \dot{x}^2 + \left[1 + \left(\frac{\partial z}{\partial y}\right)^2\right] \dot{y}^2 + 2 \frac{\partial z}{\partial x} \frac{\partial z}{\partial y} \dot{x}\dot{y} \right\}^{\frac{1}{2}} dt$$

3. A mass slides on a frictionless wire connecting points P and Q in a vertical plane. For what shape of the wire is the time of descent a minimum?   Energy is conserved, so that the potential energy lost in the descent is equal to the kinetic energy gained.   Taking the point P to be the origin of the plane and measuring y positively down, we have $\frac{1}{2}mv^2 = mgy$ or $v = \sqrt{2gy}$.   We wish to find the curve $y = y(x)$ which minimizes

$$\int_P^Q dt = \int_P^Q \frac{ds}{v} = \int_0^a \left[\frac{1 + (y')^2}{2gy}\right]^{\frac{1}{2}} dx$$

and which passes through the points $(0,0)$ and (a,b).

4. Find the positive function $y = y(x) > 0$ whose graph passes through the points (a,b) and (c,d) which produces the surface of revolution about the x axis with least area. We wish to minimize

$$\int_a^c 2\pi y \left[1 + \left(\frac{dy}{dx}\right)^2\right]^{\frac{1}{2}} dx$$

subject to $y(a) = b$ and $y(c) = d$.

5. Fermat's principle states that a light ray passes through a medium along a path which minimized the transit time.   Let $\eta(x,y)$ be the index of refraction in a two-dimensional medium, i.e., $v(x,y) = c/\eta(x,y)$, where c is a constant (velocity of light in a vacuum).   Then the time of transit between points $(0,0)$ and (a,b) is given by

$$\int_0^a \frac{ds}{v} = \frac{1}{c} \int_0^a \eta(x,y) \left[1 + \left(\frac{dy}{dx}\right)^2\right]^{\frac{1}{2}} dx$$

where $y = y(x)$ is the curve along which light is transmitted.   The problem is to find the function $y(x)$ which minimizes this integral.

6. Find the shape of a uniform hanging cable of a given length.   The cable will hang in a position which minimizes the potential energy.   The potential energy is proportional to the coordinate of the centroid in the direction of the gravitational force.   Take the y axis in the vertical direction.   The problem is then to minimize

$$\bar{y} = \frac{1}{L} \int_0^a y \, ds = \frac{1}{L} \int_0^a y \left[1 + \left(\frac{dy}{dx}\right)^2\right]^{\frac{1}{2}} dx$$

subject to the condition

$$L = \int_0^a \left[1 + \left(\frac{dy}{dx}\right)^2\right]^{\frac{1}{2}} dx$$

and with $y(0) = 0$ and $y(a) = b$.

7. Find the closed curve of given length in the xy plane which encloses the largest area. The parametric equations of the curve are $x = x(t)$, $y = y(t)$, $0 \le t \le 1$, with $x(0) = x(1)$ and $y(0) = y(1)$. The area enclosed is

$$\iint_R dx\, dy = \tfrac{1}{2} \oint_C x\, dy - y\, dx$$

by use of Green's lemma. Thus we wish to maximize

$$\tfrac{1}{2} \int_0^1 (x\dot{y} - y\dot{x})\, dt$$

subject to
$$L = \int_0^1 (\dot{x}^2 + \dot{y}^2)^{\frac{1}{2}}\, dt$$

It is understood that certain continuity conditions on the functions and/or their derivatives must be prescribed in each case in order to make the extremum meaningful. This serves to define the function space in which the extremum is sought. It may be that there exists no solution of the variation problem within the **class of admissible functions,** i.e., that function space in which the extremum is sought. For example, if we seek the positive continuous function $y = y(x)$ passing through (a,c) and (b,d) which minimizes the area between the curve and the x axis, there is no solution. This is because the function corresponding to the lower bound

$$\int_a^b y\, dx = 0$$

is $y(x) = 0, a < x < b, y(a) = c, y(b) = d$, and this is not a continuous function as prescribed by the variational problem. Continuous functions can be found which will make the area arbitrarily close to zero, but it cannot be made exactly zero for any continuous function.

The problem of finding sufficient conditions for the solution of a variational problem is one of the more difficult aspects of the calculus of variations. We shall be content to deal only with necessary conditions, i.e., assuming that a maximizing or a minimizing function exists, to find the conditions it must satisfy, and hence to find a function which satisfies these conditions. One can usually show that it is the required extremizing function within the context of the individual problem.

Problems 1, 3, 4, and 5 can all be put in the form of the following problem: to minimize

$$\int_a^b F\left(x, y, \frac{dy}{dx}\right) dx$$

by the proper choice of $y = y(x)$, which goes through the end points $y(a) = c$ and $y(b) = d$. Under suitable restrictions on F and on the class of functions

admitted to competition, we shall derive necessary conditions for the minimizing function, assuming that it exists in the class of admissible functions.
Let F have continuous second partial derivatives with respect to its arguments
x, y, and $\dfrac{dy}{dx}$. Let y have continuous second derivatives. Assuming that
there is a function $\phi(x)$, which has continuous second derivatives, passes
through the given points, and makes the functional take on its minimum
value, we have

$$I(\epsilon) = \int_a^b F(x,\, \phi + \epsilon\eta,\, \phi' + \epsilon\eta')\, dx \geq I(0) = \int_a^b F(x,\phi,\phi')\, dx$$

where we have set $y(x) = \phi(x) + \epsilon\eta(x)$. ϵ is a small scalar, and $\eta(x)$ is an
arbitrary function in the class of admissible functions, i.e., has continuous
second derivatives. Furthermore,

$$y' = \frac{dy}{dx} = \frac{d\phi}{dx} + \epsilon\frac{d\eta}{dx} = \phi' + \epsilon\eta'$$

Also, since $y(a) = \phi(a)$ and $y(b) = \phi(b)$, then $\eta(a) = \eta(b) = 0$.

$I(\epsilon)$ takes on a minimum value at $\epsilon = 0$. Therefore, $I'(0) = 0$, and we use
this to derive necessary conditions for $\phi(x)$ to be the minimizing function.

$$I'(0) = \lim_{\epsilon \to 0} \frac{I(\epsilon) - I(0)}{\epsilon}$$

$$= \lim_{\epsilon \to 0} \int_a^b \left[\frac{F(x,\, \phi + \epsilon\eta,\, \phi' + \epsilon\eta') - F(x,\phi,\phi')}{\epsilon} \right] dx$$

Since F has continuous first partial derivatives, we can write

$$I'(0) = \lim_{\epsilon \to 0} \int_a^b [F_y(x,\, \phi + \theta_1\epsilon\eta,\, \phi')\eta + F_{y'}(x,\, \phi,\, \phi' + \theta_2\epsilon\eta')\eta']\, dx$$

where F_y refers to the partial derivative of F with respect to its second argument and $F_{y'}$ refers to the partial derivative of F with respect to its third
argument. Here $0 < \theta_1 < 1$, and $0 < \theta_2 < 1$. The fact that the integral is
a continuous function of ϵ allows us to take the limit under the integral sign,
and we have

$$I'(0) = \int_a^b [F_y(x,\phi,\phi')\eta + F_{y'}(x,\phi,\phi')\eta']\, dx = 0$$

We can integrate the second term by parts, giving

$$0 = \left[F_{y'}(x,\phi,\phi')\eta \right]_a^b - \int_a^b \left[\frac{d}{dx} F_{y'}(x,\phi,\phi') - F_y(x,\phi,\phi') \right] \eta\, dx$$

Because $\eta(a) = \eta(b) = 0$, we have

$$\int_a^b \left[\frac{d}{dx} F_{y'}(x,\phi,\phi') - F_y(x,\phi,\phi') \right] \eta\, dx = 0$$

The function $\dfrac{d}{dx} F_{y'}(x,\phi,\phi') - F_y(x,\phi,\phi')$ is a continuous function of x.   When it is multiplied by an arbitrary continuous function $\eta(x)$, which vanishes at the end points, and is integrated, the result is zero.   This means that

$$\frac{d}{dx} F_{y'}(x,\phi,\phi') - F_y(x,\phi,\phi') = 0$$

in the whole interval.   If this were not so, the function would be different from zero at some point.   The continuity implies that it is of the same sign in some neighborhood of that point.   Then η can be chosen with the same sign in all or part of this neighborhood and with the value zero elsewhere.   This would imply that the integral of a positive continuous function is zero, which is clearly impossible.

The necessary condition for $y = \phi(x)$ to be the minimizing function is thus

$$\frac{d}{dx} F_{y'}(x,\phi,\phi') - F_y(x,\phi,\phi') = 0$$

which is **Euler's equation.**   It is a second-order differential equation for ϕ which, along with the boundary conditions $\phi(a) = c$ and $\phi(b) = d$, generally will yield the desired solution.

As an example, let us solve problem 1.   Here

$$F(x,y,y') = \left[1 + \left(\frac{dy}{dx}\right)^2\right]^{\frac{1}{2}}$$

The Euler equation yields

$$\frac{d}{dx} \frac{\phi'}{[1 + (\phi')^2]^{\frac{1}{2}}} = 0$$

Integrating this equation, we have

$$\frac{\phi'}{[1 + (\phi')^2]^{\frac{1}{2}}} = k$$

which can be solved for ϕ' as follows:

$$\phi' = \frac{k}{(1 - k^2)^{\frac{1}{2}}} = K$$

Integrating and using the boundary conditions $\phi(0) = 0$ and $\phi(a) = b$, we have

$$\phi = \frac{b}{a} x$$

which is to say that the straight line is the shortest curve connecting two points in the plane.

Problems 3 and 4 can likewise be solved, but first let us note a useful property of the Euler equation when F does not depend explicitly on the independent variable x. In this case,

$$\frac{d}{dx}(y'F_{y'} - F) = y''F_{y'} + y'\frac{d}{dx}F_{y'} - F_y y' - F_{y'}y'' = y'\left(\frac{d}{dx}F_{y'} - F_y\right) = 0$$

when $y = \phi$, the minimizing function. This implies that

$$\phi'F_{y'}(x,\phi,\phi') - F(x,\phi,\phi') = k$$

where k is a constant.

In problem 3,

$$F = y^{-\frac{1}{2}}[1 + (y')^2]^{\frac{1}{2}}$$

which does not depend explicitly on x. Therefore,

$$(\phi')^2\{\phi[1 + (\phi')^2]\}^{-\frac{1}{2}} - \phi^{-\frac{1}{2}}[1 + (\phi')^2]^{\frac{1}{2}} = k$$

$$\frac{-1}{\{\phi[1 + (\phi')^2]\}^{\frac{1}{2}}} = k = \frac{1}{K}$$

Solving for dx, we have

$$dx = \frac{\phi^{\frac{1}{2}}\,d\phi}{(K^2 - \phi)^{\frac{1}{2}}}$$

Making the substitution $\phi = K^2 \sin^2 t$, we have

$$x = 2K^2\int_0^t \sin^2 t\,dt = K^2\left(t - \frac{\sin 2t}{2}\right)$$

$$x = \tfrac{1}{2}K^2(2t - \sin 2t)$$

$$\phi = \tfrac{1}{2}K^2(1 - \cos 2t)$$

Therefore, the solution is a cycloid, with the constant K determined by the condition that the curve pass through the point (a,b).

Problem 2 is of the following type: to minimize

$$\int_a^b F(t,x,y,\dot{x},\dot{y})\,dt$$

by choosing properly functions $x(t)$ and $y(t)$ passing through given end values $x(a) = x_1$, $y(a) = y_1$, and $x(b) = x_2$, $y(b) = y_2$. This is a special case of the following problem in n dependent variables: to minimize

$$\int_a^b F(t,x_1,x_2, \ldots, x_n,\dot{x}_1,\dot{x}_2, \ldots ,\dot{x}_n)\,dt$$

by choosing properly function $x_1(t)$, $x_2(t)$, $\ldots$, $x_n(t)$ passing through given end points. It is possible to find necessary conditions for the minimizing functions in this more general case. We shall do this in the case of two dependent variables, and the extension to n dependent variables will be immediate.

Let F have continuous second partial derivatives with respect to its arguments t, x, y, $\dot{x}$, and $\dot{y}$, and let $x(t)$ and $y(t)$ have continuous second derivatives. Assuming that $\phi(t)$ and $\psi(t)$ are the actual minimizing functions,

$$I(\epsilon_1,\epsilon_2) = \int_a^b F(t,\ \phi + \epsilon_1\eta_1,\ \psi + \epsilon_2\eta_2,\ \dot{\phi} + \epsilon_1\dot{\eta}_1,\ \dot{\psi} + \epsilon_2,\ \dot{\eta}_2)\ dt$$

has a minimum at $\epsilon_1 = \epsilon_2 = 0$. Here ϵ_1 and ϵ_2 are scalars, and $\eta_1(t)$ and $\eta_2(t)$ are arbitrary functions with continuous second derivatives. Under the hypotheses, we can compute partial derivatives of $I(\epsilon_1,\epsilon_2)$ as in the simpler case of only one dependent variable. We have

$$I_{\epsilon_1}(0,0) = \int_a^b [F_x(t,\phi,\psi,\dot{\phi},\dot{\psi})\eta_1 + F_{\dot{x}}(t,\phi,\psi,\dot{\phi},\dot{\psi})\dot{\eta}_1]\ dt = 0$$

$$I_{\epsilon_2}(0,0) = \int_a^b [F_y(t,\phi,\psi,\dot{\phi},\dot{\psi})\eta_2 + F_{\dot{y}}(t,\phi,\psi,\dot{\phi},\dot{\psi})\dot{\eta}_2]\ dt = 0$$

Integrating by parts gives

$$\left[F_{\dot{x}}\eta_1\right]_a^b - \int_a^b \left(\frac{d}{dt}F_{\dot{x}} - F_x\right)\eta_1\ dt = 0$$

$$\left[F_{\dot{y}}\eta_2\right]_a^b - \int_a^b \left(\frac{d}{dt}F_{\dot{y}} - F_y\right)\eta_2\ dt = 0$$

Using the fact that η_1 and η_2 vanish at the end points but are otherwise arbitrary, we arrive at the pair of Euler equations

$$\frac{d}{dt}F_{\dot{x}} - F_x = 0 \qquad \frac{d}{dt}F_{\dot{y}} - F_y = 0$$

as necessary conditions for the minimizing functions $\phi(t)$ and $\psi(t)$. They represent a system of second-order differential equations for the unknown functions ϕ and ψ. In the general case with n dependent variables the necessary conditions are

$$\frac{d}{dt}F_{\dot{x}_i} - F_{x_i} = 0 \qquad i = 1, 2, \ldots, n$$

For purposes of illustration, let us solve problem 2 in the case of the cylindrical surface $z = (1 - x^2)^{\frac{1}{2}}$. The problem is to minimize

$$\int_0^1 \left[\dot{x}^2 + \dot{y}^2 + \left(\frac{\partial z}{\partial x}\dot{x} + \frac{\partial z}{\partial y}\dot{y}\right)^2\right]^{\frac{1}{2}} dt$$

here
$$F = [(1 - x^2)^{-1}\dot{x}^2 + \dot{y}^2]^{\frac{1}{2}}$$

$$\frac{\partial F}{\partial x} = \frac{1}{F}\frac{x\dot{x}^2}{(1 - x^2)^2} \qquad \frac{\partial F}{\partial y} = 0$$

$$\frac{\partial F}{\partial \dot{x}} = \frac{1}{F}\frac{\dot{x}}{(1 - x^2)} \qquad \frac{\partial F}{\partial \dot{y}} = \frac{1}{F}\dot{y}$$

It is well known that there are many ways of describing a curve parametrically. So far, what we have said holds for a general parameter t. We can simplify the problem by picking a particular parameter s, the length of arc along the shortest curve. With this choice of parameter,

$$F(\phi,\psi,\dot\phi,\dot\psi) = \left[(1 - \dot\phi^2)^{-1}\left(\frac{d\phi}{ds}\right)^2 + \left(\frac{d\psi}{ds}\right)^2\right]^{\frac{1}{2}} = 1$$

The Euler equations, written in terms of the parameter s, become

$$\frac{d}{ds}\left(\frac{\dot\phi}{1 - \dot\phi^2}\right) - \frac{\dot\phi\ddot\phi^2}{(1 - \dot\phi^2)^2} = \frac{\ddot\phi}{1 - \dot\phi^2} + \frac{\dot\phi\ddot\phi^2}{(1 - \dot\phi^2)^2} = 0$$

$$\frac{d^2}{ds^2}\psi = 0$$

where $\dot\phi = \dfrac{d\phi}{ds}$. The second equation can be integrated directly, giving $\psi = as + b$. Also, from the condition

$$\frac{\dot\phi^2}{1 - \dot\phi^2} = 1 - \left(\frac{d\psi}{ds}\right)^2 = 1 - a^2$$

we have

$$\ddot\phi = -\phi\,\frac{\dot\phi^2}{1 - \dot\phi^2} = -(1 - a^2)\phi$$

Therefore,

$$\phi = c\cos\left(\sqrt{1 - a^2}\,s + d\right)$$

If $a = 1$, $\psi = s + b$ and $\phi = k$, and we have a straight line parallel to the y axis. If $a = 0$, $\psi = b$ and $\phi = c\cos(s + d)$. However,

$$\frac{c^2\sin^2(s + d)}{1 - c^2\cos^2(s + d)} = 1$$

implies that $c = 1$. In this case we have a circle in a plane perpendicular to the axis of the cylinder. If $0 < a < 1$, we again must have $c = 1$ in order that the condition

$$\frac{(1 - a^2)c^2\sin^2\left(\sqrt{1 - a^2}\,s + d\right)}{1 - c^2\cos^2\left(\sqrt{1 - a^2}\,s + d\right)} = 1 - a^2$$

be satisfied. The parametric equations of the curve are therefore

$$\phi = \cos\left(\sqrt{1 - a^2}\,s + d\right)$$

$$\psi = as + b$$

$$\zeta = \sin\left(\sqrt{1 - a^2}\,s + d\right)$$

and we have a spiral.

An alternative approach to the solution of the last problem is a technique related to the Lagrange multiplier method of extremizing functions subject to constraints.   In the present case we wish to minimize

$$I = \int_a^b F(t,x,y,z,\dot{x},\dot{y},\dot{z}) \, dt$$

subject to a condition (constraint)

$$G(x,y,z) = 0$$

Assuming that there are minimizing functions $\phi(t)$, $\psi(t)$, $\zeta(t)$, then the first variation

$$
\begin{aligned}
dI &= I_{\epsilon_1}(0,0,0)\epsilon_1 + I_{\epsilon_2}(0,0,0)\epsilon_2 + I_{\epsilon_3}(0,0,0)\epsilon_3 \\
&= \int_a^b \left[F_x(t,\phi,\psi,\zeta,\dot{\phi},\dot{\psi},\dot{\zeta}) - \frac{d}{dt} F_{\dot{x}}(t,\phi,\psi,\zeta,\dot{\phi},\dot{\psi},\dot{\zeta}) \right] \epsilon_1 \eta_1(t) \, dt \\
&\quad + \int_a^b \left[F_y(t,\phi,\psi,\zeta,\dot{\phi},\dot{\psi},\dot{\zeta}) - \frac{d}{dt} F_{\dot{y}}(t,\phi,\psi,\zeta,\dot{\phi},\dot{\psi},\dot{\zeta}) \right] \epsilon_2 \eta_2(t) \, dt \\
&\quad + \int_a^b \left[F_z(t,\phi,\psi,\zeta,\dot{\phi},\dot{\psi},\dot{\zeta}) - \frac{d}{dt} F_{\dot{z}}(t,\phi,\psi,\zeta,\dot{\phi},\dot{\psi},\dot{\zeta}) \right] \epsilon_3 \eta_3(t) \, dt
\end{aligned}
$$

must vanish.   In this case, however, the variations $\epsilon_1 \eta_1$, $\epsilon_2 \eta_2$, $\epsilon_3 \eta_3$ are not independent, but must satisfy the constraint

$$G(\phi + \epsilon_1 \eta_1, \psi + \epsilon_2 \eta_2, \zeta + \epsilon_3 \eta_3) = 0$$

Therefore, $dG = G_x(\phi,\psi,\zeta)\epsilon_1 \eta_1 + G_y(\phi,\psi,\zeta)\epsilon_2 \eta_2 + G_x(\phi,\psi,\zeta)\epsilon_3 \eta_3 = 0$

Multiplying by an arbitrary function $\lambda(t)$ and integrating, we have

$$\int_a^b (\lambda G_x \epsilon_1 \eta_1 + \lambda G_y \epsilon_2 \eta_2 + \lambda G_z \epsilon_3 \eta_3) \, dt = 0$$

Adding this to dI,

$$
\int_a^b \left(F_x - \frac{d}{dt} F_{\dot{x}} + \lambda G_x \right) \epsilon_1 \eta_1 \, dt + \int_a^b \left[F_y - \frac{d}{dt} F_{\dot{y}} + \lambda G_y \right] \epsilon_2 \eta_2 \, dt
$$
$$
+ \int_a^b \left[F_z - \frac{d}{dt} F_{\dot{z}} + \lambda G_z \right] \epsilon_3 \eta_3 \, dt = 0
$$

λ is arbitrary, so we choose it to make

$$F_x - \frac{d}{dt} F_{\dot{x}} + \lambda G_x = 0$$

Two of the variations $\epsilon_2\eta_2$ and $\epsilon_3\eta_3$ are arbitrary, so that

$$F_y - \frac{d}{dt}F_{\dot{y}} + \lambda G_y = 0$$

$$F_z - \frac{d}{dt}F_{\dot{z}} + \lambda G_z = 0$$

λ can be eliminated between two of these equations, leaving two equations to be solved, say for ϕ and ψ. ζ is then determined from the condition $G(\phi,\psi,\zeta) = 0$.

To determine the shortest curves on the cylindrical surface of the above example, we must minimize

$$\int_a^b (\dot{x}^2 + \dot{y}^2 + \dot{z}^2)^{\frac{1}{2}}\, dt$$

subject to $\qquad\qquad G(x,y,z) = x^2 + z^2 - 1 = 0$

Then $F = (\dot{x}^2 + \dot{y}^2 + \dot{z}^2)^{\frac{1}{2}}$, and the equations become

$$-\frac{d}{dt}\frac{\dot{\phi}}{F} + 2\lambda\phi = 0$$

$$-\frac{d}{dt}\frac{\dot{\psi}}{F} = 0$$

$$-\frac{d}{dt}\frac{\dot{\zeta}}{F} + 2\lambda\zeta = 0$$

Changing to the parameter s, the arc length on the shortest curve, we have the equations

$$\ddot{\phi} = 2\lambda\phi \qquad \ddot{\psi} = 0 \qquad \ddot{\zeta} = 2\lambda\zeta$$

where the dot now refers to $\dfrac{d}{ds}$. The second equation can be integrated to give

$$\psi = as + b$$

We can show in this case that λ is a constant, for

$$\phi^2 + \zeta^2 = 1$$
$$\phi\dot{\phi} + \zeta\dot{\zeta} = 0$$
$$\phi\ddot{\phi} + \zeta\ddot{\zeta} + \dot{\phi}^2 + \dot{\zeta}^2 = 0$$
$$2\lambda(\phi^2 + \zeta^2) = \dot{\psi}^2 - 1 = a^2 - 1$$
$$\lambda = \frac{a^2 - 1}{2}$$

Therefore, $\ddot{\phi} = (a^2 - 1)\phi$, $\ddot{\zeta} = (a^2 - 1)\zeta$, and we have

$$\phi = \cos(\sqrt{1 - a^2}\, s + d) \qquad \zeta = \sin(\sqrt{1 - a^2}\, s + d)$$

the same solution as before.

Still another alternative is to work the problem in cylindrical coordinates, since the calculus-of-variation technique is independent of the particular set of coordinates used to describe the surface. Let us minimize

$$\int_a^b (\dot{r}^2 + r^2\dot{\theta}^2 + \dot{y}^2)^{\frac{1}{2}}\, dt$$

subject to $r = 1$, where $x = r \cos \theta, y = y, z = r \sin \theta.$*

Because of the constraint, $\dot{r} = 0$, and hence we are to minimize

$$\int_{\theta_1}^{\theta_2} \left[1 + \left(\frac{dy}{d\theta}\right)^2\right]^{\frac{1}{2}} d\theta$$

This is the same as problem 1 above, and therefore

$$\psi = A \cos^{-1} \phi + B$$

$$\phi = \cos\left(\frac{\psi - B}{A}\right)$$

which is the spiral solution obtained by the other methods.

In problems 6 and 7, we are to minimize a certain integral subject to a subsidiary condition. The problem is to minimize

$$\int_a^b F(x,y,y')\, dx$$

subject to

$$\int_a^b G(x,y,y')\, dx = k$$

k being a constant. Let F and G both have continuous second partial derivatives with respect to their arguments, and let y have a continuous second derivative.

If $\phi(x)$ is the solution of the problem, then

$$I(\epsilon_1,\epsilon_2) = \int_a^b F(x,\ \phi + \epsilon_1\eta_1 + \epsilon_2\eta_2,\ \phi' + \epsilon_1\eta_1' + \epsilon_2\eta_2')\, dx$$

has a minimum at $\epsilon_1 = \epsilon_2 = 0$, while

$$J(\epsilon_1,\epsilon_2) = \int_a^b G(x,\ \phi + \epsilon_1\eta_1 + \epsilon_2\eta_2,\ \phi' + \epsilon_1\eta_1' + \epsilon_2\eta_2')\, dx = k$$

This is equivalent to a problem in Lagrange multipliers, i.e., to minimize $I(\epsilon_1,\epsilon_2)$ subject to $J(\epsilon_1,\epsilon_2) = k$. If this has a solution for $\epsilon_1 = \epsilon_2 = 0$, then

$$\left(\frac{\partial I}{\partial \epsilon_1} + \lambda \frac{\partial J}{\partial \epsilon_1}\right)_{\epsilon_1 = \epsilon_2 = 0} = 0$$

$$\left(\frac{\partial I}{\partial \epsilon_2} + \lambda \frac{\partial J}{\partial \epsilon_2}\right)_{\epsilon_1 = \epsilon_2 = 0} = 0$$

$$(J - k)_{\epsilon_1 = \epsilon_2 = 0} = 0$$

* These are not the usual cylindrical coordinates because of the choice of the y axis as the axis of the cylinder.

The first of these equations gives

$$\int_a^b \left[\left(\frac{d}{dx} F_{y'} - F_y \right) + \lambda \left(\frac{d}{dx} G_{y'} - G_y \right) \right] \eta_1 \, dx = 0$$

Unless $\dfrac{d}{dx} G_{y'} - G_y \equiv 0$, η_1 can be chosen so that $\displaystyle\int_a^b \left(\frac{d}{dx} G_{y'} - G_y \right) \eta_1 \, dx \neq 0$.
This equation can then be used to define λ. Using this λ in the second equation, we have

$$\int_a^b \left[\left(\frac{d}{dx} F_{y'} - F_y \right) + \lambda \left(\frac{d}{dx} G_{y'} - G_y \right) \right] \eta_2 \, dx = 0$$

for arbitrary η_2 vanishing at the end points. Hence, our necessary condition is

$$\frac{d}{dx} \frac{\partial}{\partial y'} (F + \lambda G) - \frac{\partial}{\partial y} (F + \lambda G) = 0$$

which is the necessary condition for a minimum of the functional

$$\int_a^b (F + \lambda G) \, dx$$

without regard to the subsidiary condition. In actual practice, the parameter λ is determined from the condition

$$\int_a^b G(x,\phi,\phi') \, dx = k$$

after we have first solved the Euler equation for ϕ in terms of λ.

To illustrate the problem of the calculus of variations with a subsidiary condition, let us solve problem 7. Let

$$H = F + \lambda G = \tfrac{1}{2}(x\dot{y} - y\dot{x}) + \lambda(\dot{x}^2 + \dot{y}^2)^{\frac{1}{2}}$$

Then

$$\frac{\partial H}{\partial x} = \tfrac{1}{2}\dot{y}$$

$$\frac{\partial H}{\partial y} = -\tfrac{1}{2}\dot{x}$$

$$\frac{\partial H}{\partial \dot{x}} = -\tfrac{1}{2}y + \frac{\lambda \dot{x}}{(\dot{x}^2 + \dot{y}^2)^{\frac{1}{2}}}$$

$$\frac{\partial H}{\partial \dot{y}} = \tfrac{1}{2}x + \frac{\lambda \dot{y}}{(\dot{x}^2 + \dot{y}^2)^{\frac{1}{2}}}$$

If we now pick a special parameter s, the arc length along the solution curve, then $(\dot{\phi}^2 + \dot{\psi}^2)^{\frac{1}{2}} = 1$, and the Euler equations become

$$\lambda \ddot{\phi} - \dot{\psi} = 0$$

$$\lambda \ddot{\psi} + \dot{\phi} = 0$$

Integrating these, we have

$$\lambda \dot{\phi} - \psi = c_1$$
$$\lambda \dot{\psi} + \phi = c_2$$

Eliminating ψ, we have

$$\lambda^2 \ddot{\phi} + \phi - c_2 = 0$$

which has the solution

$$\phi = A \sin \frac{1}{\lambda} s + B \cos \frac{1}{\lambda} s + c_2$$

Solving for ψ, we have

$$\psi = A \cos \frac{1}{\lambda} s + B \sin \frac{1}{\lambda} s - c_1$$

Let $\phi(0) = c_2$; then $B = 0$, and $\psi(0) = A - c_1$. Finally, $\phi(0) = \phi(L)$, $\psi(0) = \psi(L)$ implies that $\sin (1/\lambda)L = 0$ and $\cos (1/\lambda)L = 1$, so that $\lambda = L/2\pi$ and the desired maximizing curve is a circle.

Before this section is concluded, a few words about notation are in order. Going back to the first class of problem treated in this section, we asked for necessary conditions for stationary values of the functional

$$\int_a^b F\left(x, y, \frac{dy}{dx}\right) dx$$

Assuming the existence of an extremizing function $\phi(x)$, we let

$$y(x) = \phi(x) + \epsilon\eta(x) = \phi(x) + \delta y(x)$$

Then

$$I(\epsilon) = \int_a^b F\left(x, \phi + \delta y, \phi' + \delta y'\right) dx$$

has a stationary value at $\epsilon = 0$, a necessary condition for which is that the first variation

$$\delta I = I'(0)\epsilon = \int_a^b \left[F_y(x, \phi, \phi') - \frac{d}{dx} F_{y'}(x, \phi, \phi')\right] \epsilon\eta \, dx = 0$$

from which the Euler equation follows, since $\epsilon\eta$ is arbitrary. This argument is often abbreviated as follows:

$$\delta I = \delta \int_a^b F \, dx = \int_a^b \delta F \, dx = \int_a^b \left(F_y - \frac{d}{dx} F_{y'}\right) \delta y \, dx = 0$$

This notation has become standard, so that the reader should be able to use it without losing sight of the basic arguments behind it.

Exercises 2.2

1. Show that if $F(x, y, y')$ does not depend explicitly on y, then the Euler equation has a first integral $F_{y'} = c$.

2. Solve problem 4 of the text.

3. Find the light ray passing through the two-dimensional medium between the points $(0,0)$ and (a,b) if the index of refraction is $\eta(x,y) = k(x + 1)$.

4. Find the **geodesics** (shortest curves) on the surface of a sphere.

5. Find the geodesics on the surface of a cone.

6. Solve problem 6 of the text.

7. What are the necessary conditions for an extreme value of

$$\int_a^b F\left(x, y, \frac{dy}{dx}, \frac{d^2y}{dx^2}\right) dx$$

for functions $y(x)$ with continuous fourth derivatives passing through the points (a,c) and (b,d) and having specified first derivatives at $x = a$ and $x = b$?

2.3   Hamilton's Principle.   Lagrange's Equations

One of the reasons the calculus of variations plays such an important role in mathematical physics is that a large number of problems in mechanics can be stated in terms of a variational principle known as **Hamilton's principle.** Consider a system of n particles with masses $m_1, m_2, \ldots, m_n$ and displacement vectors $\mathbf{X}_1, \mathbf{X}_2, \ldots, \mathbf{X}_n$ referred to some inertial (unaccelerating) coordinate system. Under the action of forces $\mathbf{F}_1, \mathbf{F}_2, \ldots, \mathbf{F}_n$, referred to the same coordinate system, Newtonian mechanics tells us that the equations of motion of the system are

$$m_\alpha \ddot{\mathbf{X}}_\alpha = \mathbf{F}_\alpha \qquad \alpha = 1, 2, 3, \ldots, n$$

Each displacement vector consists of a triple of numbers, each of which is, in general, a function of time. Hence, the configuration (the positions of all the particles) of the system can be described at any time by $3n$ coordinates. However, the system may be subject to certain constraints, which would imply that not all the $3n$ coordinates are independent. Suppose that there are k relations of the type

$$\phi_i(\mathbf{X}_1, \mathbf{X}_2, \ldots, \mathbf{X}_n, t) = 0 \qquad i = 1, 2, \ldots, k$$

which must be satisfied by the coordinates due to the constraints.[1] Then there are only $3n - k = p$ independent coordinates, and we can find a set of p independent **generalized coordinates** q_i, in terms of which the displacement vectors can be written

$$\mathbf{X}_i = \mathbf{X}_i(q_1, q_2, \ldots, q_p, t)$$

The forces acting on the particles consist of applied forces $\mathbf{F}_\alpha^{(a)}$ and forces of constraint $\mathbf{F}_\alpha^{(c)}$, so we may write

$$m_\alpha \ddot{\mathbf{X}}_\alpha = \mathbf{F}_\alpha^{(a)} + \mathbf{F}_\alpha^{(c)}$$

---

[1] When this is the case, the constraints are called **holonomic.** For a discussion of nonholonomic constraints, see Herbert Goldstein, "Classical Mechanics," Addison-Wesley Publishing Company, Reading, Mass., 1950.

Let the actual path of the system between times t_1 and t_2 be given by the functions $\mathbf{X}_\alpha(t)$. Now consider some virtual (fictitious) path

$$\mathbf{X}_\alpha(t) + \epsilon\mathbf{Y}_\alpha(t) = \mathbf{X}_\alpha(t) + \delta\mathbf{X}_\alpha(t)$$

between t_1 and t_2 slightly different from the actual motion, but having the same configuration at the ends of the time interval, i.e.,

$$\delta\mathbf{X}_\alpha(t_1) = \delta\mathbf{X}_\alpha(t_2) = \mathbf{0}$$

We shall also require that the virtual displacements satisfy the constraints. We can now write

$$\sum_{\alpha=1}^{n} [m_\alpha(\ddot{\mathbf{X}}_\alpha,\delta\mathbf{X}_\alpha) - (\mathbf{F}_\alpha^{(a)},\delta\mathbf{X}_\alpha) - (\mathbf{F}_\alpha^{(c)},\delta\mathbf{X}_\alpha)] = 0$$

If we restrict ourselves to systems in which the forces of constraint do no work,[1] the last term in this expression vanishes, and we have

$$\sum_{\alpha=1}^{n} [m_\alpha(\ddot{\mathbf{X}}_\alpha,\delta\mathbf{X}_\alpha) - (\mathbf{F}_\alpha^{(a)},\delta\mathbf{X}_\alpha)] = 0$$

for any time t. This is known as **D'Alembert's principle.** Integrating between t_1 and t_2, we have

$$\int_{t_1}^{t_2} \sum_{\alpha=1}^{n} [m_\alpha(\ddot{\mathbf{X}}_\alpha,\delta\mathbf{X}_\alpha) - (\mathbf{F}_\alpha^{(a)},\delta\mathbf{X}_\alpha)] \, dt = 0$$

Integrating the first term by parts,

$$\left[\sum_{\alpha=1}^{n} m_\alpha(\dot{\mathbf{X}}_\alpha,\delta\mathbf{X}_\alpha)\right]_{t_1}^{t_2} - \int_{t_1}^{t_2} \sum_{\alpha=1}^{n} [m_\alpha(\dot{\mathbf{X}}_\alpha,\delta\dot{\mathbf{X}}_\alpha) + (\mathbf{F}_\alpha^{(a)},\delta\mathbf{X}_\alpha)] \, dt = 0$$

Making use of the fact that the virtual displacements vanish at t_1 and t_2, we have

$$\int_{t_1}^{t_2} \sum_{\alpha=1}^{n} [m_\alpha(\dot{\mathbf{X}}_\alpha,\delta\dot{\mathbf{X}}_\alpha) + (\mathbf{F}_\alpha^{(a)},\delta\mathbf{X}_\alpha)] \, dt = 0$$

We define the kinetic energy T as follows:

$$T = \frac{1}{2} \sum_{\alpha=1}^{n} m_\alpha(\dot{\mathbf{X}}_\alpha,\dot{\mathbf{X}}_\alpha)$$

Then the first-order change in the kinetic energy induced by the virtual displacements is

$$\delta T = \sum_{\alpha=1}^{n} m_\alpha(\dot{\mathbf{X}}_\alpha,\delta\dot{\mathbf{X}}_\alpha)$$

---

[1] For example, the normal reaction of a plane on a particle constrained to move on a plane surface, the tension in an inextensible pendulum cord, the internal forces in a rigid body, etc.

Hence we have

$$\int_{t_1}^{t_2}\left[\delta T + \sum_{\alpha=1}^{n}(\mathbf{F}_\alpha^{(a)},\delta\mathbf{X}_\alpha)\right]dt = 0$$

If the applied forces are derivable from a **potential function** V, i.e., if the force field is **conservative**, then[1]

$$\mathbf{F}_\alpha^{(a)} = -\left(\frac{\partial V}{\partial x_{\alpha 1}},\frac{\partial V}{\partial x_{\alpha 2}},\frac{\partial V}{\partial x_{\alpha 3}}\right)$$

and

$$\sum_{\alpha=1}^{n}(\mathbf{F}_\alpha^{(a)},\delta\mathbf{X}_\alpha) = -\delta V$$

Then

$$\int_{t_1}^{t_2}\delta(T - V)\,dt = \delta\int_{t_1}^{t_2}(T - V)\,dt = 0$$

This is **Hamilton's principle** for a conservative system. It may be stated as follows: *The motion of a conservative system between time t_1 and t_2 proceeds in such a way that* $\int_{t_1}^{t_2}(T - V)\,dt$ *is stationary with respect to arbitrary small changes in the motion consistent with the constraints and vanishing at t_1 and t_2.*

From Hamilton's principle we can derive **Lagrange's equations.** We first define the **Lagrangian function**

$$L = T - V$$

which can be defined in terms of the generalized coordinates $q_1, q_2, \ldots, q_p$. We have

$$\dot{\mathbf{X}}_\alpha = \frac{\partial\mathbf{X}_\alpha}{\partial q_j}\dot{q}_j + \frac{\partial\mathbf{X}_\alpha}{\partial t} \qquad \alpha = 1, 2, \ldots, n$$
$$j = 1, 2, \ldots, p$$

Hence

$$T = \tfrac{1}{2}\sum_{\alpha=1}^{n}m_\alpha(\dot{\mathbf{X}}_\alpha,\dot{\mathbf{X}}_\alpha) = T(q_1,q_2,\ldots,q_p,\dot{q}_1,\dot{q}_2,\ldots,\dot{q}_p,t)$$

Likewise,

$$V = V(\mathbf{X}_1,\mathbf{X}_2,\ldots,\mathbf{X}_n) = V(q_1,q_2,\ldots,q_p,t)$$

so that L is a function of the generalized coordinates q_i, the **generalized velocities** $\dot{q}_i$, and time. Using the notation of the calculus of variations, we have

$$\delta\int_{t_1}^{t_2}L\,dt = \int_{t_1}^{t_2}\left(\frac{\partial L}{\partial q_i} - \frac{d}{dt}\frac{\partial L}{\partial\dot{q}_i}\right)\delta q_i\,dt = 0$$

Since the δq_i are independent, we have

$$\frac{d}{dt}\frac{\partial L}{\partial\dot{q}_i} - \frac{\partial L}{\partial q_i} = 0 \qquad i = 1, 2, \ldots, p$$

These are the **Lagrange equations** for a conservative system.

[1] Here $x_{\alpha 1}, x_{\alpha 2}, x_{\alpha 3}$ are the three rectangular cartesian coordinates of the αth particle.

As an example of the use of Lagrange's equations, consider the small vibrations of the following system of coupled pendulums, assuming the pendulum rods weightless:

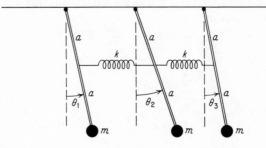

FIGURE 2

The generalized coordinates can be taken as θ_1, θ_2, θ_3. The kinetic and potential energies are then

$$T = 2ma^2(\dot{\theta}_1^2 + \dot{\theta}_2^2 + \dot{\theta}_3^2)$$
$$V = \tfrac{1}{2}ka^2(\sin\theta_1 - \sin\theta_2)^2 + \tfrac{1}{2}ka^2(\sin\theta_2 - \sin\theta_3)^2$$
$$+ 2mga[(1 - \cos\theta_1) + (1 - \cos\theta_2) + (1 - \cos\theta_3)]$$

For small vibrations we can make the approximations $\sin\theta \approx \theta$ and

$$1 - \cos\theta = 2\sin^2\frac{\theta}{2} \approx \frac{\theta^2}{2}$$

Then

$$V = \tfrac{1}{2}ka^2[(\theta_1 - \theta_2)^2 + (\theta_2 - \theta_3)^2] + mga(\theta_1^2 + \theta_2^2 + \theta_3^2)$$

and the equations of motion are

$$4ma^2\ddot{\theta}_1 = -ka^2(\theta_1 - \theta_2) - 2mga\theta_1$$
$$4ma^2\ddot{\theta}_2 = -ka^2(2\theta_2 - \theta_1 - \theta_3) - 2mga\theta_2$$
$$4ma^2\ddot{\theta}_3 = -ka^2(\theta_3 - \theta_2) - 2mga\theta_3$$

The solution can then be found by the methods developed in Sec. 1.11. We shall return to the general theory of small vibrations in the next section.

It is possible to derive Lagrange equations even if the field is not conservative. In the absence of a potential function V, we can write

$$\sum_{\alpha=1}^{n}(\mathbf{F}_\alpha^{(a)}, \delta\mathbf{X}_\alpha) = Q_k\delta q_k \qquad k = 1, 2, \ldots, p$$

with

$$\delta\mathbf{X}_\alpha = \frac{\partial\mathbf{X}_\alpha}{\partial q_k}\delta q_k$$

so that
$$Q_k = \sum_{\alpha=1}^{n} \left(\mathbf{F}_\alpha^{(a)}, \frac{\partial \mathbf{X}_\alpha}{\partial q_k} \right)$$

We call Q_k the **generalized forces.** They do not necessarily have the dimensions of a force, since the δq_k do not necessarily have dimensions of length. However, $Q_k \delta q_k$ must have the dimensions of work.

Introducing the generalized forces, we have

$$\int_{t_1}^{t_2} (\delta T + Q_k \delta q_k)\, dt = 0$$

or
$$\int_{t_1}^{t_2} \left(\frac{\partial T}{\partial q_k} - \frac{d}{dt}\frac{\partial T}{\partial \dot{q}_k} + Q_k \right) \delta q_k\, dt = 0$$

Thus
$$\frac{d}{dt}\frac{\partial T}{\partial \dot{q}_k} - \frac{\partial T}{\partial q_k} = Q_k$$

are the equations of motion when the field is not conservative.

Consider next a conservative system in which the constraints are not functions of time, and hence
$$\mathbf{X}_i = \mathbf{X}_i(q_1, q_2, \ldots, q_p)$$

are not explicitly functions of time. In this case, V is not explicitly a function of time, nor is it a function of the generalized velocities $\dot{q}_i$. Then

$$\frac{dL}{dt} = \frac{\partial L}{\partial q_i}\dot{q}_i + \frac{\partial L}{\partial \dot{q}_i}\ddot{q}_i$$

From Lagrange's equations we have

$$\frac{\partial L}{\partial q_i} = \frac{d}{dt}\frac{\partial L}{\partial \dot{q}_i}$$

so that
$$\frac{dL}{dt} = \left(\frac{d}{dt}\frac{\partial L}{\partial \dot{q}_i} \right)\dot{q}_i + \frac{\partial L}{\partial \dot{q}_i}\ddot{q}_i = \frac{d}{dt}\left(\dot{q}_i \frac{\partial L}{\partial \dot{q}_i} \right)$$

Hence we have
$$\frac{d}{dt}\left(\dot{q}_i \frac{\partial L}{\partial \dot{q}_i} - L \right) = 0$$

which implies that
$$\dot{q}_i \frac{\partial L}{\partial \dot{q}_i} - L = H$$

where H is a constant. This statement can be put in a simpler form, for under the given hypotheses,

$$\frac{\partial L}{\partial \dot{q}_i} = \frac{\partial T}{\partial \dot{q}_i}$$

and we have
$$H = \dot{q}_i \frac{\partial T}{\partial \dot{q}_i} - T + V$$

But
$$T = \frac{1}{2} \sum_{\alpha=1}^{n} m_\alpha (\dot{\mathbf{X}}_\alpha, \dot{\mathbf{X}}_\alpha)$$

$$= \frac{1}{2} \sum_{\alpha=1}^{n} m_\alpha \left(\frac{\partial \mathbf{X}_\alpha}{\partial q_j}, \frac{\partial \mathbf{X}_\alpha}{\partial q_k} \right) \dot{q}_j \dot{q}_k$$

$$= \tfrac{1}{2} a_{jk}(q_1, q_2, \ldots, q_p) \dot{q}_j \dot{q}_k$$

and
$$\dot{q}_i \frac{\partial T}{\partial \dot{q}_i} = a_{ik} \dot{q}_i \dot{q}_k = 2T$$

Hence, we have the **conservation-of-energy principle**

$$T + V = H$$

a constant.

There are many reasons why the formulation of mechanics as a variational principle is extremely important. First, it gives us a formulation which is independent of the particular coordinate system in terms of which the motion is described. In other words, if we change the generalized coordinates to a new set by a coordinate transformation

$$\bar{q}_i = \bar{q}_i(q_1, q_2, \ldots, q_p) \qquad i = 1, 2, \ldots, p$$

then Hamilton's principle

$$\delta \int (T - V)\, dt = 0$$

will yield the equations of motion

$$\frac{d}{dt} \frac{\partial L}{\partial \dot{\bar{q}}_i} - \frac{\partial L}{\partial \bar{q}_i} = 0$$

and the form of the equations is the same, as it should be if the theory is to be independent of the particular mathematical description.

Second, the variational calculus approach is one which is more easily generalized to situations other than the equations of motion as such. Indeed new theories have been developed in areas unrelated to mechanics by means of variational principles. For example, various field theories can be based on variational principles.

Third, it gives us numerical techniques for approximating certain physical constants by means of establishing upper and lower bounds, which are easily computed from the functionals involved in the variational problem. Some of these methods will be illustrated in Sec. 2.9.

Exercises 2.3

1. Rework the example of this section, taking into account the mass of the rods and assuming the linear density of the rods uniform. The kinetic energy of the rods can be expressed as the rotational kinetic energy $\frac{1}{2}I\dot{\theta}^2$, where I is the moment of inertia about the point of rotation.

2. Assume a change of generalized coordinates $\bar{q}_i = \bar{q}_i(q_1, q_2, \ldots, q_p)$ and show the following:

a. $\dot{\bar{q}}_i = \dfrac{\partial \bar{q}_i}{\partial q_j}\dot{q}_j$ and $\dot{q}_i = \dfrac{\partial q_i}{\partial \bar{q}_j}\dot{\bar{q}}_j$

b. $\dfrac{\partial \dot{q}_i}{\partial \bar{q}_j} = \dfrac{\partial^2 q_i}{\partial \bar{q}_j \partial \bar{q}_k}\dot{\bar{q}}_k$

Hence, show directly that the form of Lagrange's equations is independent of the coordinate system.

3. The notion of generalized coordinates can be used to derive equations of motion in various coordinate systems. In spherical coordinates

$$T = \tfrac{1}{2}\sum_{\alpha=1}^{n} m_\alpha(\dot{r}_\alpha^2 + r_\alpha^2 \sin^2\phi_\alpha \dot{\theta}_\alpha^2 + r_\alpha^2\dot{\phi}_\alpha^2)$$

Use this to derive equations of motion for a system of particles referred to spherical coordinates.

4. Suppose that additional conditions of constraint

$$\phi_i(q_1, q_2, \ldots, q_p) = 0 \qquad i = 1, 2, \ldots, k < p$$

are imposed on a system. Derive the equations of motion

$$\frac{d}{dt}\frac{\partial T}{\partial \dot{q}_j} - \frac{\partial T}{\partial q_j} - Q_j = \lambda_i \frac{\partial \phi_i}{\partial q_j} \qquad i = 1, 2, \ldots, k$$

$$j = 1, 2, \ldots, p$$

5. Define the **generalized momentum** $p_i = \dfrac{\partial T}{\partial \dot{q}_i}$ and the **Hamiltonian** for a conservative system $H = p_i\dot{q}_i - L$. Show that

a. $\dfrac{\partial H}{\partial \dot{q}_i} = 0$

b. $\dfrac{\partial H}{\partial p_i} = \dot{q}_i$

c. $\dfrac{\partial H}{\partial q_i} = -\dot{p}_i$

d. $\dfrac{\partial H}{\partial t} = -\dfrac{\partial L}{\partial t}$

On the basis of these equations give an alternative proof of conservation of energy when the constraints do not depend explicitly on time.

2.4   Theory of Small Vibrations

We next turn our attention to the general theory of small vibrations of conservative systems near a position of stable equilibrium.[1] Consider a conservative system in which the constraints are not functions of time and hence the potential energy is not explicitly a function of time. Suppose the system is in a configuration of stable equilibrium. Equilibrium occurs when the forces on all the particles are zero. Hence, in a small virtual displacement at equilibrium

$$\delta W = \sum_{\alpha=1}^{n} (\mathbf{F}_{\alpha}, \delta \mathbf{X}_{\alpha}) = 0$$

$$= \sum_{\alpha=1}^{n} (\mathbf{F}_{\alpha}^{(a)} + \mathbf{F}_{\alpha}^{(c)}, \delta \mathbf{X}_{\alpha}) = 0$$

$$= \sum_{\alpha=1}^{n} (\mathbf{F}_{\alpha}^{(a)}, \delta \mathbf{X}_{\alpha}) = 0$$

since the forces of constraint are assumed to do no work. In terms of generalized forces Q_k and generalized coordinates q_k

$$\delta W = Q_k \delta q_k = 0$$

for arbitrary δq_k at equilibrium. Hence the condition for equilibrium can be stated as

$$Q_k = -\frac{\partial V}{\partial q_k} = 0$$

Therefore, V is stationary at equilibrium. That it is a relative minimum follows from the fact that we are assuming stable equilibrium. If not, a small displacement would decrease V and hence increase T, since energy $H = T + V$ is conserved. This would imply that a small displacement would cause the system to run away, contrary to assumption.

If we choose the generalized coordinates so that they vanish in the equilibrium position and choose V so that it vanishes at equilibrium, then

$$V(q_1, q_2, \ldots, q_p) = \frac{1}{2} \frac{\partial^2 V}{\partial q_i \, \partial q_j} q_i q_j$$

$$= \tfrac{1}{2} a_{ij} q_i q_j$$

neglecting higher-order terms in the small displacements from equilibrium. The a_{ij} are constants, since the second partial derivatives are evaluated at the

---

[1] This means that, if the system is slightly displaced, it will tend to return to the equilibrium state rather than run away.

equilibrium position $q_1 = q_2 = \cdots = q_p = 0$. The square matrix A with elements a_{ij} is real and symmetric. The potential energy is, therefore, a quadratic form in the displacements.

Since the constraints do not depend on time, the kinetic energy is

$$T = \tfrac{1}{2} b_{ij} \dot{q}_i \dot{q}_j$$

where
$$b_{ij} = \sum_{\alpha=1}^{n} m_\alpha \left(\frac{\partial \mathbf{X}_\alpha}{\partial q_i}, \frac{\partial \mathbf{X}_\alpha}{\partial q_j} \right)$$

In the case of small vibrations about equilibrium, we can evaluate b_{ij} at the equilibrium position. Hence, the b_{ij} are constants and the matrix B with elements b_{ij} is real and symmetric. From the definition of kinetic energy we see that it is positive unless all the velocities are zero. Therefore, B has only positive eigenvalues.

The Lagrangian is equal to

$$L = T - V = \tfrac{1}{2} b_{ij} \dot{q}_i \dot{q}_j - \tfrac{1}{2} a_{ij} q_i q_j$$

and the Lagrange equations yield

$$b_{ij} \ddot{q}_j + a_{ij} q_j = 0$$

Suppose we attempt to separate out the time-dependent part of the solution, i.e., we look for a solution of the form

$$q_j = y_j f(t)$$

Then the equations of motion become

$$b_{ij} y_j \ddot{f} + a_{ij} y_j f = 0$$

For each i we can then write

$$\frac{\ddot{f}}{f} = -\frac{a_{ij} y_j}{b_{ij} y_j} = -\lambda$$

from which it follows that

$$\ddot{f}(t) + \lambda f(t) = 0$$

$$a_{ij} y_j = \lambda b_{ij} y_j$$

We are thus led to the eigenvector problem

$$AY = \lambda BY$$

with characteristic equation

$$|A - \lambda B| = 0$$

which has p real solutions. There are thus p separation constants λ_α corresponding to p **normal modes** of vibration of the system

$$y_{\alpha j} f_\alpha(t) = y_{\alpha j} \sin (\sqrt{\lambda_\alpha} t + \phi_\alpha) \qquad \alpha = 1, 2, \ldots, p$$

The general solution is a linear combination of these normal modes:

$$q_j = \sum_{\alpha=1}^{p} c_\alpha y_{\alpha j} \sin (\sqrt{\lambda_\alpha} t + \phi_\alpha)$$

for

$$\ddot{q}_j = -\sum_{\alpha=1}^{p} \lambda_\alpha c_\alpha y_{\alpha j} \sin (\sqrt{\lambda_\alpha} t + \phi_\alpha)$$

and

$$b_{kj} \ddot{q}_j = -\sum_{\alpha=1}^{p} \lambda_\alpha c_\alpha b_{kj} y_{\alpha j} \sin (\sqrt{\lambda_\alpha} t + \phi_\alpha)$$

$$= -\sum_{\alpha=1}^{p} c_\alpha a_{kj} y_{\alpha j} \sin (\sqrt{\lambda_\alpha} t + \phi_\alpha)$$

$$= -a_{kj} q_j$$

Alternatively, we could have performed the coordinate transformation

$$q_i = t_{ij} \bar{q}_j$$
$$\dot{q}_i = t_{ij} \dot{\bar{q}}_j$$

which will simultaneously reduce the potential and kinetic energy quadratic forms to the diagonal form

$$T = \tfrac{1}{2} \delta_{ij} \dot{\bar{q}}_i \dot{\bar{q}}_j$$
$$V = \tfrac{1}{2} d_{ij} \bar{q}_i \bar{q}_j$$

Then the equations of motion give

$$\ddot{\bar{q}}_\alpha + \lambda_\alpha \bar{q}_\alpha = 0$$

The $\bar{q}$'s are called the **normal coordinates** for the system. We solve for them as follows:

$$\bar{q}_\alpha = c_\alpha \sin (\sqrt{\lambda_\alpha} t + \phi_\alpha)$$

That the λ's are positive follows from the fact that V is positive-definite.

A third approach is to obtain the normal modes as a solution of a problem in the calculus of variations. The normal modes are characterized by the fact that they are solutions with periodic time dependence. Let

$$q_i = y_i \sin (\sqrt{\lambda} t + \phi)$$

Then

$$2T = \lambda b_{ij} y_i y_j \cos^2 (\sqrt{\lambda} t + \phi)$$
$$2V = a_{ij} y_i y_j \sin^2 (\sqrt{\lambda} t + \phi)$$

If y_i are the components of one of the eigenvectors of the problem

$$AY = \lambda BY$$

then

$$2V = \lambda b_{ij} y_i y_j \sin^2 (\sqrt{\lambda} t + \phi)$$

and $\bar{V} = \bar{T}$, where $\bar{V}$ and $\bar{T}$ are the mean potential and kinetic energies over one period τ in periodic motion.

$$2\bar{V} = \frac{1}{\tau} \int_0^\tau a_{ij} y_i y_j \sin^2 (\sqrt{\lambda} t + \phi)\, dt$$

$$2\bar{T} = \frac{1}{\tau} \int_0^\tau \lambda b_{ij} y_i y_j \cos^2 (\sqrt{\lambda} t + \phi)\, dt$$

Then
$$\frac{a_{ij} y_i y_j}{b_{ij} y_i y_j} = \frac{\bar{V}}{\bar{U}} = \lambda$$

where $\bar{T} = \lambda \bar{U}$. For a normal mode with a natural frequency $\sqrt{\lambda}/2\pi$

$$\bar{V} = \lambda \bar{U}$$

and furthermore, λ is a stationary value of $\bar{V}/\bar{U}$ or, alternatively, a stationary value of $\bar{V}$ subject to $\bar{U} = 1$. These properties have already been developed in Sec. 2.1. Thus, the eigenvalues and eigenvectors can be defined by any one of three problems in the calculus of variations:

1. Minimize $\dfrac{\bar{V}}{\bar{U}} = \dfrac{a_{ij} x_i x_j}{a_{ij} x_i x_j}$ subject to $X'BY_j = 0, j = 1, 2, \ldots, k - 1$.

2. Minimize $\bar{V} = a_{ij} x_i x_j$ subject to $\bar{U} = b_{ij} x_i x_j = 1$ and $X'BY_j = 0$, $j = 1, 2, \ldots, k - 1$.

3. Find the minimum of $\bar{V}/\bar{U}$ subject to $X'BV_j = 0, j = 1, 2, \ldots, k - 1$, where V_j are any set of linearly independent vectors. Then find the maximum of the minima as the V's are allowed to change.

Exercises 2.4

1. Find the natural frequencies and normal modes of small vibrations about equilibrium of the double pendulum with identical masses and rods, assuming plane motion.

2. Find the natural frequencies and normal modes of small transverse vibrations of a system consisting of two identical rods hinged together and supported by three identical springs, one at the hinge and the others at the ends of the rods. Assume plane motion. HINT: The kinetic energy of a rod is the sum of the translational energy of the center of mass and the rotational energy about the center of mass.

3. A simple pendulum is suspended from a point and is free to move so that the mass remains on the surface of a sphere with a diameter equal to the length of the pendulum rod. Analyze small vibrations about equilibrium.

2.5   The Vibrating String

Most of the above ideas for systems of particles can be carried over to the case of continuous distributions of mass. Consider, for example, a string of uniform density ρ stretched between two fixed points $x = 0$ and $x = L$, with a tension σ. The density and tension will be assumed constant, and we shall ignore the weight of the string. The kinetic energy per unit length is $\frac{1}{2}\rho\dot{y}^2$, where y is the displacement from equilibrium. Hence, the total kinetic energy is

$$T = \tfrac{1}{2}\rho\int_0^L \dot{y}^2\,dx$$

The potential energy can be computed as the negative of the work done in the displacement. Consider an element of string subject to tension σ on the ends.

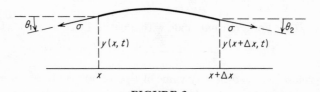

FIGURE 3

The force in the direction of the displacement is

$$F = \sigma(\sin\theta_2 + \sin\theta_1) \approx \sigma(\tan\theta_2 + \tan\theta_1)$$

Therefore,
$$F \approx \sigma[-y'(x + \Delta x) + y'(x)]$$

$$\approx -\sigma y''(x)\,\Delta x = -\sigma p\,\frac{dp}{dy}\,\Delta x$$

where $p = y'$. The work done per unit length is then

$$-\sigma\int_0^y p\,\frac{dp}{dy}\,dy = -\sigma\,\frac{p^2}{2} = \frac{-\sigma(y')^2}{2}$$

The total potential energy is thus

$$V = \tfrac{1}{2}\int_0^L \sigma(y')^2\,dx$$

The equilibrium position is a stationary value of V. Therefore,

$$\delta V = \tfrac{1}{2}\delta\int_0^L \sigma(y')^2\,dx = 0$$

will tell us what the equilibrium configuration is. The Euler equation for this problem is $y'' = 0$, which implies that $y = 0$ for equilibrium, assuming that the ends are on the x axis.

Hamilton's principle for this problem states the following:

$$\delta\int_{t_1}^{t_2}\int_0^L (\tfrac{1}{2}\rho\dot{y}^2 - \tfrac{1}{2}\sigma y'^2)\,dx\,dt = 0$$

Let $y(x,t) = \phi(x,t) + \epsilon\eta(x,t)$, where ϕ is assumed to be the solution of the variational problem. The boundary conditions are

$$y(0,t) = \phi(0,t) = y(L,t) = \phi(L,t) = 0$$

Hence, $\eta(0,t) = \eta(L,t) = 0$. Also we must have $\eta(x,t_1) = \eta(x,t_2) = 0$. We know that

$$I(\epsilon) = \int_{t_1}^{t_2} \int_0^L [\tfrac{1}{2}\rho(\dot\phi + \epsilon\dot\eta)^2 - \tfrac{1}{2}\sigma(\phi' + \epsilon\eta')^2]\, dx\, dt$$

has a stationary value at $\epsilon = 0$. Therefore,

$$I'(0) = \int_{t_1}^{t_2} \int_0^L [\rho\dot\phi\dot\eta - \sigma\phi'\eta']\, dx\, dt = 0$$

Integrating by parts and using the boundary conditions, we have

$$\int_{t_1}^{t_2} \int_0^L (\rho\ddot\phi - \sigma\phi'')\eta\, dx\, dt = 0$$

Since η is arbitrary, the Euler equation becomes the following partial differential equation:

$$\frac{\partial^2\phi}{\partial x^2} = \frac{\rho}{\sigma}\frac{\partial^2\phi}{\partial t^2}$$

This is the **wave equation** which must be satisfied by the displacement function on the string. To determine the solution, we must also have boundary conditions and initial conditions. In this case the boundary conditions are $\phi(0,t) = \phi(L,t) = 0$. The initial conditions are $\phi(x,0) = g(x)$ and $\dot\phi(x,0) = h(x)$, where $g(x)$ and $h(x)$ are some prescribed functions which give the initial displacements and initial velocities along the string.

We can solve the string problem by techniques analogous to those used in the case of systems of particles. We attempt to find fundamental solutions in the form of simple periodic functions by performing a separation of variables. Let $\phi(x,t) = \psi(x)f(t)$. Then

$$f\psi'' = \frac{\rho}{\sigma}\psi\ddot f$$

so that

$$\frac{\psi''}{\psi} = \frac{\rho}{\sigma}\frac{\ddot f}{f} = -\lambda$$

The time-dependent part $f(t)$ must then satisfy the equation

$$\ddot f + \frac{\sigma\lambda}{\rho}f = 0$$

and the space-dependent part $\psi(x)$ must satisfy the equation

$$\psi'' + \lambda\psi = 0$$

If $\lambda = 0$, then $\psi = c_1 x + c_2$, and the boundary conditions would imply that c_1 and c_2 are both zero. If λ were negative, then

$$\psi = c_1 \sinh \sqrt{-\lambda}x + c_2 \cosh \sqrt{-\lambda}x$$

and again the boundary conditions would imply that $c_1 = c_2 = 0$. For λ positive

$$\psi(x) = c \sin (\sqrt{\lambda}x + \theta) = A \sin \sqrt{\lambda}x + B \cos \sqrt{\lambda}x$$

$\psi(0) = 0$ implies $B = 0$, and $\psi(L) = 0$ implies

$$\lambda = \frac{k^2 \pi^2}{L^2}$$

There are, therefore, an infinite number of discrete separation constants possible with $k = 1, 2, 3, \ldots$.

The time-dependent part of the fundamental solution is

$$f_k = \sin (\omega_k t + \theta_k)$$

with $\omega_k = \frac{k\pi}{L}\sqrt{\frac{\sigma}{\rho}}$. These are the **natural frequencies** corresponding to the **normal modes**

$$\phi_k = c_k \sin \frac{k\pi}{L} x \sin (\omega_k t + \theta_k)$$

Any linear combination of normal modes will satisfy the partial differential equation and the boundary conditions. We must find out which of all possible such functions satisfies the initial conditions. To this end, we use the theory of Fourier series developed in Sec. 1.9. Consider the series

$$\phi(x,t) = \sum_{k=1}^{\infty} \sin \frac{k\pi x}{L} (a_k \cos \omega_k t + b_k \sin \omega_k t)$$

If this represents the solution, then

$$\phi(x,0) = g(x) = \sum_{k=1}^{\infty} a_k \sin \frac{k\pi x}{L}$$

If this is the Fourier sine series for $g(x)$, then

$$a_k = \frac{2}{L} \int_0^L g(x) \sin \frac{k\pi x}{L} dx$$

Also, we must have

$$\dot{\phi}(x,0) = h(x) = \sum_{k=1}^{\infty} \omega_k b_k \sin \frac{k\pi x}{L}$$

and
$$b_k = \frac{2}{\omega_k L} \int_0^L h(x) \sin \frac{k\pi x}{L} \, dx$$

These series will converge to the given functions $g(x)$ and $h(x)$ if both are continuous and have a piecewise continuous derivative.

We have thus obtained an infinite series which converges to the given initial conditions. To show that this is the solution to our problem, we proceed as follows:

$$\phi(x,t) = \sum_{k=1}^{\infty} \frac{a_k}{2} \left[\sin \frac{k\pi}{L} (x - ct) + \sin \frac{k\pi}{L} (x + ct) \right]$$

$$+ \sum_{k=1}^{\infty} \frac{b_k}{2} \left[\cos \frac{k\pi}{L} (x - ct) - \cos \frac{k\pi}{L} (x + ct) \right]$$

where $c = \sqrt{\sigma/\rho}$. Since a_k is the Fourier coefficient of $g(x)$, the first sum is obviously $\frac{1}{2}[g(x - ct) + g(x + ct)]$, where we must extend the definition of $g(x)$ to the interval $-L \le x \le 0$ as an odd function and from there to any other interval as a periodic function with period $2L$. The other series can also be summed in closed form. To see this, extend the definition of $h(x)$ first to the interval $-L \le x \le 0$ as an odd function and then to any other interval as a periodic function with period $2L$. Define

$$H(x) = \int_0^x h(\xi) \, d\xi$$

Then $H(x)$ is continuous, even, and periodic with perod $2L$ and has a continuous derivative and a piecewise continuous second derivative. Now

$$H(x + ct) - H(x - ct) = \int_{x-ct}^{x+ct} h(\xi) \, d\xi$$

$$= \int_{x-ct}^{x+ct} \sum_{k=1}^{\infty} \omega_k b_k \sin \frac{k\pi\xi}{L} \, d\xi$$

$$= c \sum_{k=1}^{\infty} b_k \left[\cos \frac{k\pi}{L} (x - ct) - \cos \frac{k\pi}{L} (x + ct) \right]$$

Hence, $\quad \phi(x,t) = \frac{1}{2}[g(x - ct) + g(x + ct)] + \frac{1}{2c} \int_{x-ct}^{x+ct} h(\xi) \, d\xi$

It can be shown by direct substitution that this is a solution of the problem if $g(x)$ is twice differentiable and $h(x)$ is once differentiable.

We can analyze the natural frequencies and normal modes of the string problem, using the calculus of variations.

For a fundamental solution ϕ_k the average potential and kinetic energies over one period τ_k are equal, i.e.,

$$\bar{T} = \frac{1}{\tau_k} \int_0^{\tau_k} \int_0^L \frac{\omega_k^2}{2} \rho \sin^2 \frac{k\pi}{L} x \cos^2 (\omega_k t + \theta_k) \, dx \, dt$$

$$= \frac{\omega_k^2 \rho L}{8}$$

$$\bar{V} = \frac{1}{\tau_k} \int_0^{\tau_k} \int_0^L \left(\frac{k\pi}{L}\right)^2 \frac{\sigma}{2} \cos^2 \frac{k\pi}{L} x \sin^2 (\omega_k t + \theta_k) \, dx \, dt$$

$$= \frac{k^2 \pi^2}{L^2} \frac{\sigma L}{8} = \frac{\omega_k^2 \rho L}{8}$$

Integrating out the time-dependent part, we have

$$\bar{T} = \frac{\omega_k^2 \rho}{4} \int_0^L \psi_k^2 \, dx$$

$$\bar{V} = \frac{\sigma}{4} \int_0^L \psi_k'^2 \, dx$$

so that

$$\frac{\sigma}{\rho \omega_k^2} \frac{\int_0^L \psi_k'^2 \, dx}{\int_0^L \psi_k^2 \, dx} = 1$$

or

$$\frac{Q(\psi_k)}{N(\psi_k)} = \omega_k^2 \frac{\rho}{\sigma} = \frac{k^2 \pi^2}{L^2} = \lambda_k$$

where

$$Q(\psi_k) = \int_0^L \psi_k'^2 \, dx \quad \text{and} \quad N(\psi_k) = \int_0^L \psi_k^2 \, dx$$

We are led to speculate that the eigenvalues λ_k are stationary values of $Q(\psi)/N(\psi)$ or, alternatively, stationary values of $Q(\psi)$ subject to $N(\psi) = 1$. This is indeed the case, as we shall now show.

Let F be the function space of real-valued functions defined on the interval $0 \le x \le L$, which are continuous and have piecewise continuous first and second derivatives[1] and vanish at $x = 0$ and $x = L$. Then $\lambda_k = k^2 \pi^2 / L^2$,

---

[1] Using more sophisticated methods, we would not have to assume the piecewise continuity of the second derivative.

$k = 1, 2, 3, \ldots$ are stationary values of $Q(f)$ over F subject to $N(f) = 1$ and $N(f, \psi_j) = 0, j = 1, 2, 3, \ldots, k - 1$, where

$$\psi_k = \left(\frac{2}{L}\right)^{\frac{1}{2}} \sin \frac{k\pi x}{L}$$

are the eigenfunctions of the variational problem. We prove this as follows.

We first extend the definition of every function in F into the interval $-L \leq x \leq 0$ as an odd function. Then, since the trigonometric functions $\sin (k\pi x)/L$ are complete with respect to this set of odd functions,

$$\frac{1}{L} \int_{-L}^{L} [f(x)]^2 \, dx = \sum_{k=1}^{\infty} b_k^2$$

where

$$b_k = \frac{1}{L} \int_{-L}^{L} f(x) \sin \frac{k\pi x}{L} \, dx$$

Furthermore, $f'(x)$ is even, and the functions $\cos (k\pi x/L)$, $k = 0, 1, 2, \ldots$ are complete with respect to this set of functions. Hence,

$$\frac{1}{L} \int_{-L}^{L} [f'(x)]^2 \, dx = \frac{a_0^2}{2} + \sum_{k=1}^{\infty} a_k^2$$

where

$$a_k = \frac{1}{L} \int_{-L}^{L} f'(x) \cos \frac{k\pi x}{L} \, dx$$

$$= \frac{1}{L} \left[f(x) \cos \frac{k\pi x}{L} \right]_{-L}^{L} + \frac{k\pi}{L^2} \int_{-L}^{L} f(x) \sin \frac{k\pi x}{L} \, dx$$

$$= \frac{k\pi}{L} b_k$$

Therefore,

$$Q(f) = \int_0^L [f'(x)]^2 \, dx = \frac{1}{2} \int_{-L}^{L} [f'(x)]^2 \, dx$$

$$= \frac{L}{2} \sum_{k=1}^{\infty} \frac{k^2 \pi^2}{L^2} b_k^2$$

$$N(f) = \int_0^L [f(x)]^2 \, dx = \frac{1}{2} \int_{-L}^{L} [f(x)]^2 \, dx$$

$$= \frac{L}{2} \sum_{k=1}^{\infty} b_k^2$$

Now consider
$$\psi_1(x) = \left(\frac{2}{L}\right)^{\frac{1}{2}} \sin \frac{\pi x}{L}$$

$$N(\psi_1) = \frac{2}{L} \int_0^L \sin \frac{2\pi x}{L} \, dx$$

$$= \frac{1}{L} \int_0^L \left(1 - \cos \frac{2\pi x}{L}\right) dx = 1$$

$$Q(\psi_1) = \frac{2\pi^2}{L^3} \int_0^L \cos^2 \frac{\pi x}{L} \, dx$$

$$= \frac{\pi^2}{L^3} \int_0^L \left(1 + \cos \frac{2\pi x}{L}\right) dx$$

$$= \frac{\pi^2}{L^2}$$

For any normalized $f(x)$ in F

$$N(f) = \frac{L}{2} \sum_{k=1}^{\infty} b_k^2 = 1$$

and
$$Q(f) - Q(\psi_1) = \frac{L}{2} \sum_{k=1}^{\infty} \frac{k^2 \pi^2}{L^2} b_k^2 - \frac{L}{2} \sum_{k=1}^{\infty} \frac{\pi^2}{L^2} b_k^2$$

$$= \frac{L}{2} \sum_{k=2}^{\infty} \frac{(k^2 - 1)\pi^2}{L^2} b_k^2 \geq 0$$

This proves that $Q(\psi_1) = \pi^2/L^2$ is the minimum over the whole space subject to $N(f) = 1$.

Next consider the subspace of F such that $N(f) = 1$ and $N(f,\psi_1) = 0$. The latter condition implies that $b_1 = 0$. Let $\psi_2(x) = \left(\frac{2}{L}\right)^{\frac{1}{2}} \sin \frac{2\pi x}{L}$. Then

$$N(\psi_2) = 1 \qquad Q(\psi_2) = \frac{4\pi^2}{L^2}$$

$$Q(f) - Q(\psi_2) = \frac{L}{2} \sum_{k=2}^{\infty} \frac{k^2 \pi^2}{L^2} b_k^2 - \frac{L}{2} \sum_{k=2}^{\infty} \frac{4\pi^2}{L^2} b_k^2$$

$$= \frac{L}{2} \sum_{k=3}^{\infty} \frac{(k^2 - 4)\pi^2}{L^2} b_k^2 \geq 0$$

This proves the $Q(\psi_2) = 4\pi^2/L^2$ is the minimum over the subspace   More generally, consider the subspace such that $N(f) = 1$ and $N(f,\psi_j) = 0$,

$j = 1, 2, 3, \ldots, k - 1$, where $\psi_j = \left(\dfrac{2}{L}\right)^{\frac{1}{2}} \sin \dfrac{j\pi x}{L}$.   The latter condition implies that $b_1 = b_2 = \cdots = b_{k-1} = 0$.   Let $\psi_k(x) = \left(\dfrac{2}{L}\right)^{\frac{1}{2}} \sin \dfrac{k\pi x}{L}$.

Then
$$N(\psi_k) = 1 \qquad Q(\psi_k) = \frac{k^2 \pi^2}{L^2}$$

$$Q(f) - Q(\psi_k) = \frac{L}{2} \sum_{m=k}^{\infty} \frac{m^2 \pi^2}{L^2} b_m^2 - \frac{L}{2} \sum_{m=k}^{\infty} \frac{k^2 \pi^2}{L^2} b_m^2$$

$$= \frac{L}{2} \sum_{m=k+1}^{\infty} \frac{(m^2 - k^2)\pi^2}{L^2} b_m^2 \geq 0$$

This proves that $Q(\psi_k)$ is a solution of the kth minimum problem.

Notice that by the fortuitous choice of the trigonometric functions as the complete set of functions in the space F we obtained the quadratic forms $Q(f)$ and $N(f)$ in diagonal form.   For another complete set of functions these forms would not have been diagonal.   Hence, the variational problem is essentially equivalent to the simultaneous reduction of $Q(f)$ and $N(f)$ to diagonal form.

It should also be mentioned that the eigenvalues and eigenfunctions of the variational problem can be formulated in terms of a minimax definition.

Exercises 2.5

1. A string of length L and fixed ends is started into oscillation with no initial velocity but with an initial displacement $g(x) = \epsilon x(L - x)$.   Find the displacement for any time $t > 0$.

*2. Using direct methods (not Euler's equation), show that $\left(\dfrac{1}{L}\right)^{\frac{1}{2}}, \left(\dfrac{2}{L}\right)^{\frac{1}{2}} \cos \dfrac{k\pi x}{L}$,

$k = 1, 2, 3, \ldots$ are solutions of the following variational problem: Over the space of real-valued functions defined on the interval $0 \leq x \leq L$, which are continuous and have piecewise continuous first and second derivatives, minimize

$$Q(f) = \int_0^L [f'(x)]^2 \, dx$$

subject to $N(f) = \displaystyle\int_0^L [f(x)]^2 \, dx = 1$ and $N(f, \psi_j) = 0, j = 0, 1, 2, \ldots, k - 1$, where

$$\psi_0 = \left(\frac{1}{L}\right)^{\frac{1}{2}} \qquad \psi_j = \left(\frac{2}{L}\right)^{\frac{1}{2}} \cos \frac{j\pi x}{L}$$

*3. Formulate and establish the minimax definition of the eigenvalues and eigenfunctions for the string problem with fixed ends.

*4. If a force of linear density $f(x)$ is applied to a string stretched between two fixed points with tension σ, show that the total potential energy is

$$\int_0^L \left[\frac{\sigma}{2} \left(\frac{dy}{dx} \right)^2 - f(x)y \right] dx$$

Hence show that the equation for the equilibrium deflection of the string is

$$\sigma \frac{d\phi^2}{dx^2} = -f(x).$$

*5. Obtain the differential equation for the longitudinal displacement y of the cross section of a rod with fixed ends, if the potential energy per unit length is $\frac{1}{2} EA \left(\dfrac{\partial y}{\partial x} \right)^2$, where E is Young's modulus and A is the area of the cross section.

*6. Obtain the differential equation for the transverse displacement y of a beam built in at the ends, if the potential energy per unit length is

$$\tfrac{1}{2} EI \left(\frac{\partial^2 y}{\partial x^2} \right)^2$$

where E is Young's modulus and I is the moment of inertia of the cross section. The boundary conditions are $y(0,t) = y(L,t) = y'(0,t) = y'(L,t) = 0$.

2.6 Boundary-value Problems of Mathematical Physics

In the last section, we arrived at the partial differential equation for the displacement of a stretched string in small vibrations by an application of Hamilton's principle to the continuous system of masses representing the string.   By a similar analysis we can obtain the equation for the displacement of a stretched elastic membrane.   Let us say that the membrane covers the region R in the xy plane, bounded by a simple closed curve[1] C.   The displacement from equilibrium is measured in the z direction.   The membrane is assumed to have uniform and constant density ρ, and, therefore, the total kinetic energy is given by

$$T = \tfrac{1}{2} \rho \iint_R \left(\frac{\partial z}{\partial t} \right)^2 dx\, dy$$

The tension σ, in small vibrations, is assumed constant, and by an extension of the argument given for the string the total potential energy is

$$V = \tfrac{1}{2} \sigma \iint_R \left[\left(\frac{\partial z}{\partial x} \right)^2 + \left(\frac{\partial z}{\partial y} \right)^2 \right] dx\, dy$$

[1] By a simple closed curve we mean a curve consisting of a finite number of arcs with continuously turning tangents, joined at the end points, but not crossing over itself.

Hamilton's principle then states

$$\delta \int_{t_1}^{t} \iint_R \left\{ \rho \left(\frac{\partial z}{\partial t} \right)^2 - \sigma \left[\left(\frac{\partial z}{\partial x} \right)^2 + \left(\frac{\partial z}{\partial x} \right)^2 \right] \right\} dx \, dy \, dt = 0$$

If we assume that there is a function $\phi(x,y,t)$, with continuous second partial derivatives, which makes this integral stationary, then

$$I(\epsilon) = \int_{t_1}^{t_2} \iint_R \left\{ \rho(\phi_t + \epsilon \eta_t)^2 - \sigma[(\phi_x + \epsilon \eta_x)^2 + (\phi_y + \epsilon \eta_y)^2] \right\} dx \, dy \, dt$$

has a stationary value at $\epsilon = 0$. Let us assume that the membrane is held fixed to the boundary curve C. Hence, the solution ϕ and the virtual displacement $\phi + \epsilon \eta$ must vanish on C. Also in the formulation of Hamilton's principle $\eta(x,y,t_1) = \eta(x,y,t_2) = 0$. Otherwise η is arbitrary, except that it must have continuous first partial derivatives. The necessary condition for I to have a stationary value at $\epsilon = 0$ is

$$I'(0) = \int_{t_1}^{t_2} \iint_R \left(\rho \frac{\partial \phi}{\partial t} \frac{\partial \phi}{\partial t} - \sigma \frac{\partial \phi}{\partial x} \frac{\partial \eta}{\partial x} - \sigma \frac{\partial \phi}{\partial y} \frac{\partial \eta}{\partial y} \right) dx \, dy \, dt = 0$$

Integrating the first term by parts with respect to t and using the conditions $\eta(x,y,t_1) = \eta(x,y,t_2) = 0$, we have

$$\int_{t_1}^{t_2} \left[\iint_R \left(\rho \frac{\partial^2 \phi}{\partial t^2} \eta + \sigma \nabla \phi \cdot \nabla \eta \right) dx \, dy \right] dt = 0$$

Next we use the following Green's identity:

$$\iint_R \nabla u \cdot \nabla v \, dx \, dy = - \iint_R v \nabla^2 u \, dx \, dy + \int_C v \frac{du}{dn} \, ds$$

plus the fact that η vanishes on C to allow us to write

$$\int_{t_1}^{t_2} \iint_R \left(\rho \frac{\partial^2 \phi}{\partial t^2} - \sigma \frac{\partial^2 \phi}{\partial x^2} - \sigma \frac{\partial^2 \phi}{\partial y^2} \right) \eta \, dx \, dy \, dt = 0$$

Since η is arbitrary, we have the necessary condition

$$\frac{\rho}{\sigma} \frac{\partial^2 \phi}{\partial t^2} = \frac{\partial^2 \phi}{\partial x^2} + \frac{\partial^2 \phi}{\partial y^2} = \nabla^2 \phi$$

which is the wave equation in two dimensions.

To solve for the displacement of the membrane, we can again try a separation of the time-dependent part of the function and write

$$\phi(x,y,t) = \psi(x,y)f(t)$$

Substituting, we have

$$\frac{\nabla^2 \psi}{\psi} = \frac{\rho}{\sigma}\frac{\ddot{f}}{f} = -\lambda$$

where λ is a constant.   If this is to hold

$$\ddot{f} + \frac{\sigma}{\rho}\lambda f = 0$$

$$\nabla^2 \psi + \lambda \psi = 0$$

The first equation is a simple second-order ordinary differential equation which will yield a sinusoidal solution if λ is positive.   That λ is positive follows, since

$$\lambda \iint_R \psi^2 \, dx \, dy = -\iint_R \psi \nabla^2 \psi \, dx \, dy$$

$$= \iint_R \nabla \psi \cdot \nabla \psi \, dx \, dy - \int_C \psi \frac{d\psi}{dn} \, ds$$

$$= \iint_R \|\nabla \psi\|^2 \, dx \, dy \geq 0$$

The line integral over the boundary curve C vanishes because of the boundary condition $\psi = 0$ on C.   If

$$\iint_R \|\nabla \psi\|^2 \, dx \, dy = \iint_R \left[\left(\frac{\partial \psi}{\partial x}\right)^2 + \left(\frac{\partial \psi}{\partial y}\right)^2 \right] dx \, dy = 0$$

then $\dfrac{\partial \psi}{\partial x} = \dfrac{\partial \psi}{\partial y} = 0$ in R, which implies that $\psi = k$, a constant, in R.   To satisfy the boundary condition, k would then have to be zero.   This leads to the trivial solution $\psi \equiv 0$ in R.

The space-dependent functions ψ and the separation constants λ are determined by solving the following **boundary-value problem**:[1]

$$\nabla^2 \psi + \lambda \psi = 0 \qquad \text{in } R$$

$$\psi = 0 \qquad \text{on } C$$

The solution will depend on the geometry of the region R.   We shall find, in general, an infinite set of nontrivial fundamental solutions (**eigenfunctions**) $\psi_1, \psi_2, \psi_3, \ldots$ corresponding to a discrete set of separation constants (**eigenvalues**) $0 < \lambda_1 \leq \lambda_2 \leq \lambda_3 \leq \ldots$.   The general solution is then a superposition of these eigenfunctions multiplied by the corresponding time-dependent functions

$$f_\alpha = A_\alpha \sin \omega_\alpha t + B_\alpha \cos \omega_\alpha t$$

---

[1] The first equation is a partial differential equation known as **Helmholtz's equation.**

where
$$\omega_\alpha = \sqrt{\frac{\sigma}{\rho}}\,\lambda_\alpha$$

or
$$\phi(x,y,t) = \sum_{\alpha=1}^{\infty} (A_\alpha \sin \omega_\alpha t + B_\alpha \cos \omega_\alpha t)\psi_\alpha(x,y)$$

A_α and B_α are determined by the initial conditions. Under suitable restrictions on the initial conditions, the infinite series will converge and represent the displacement of the membrane. Before turning to the solution of this problem, we shall cite several other physical problems which lead to this type or related types of boundary-value problems, hence indicating that the analysis to follow is really much more general than we have already indicated.

In a large number of physical situations we seek a solution of the **wave equation** with various boundary conditions prescribed and subject to certain prescribed initial values of the function and its first derivative with respect to time. The wave equation in rectangular coordinates is

$$\nabla^2\phi = \frac{\partial^2\phi}{\partial x^2} + \frac{\partial^2\phi}{\partial y^2} + \frac{\partial^2\phi}{\partial z^2} = \frac{1}{a^2}\frac{\partial^2\phi}{\partial t^2}$$

Some of these situations are the following:

1. *The Vibrating String.* We have already seen in Sec. 2.5 that the displacement of the string satisfies the one-dimensional wave equation. The boundary condition for a fixed end is $\phi = 0$. If the end is completely free, the boundary condition is $\dfrac{\partial\phi}{\partial x} = 0$, since there will then be no force exerted at this point, and the force is proportional to the first derivative of the displacement. If the end is only partially free, i.e., if the end is held by an elastic support, then by Hooke's law for the support, the restoring force is proportional to the displacement, and this is equal to the force on the end of the string, which in turn is proportional to the derivative of displacement. Hence, $\dfrac{\partial\phi}{\partial x} = -\alpha\phi$ is the boundary condition for an elastically supported end.

2. *The Vibrating Membrane.* We have seen in this section that the displacement of the membrane satisfies the two-dimensional wave equation. The boundary condition for a fixed boundary is $\phi = 0$ on C, the boundary curve. If a part of the boundary is free, then there is no force at the boundary, and hence $\dfrac{d\phi}{dn} = 0$. For an elastically supported boundary, $\dfrac{d\phi}{dn} = -\alpha\phi$.

3. *Acoustic Problems.* In acoustics the velocity potential for the flow of fluid through which sound is being transmitted is a scalar function whose gradient gives the velocity of the flow. The velocity potential satisfies the three-dimensional wave equation where a is the velocity of sound in the medium. For a rigid boundary there is no flow at right angles to the boundary,

and hence the boundary condition $\dfrac{d\phi}{dn} = 0$ must be satisfied. The opposite of a rigid boundary is a boundary at which all the flow is normal. This would imply that $\phi = k$, a constant, on such a boundary. Then $\Phi = \phi - k$ would satisfy the wave equation and satisfy $\Phi = 0$ on the boundary. For a "soft" boundary, the appropriate boundary condition is $\dfrac{d\phi}{dn} = -\alpha\phi$.

4. *Longitudinal Vibrations of an Elastic Rod.* The longitudinal displacement of a cross section of an elastic rod in small vibrations satisfies the one-dimensional wave equation

$$\frac{\partial^2 \phi}{\partial x^2} = \frac{\rho}{EA}\frac{\partial^2 \phi}{\partial t^2}$$

where ρ is the linear density, E is Young's modulus, and A is the cross-sectional area. At a fixed end $\phi = 0$. At a free end $\dfrac{\partial \phi}{\partial x} = 0$, and at an elastically upported end $\dfrac{\partial \phi}{\partial x} = -\alpha\phi$.

5. *Electromagnetic Cavity.* The electric field $\mathbf{E}$ and the magnetic field $\mathbf{H}$ satisfy the three-dimensional wave equation in a vacuum in the absence of charge and dielectric, i.e.,

$$\nabla^2 \mathbf{E} = \frac{1}{c^2}\frac{\partial^2 \mathbf{E}}{\partial t^2}$$

$$\nabla^2 \mathbf{H} = \frac{1}{c^2}\frac{\partial^2 \mathbf{H}}{\partial t^2}$$

where c is the velocity of light in a vacuum. In addition, they must satisfy

$$\nabla \cdot \mathbf{E} = 0$$

$$\nabla \cdot \mathbf{H} = 0$$

On a boundary consisting of a perfect conductor

$$\mathbf{n} \times \mathbf{E} = \mathbf{0}$$

$$\mathbf{n} \cdot \mathbf{H} = 0$$

where $\mathbf{n}$ is a unit vector normal to the boundary.

In the case of the **heat** or **diffusion equation,** the first derivative with respect to time enters; i.e.,

$$\nabla^2 \phi = \frac{1}{a^2}\frac{\partial \phi}{\partial t}$$

However, a separation of the time dependence still yields Helmholtz's equation, with the time-dependent part satisfying the first-order equation

$$\dot{f} + a^2 \lambda f = 0$$

yielding a solution $f = Ce^{-a^2\lambda t}$. In the case of heat flow, ϕ represents the temperature. At a boundary of constant temperature, the zero of temperature may be so chosen that $\phi = 0$. Flow of heat takes place in the direction of negative temperature gradient. Therefore, at a perfectly insulated boundary, $\dfrac{d\phi}{dn} = 0$, since there is no flow of heat across such a boundary. For a partially insulated boundary, the appropriate boundary condition is

$$\frac{d\phi}{dn} = -\alpha\phi$$

The partial differential equation governing the flow of electricity along a cable is the **telegrapher's equation**

$$\frac{\partial^2 \phi}{\partial x^2} = a\phi + b\frac{\partial \phi}{\partial t} + c\frac{\partial^2 \phi}{\partial t^2}$$

Both the current I and the voltage V satisfy an equation of this type. At a point where the cable is shorted, the boundary conditions are $V = 0$ and $\dfrac{\partial I}{\partial x} = 0$. At a point where the cable is open, the boundary conditions are $I = 0$ and $\dfrac{\partial V}{\partial x} = 0$.

In each of the above examples, we are attempting to solve a partial differential equation of the general type

$$\nabla^2 \phi = a\phi + b\frac{\partial \phi}{\partial t} + c\frac{\partial^2 \phi}{\partial t^2}$$

subject to boundary conditions of one of the types

$$\phi = 0 \qquad \frac{d\phi}{dn} = 0 \qquad \text{or} \qquad \frac{d\phi}{dn} + \alpha\phi = 0$$

Such a problem is an example of a **homogeneous problem.**[1] The differential equation and the boundary conditions are said to be homogeneous. Such a problem has the following important property. If ϕ_1 and ϕ_2 are both solutions of the differential equation satisfying the boundary conditions, then $\gamma_1\phi_1 + \gamma_2\phi_2$, where γ_1 and γ_2 are constants, also satisfies the differential equation and boundary conditions, for

$$\left(\nabla^2 - a - b\frac{\partial}{\partial t} - c\frac{\partial^2}{\partial t^2}\right)(\gamma_1\phi_1 + \gamma_2\phi_2)$$

$$= \gamma_1\left(\nabla^2\phi_1 - a\phi_1 - b\frac{\partial \phi_1}{\partial t} - c\frac{\partial^2 \phi_1}{\partial t^2}\right)$$

$$+ \gamma_2\left(\nabla^2\phi_2 - a\phi_2 - b\frac{\partial \phi_2}{\partial t} - c\frac{\partial^2 \phi_2}{\partial t^2}\right) = 0$$

[1] Nonhomogeneous boundary-value problems will be treated in Chap. 4.

and
$$\gamma_1\phi_1 + \gamma_2\phi_2 = 0$$

or
$$\frac{d}{dn}(\gamma_1\phi_1 + \gamma_2\phi_2) = \gamma_1\frac{d\phi_1}{dn} + \gamma_2\frac{d\phi_2}{dn} = 0$$

or
$$\left(\frac{d}{dn} + \alpha\right)(\gamma_1\phi_1 + \gamma_2\phi_2) = \gamma_1\left(\frac{d\phi_1}{dn} + \alpha\phi_1\right) + \gamma_2\left(\frac{d\phi_2}{dn} + \alpha\phi_2\right) = 0$$

Because of this property, we expect to find the general solution of the boundary-value problem as a superposition of fundamental solutions. To determine the particular solution which fits a given physical situation, one must specify initial conditions on the solution and its first derivative with respect to time. The fundamental solutions of the boundary-value problem are found by separating out the time dependence. Let

$$\phi(x,y,z,t) = \psi(x,y,z)f(t)$$

Then
$$\frac{\nabla^2\psi}{\psi} = \frac{a\ddot{f} + b\dot{f} + cf}{f} = -\lambda$$

or
$$c\ddot{f} + b\dot{f} + (a + \lambda)f = 0$$

and
$$\nabla^2\psi + \lambda\psi = 0$$

The boundary conditions on ψ will be one of the following types: $\psi = 0$, $\frac{d\psi}{dn} = 0, \frac{d\psi}{dn} + \alpha\psi = 0$, or a mixture of these. We shall consider the solution of the boundary-value problem for the space-dependent part in the next section, from the point of view of the calculus of variations.

There are many other problems which do not exactly fit the above general theory but nevertheless are quite closely related. Some of these are listed below according to the basic partial differential equation involved.

1. *Schrödinger's Wave Equation.* In nonrelativistic quantum mechanics the fundamental equation is Schrödinger's wave equation

$$i\hbar\frac{\partial\phi}{\partial t} = -\frac{\hbar^2}{2m}\nabla^2\phi + V(x,y,z)\phi$$

where $\hbar = h/2\pi$, h is Planck's constant, V is the potential energy, and m is the mass of the particle whose wave function if ϕ. ϕ has the interpretation that $|\phi|^2 \, dx \, dy \, dz$ is the probability that the particle may be found in the volume element $dx \, dy \, dz$ at any particular time. It must satisfy the normalizing condition

$$\iiint\limits_{\text{all space}} |\phi|^2 \, dx \, dy \, dz = 1$$

Although only the first derivative with respect to time enters the equation, by assuming a complex time dependence of the form $e^{-iEt/\hbar}$, where E is constant, we get a separation of variables which leads to the equation

$$\frac{\hbar^2}{2m} \nabla^2 \psi + (E - V)\psi = 0$$

for the space-dependent part of the wave function. If V is zero, we have Helmholtz's equation. In any case, the requirement that ψ satisfy certain boundary conditions may lead to discrete values of E, i.e., discrete quantum energy states. The eigenvalue problem is hence fundamental in quantum mechanics.

2. *Laplace's Equation.*   Laplace's equation, $\nabla^2 \phi = 0$, is satisfied by the equilibrium deplacement of a membrane when the displacement on the boundary curve is specified, by the temperature in steady-state heat flow in the absence of sources or sinks of heat, by the velocity potential for an incompressible, irrotational, homogeneous fluid in the absence of sources or sinks, by the electrostatic potential in the absence of charge, by the gravitational potential in the absence of mass, and in many other situations. This is a special case of Helmholtz's equation with λ equal to zero. Hence, it appears as though the eigenvalue problem does not occur here. However, separation of space variables may lead to eigenvalue problems quite similar to those for the Helmholtz equation.

3. *Poisson's Equation.*   Poisson's equation, $\nabla^2 \phi = f(x,y,z)$, where $f(x,y,z)$ is a known function, is satisfied by the equilibrium displacement of a membrane under distributed forces, by the electrostatic potential in the presence of distributed charge, by the velocity potential for an incompressible, irrotational, homogeneous fluid in the presence of distributed sources or sinks, by the gravitational potential in the presence of distributed matter, by the steady-state temperature in the presence of distributed sources or sinks of heat, and in many other situations. This is a nonhomogeneous problem, and its solution will be discussed when we take up the general study of nonhomogeneous problems and their solutions by Green's functions. It is mentioned here merely for completeness.

4. *Biharmonic Wave Equation.*   In elasticity the biharmonic wave equation is extremely important. For example, the displacement of a thin flat elastic plate in small vibrations satisfies the equation

$$\nabla^4 \phi = \nabla^2 \nabla^2 \phi = \nabla^2 \left(\frac{\partial^2 \phi}{\partial x^2} + \frac{\partial^2 \phi}{\partial y^2} \right) = -\frac{1}{a^2} \frac{\partial^2 \phi}{\partial t^2}$$

The boundary conditions for a clamped plate are $\phi = 0$ and $\dfrac{d\phi}{dn} = 0$ on the boundary.   The corresponding problem in one space variable is the transverse vibrations of an elastic beam built in at the ends.   Here the differential equation is

$$\frac{\partial^4 \phi}{\partial x^4} = -\frac{\rho}{EI}\frac{\partial^2 \phi}{\partial t^2}$$

where ρ is the linear density, E Young's modulus, and I the moment of inertia of the cross section.   The end conditions are $\phi = \dfrac{\partial \phi}{\partial x} = 0$.   If an end were free, the boundary condition would be $\dfrac{\partial^2 \phi}{\partial x^2} = \dfrac{\partial^3 \phi}{\partial x^3} = 0$.   If an end were hinged, the boundary condition would be $\phi = \dfrac{\partial^2 \phi}{\partial x^2} = 0$.

Exercises 2.6

*1. Assuming a separation of space variables for a rectangular membrane of length a and width b, write $\psi(x,y) = X(x)Y(y)$ and find the normal modes of vibration and the natural frequencies if the membrane is (a) clamped on the edges and (b) free on the edges.

*2. Consider acoustic vibrations of a rectangular room with dimensions a, b, and c.   Assume the walls to be rigid boundaries.   Find the normal modes and natural frequencies of the room.

*3. Suppose a certain boundary-value problem for a partial differential equation leads to the Helmholtz' equation for the space-dependent part of the function

$$\nabla^2 \psi + \lambda \psi = 0$$

with the boundary condition $\dfrac{d\psi}{dn} + \alpha\psi = 0$ with $\alpha > 0$.   Show that the separation constant λ is positive.

*4. If an external force of density $f(x,y,t)$ is acting on an elastic membrane, a term

$$-\iint\limits_R f(x,y,t)z \, dx \, dy$$

must be added to the potential energy.   Use Hamilton's principle to derive the differential equation

$$\rho\frac{\partial^2 \phi}{\partial t^2} - \sigma\nabla^2 \phi = f(x,y,t)$$

for forced vibrations of the membrane with clamped edges.

*5. If an external force of density $f(x,y)$ is acting on an elastic membrane, derive the equation for the equilibrium displacement of the membrane

$$\nabla^2 \phi = -\frac{1}{\sigma}f(x,y)$$

from the minimum principle for potential energy.

*6. Suppose the boundary of a membrane is elastically supported.   If a part of the boundary of length ds is displaced by an amount z, the restoring force is $kz \, ds$.

Add the appropriate term to the potential energy and show that the boundary condition $\dfrac{d\phi}{dn} = -\dfrac{k}{\sigma}\,\phi$ can be derived directly from Hamilton's principle. When this is the case, we say that it is a **natural boundary condition**.

2.7 Eigenvalues and Eigenfunctions

In this section, we shall investigate the solution of the boundary-value problem

$$\nabla^2 \psi + \lambda \psi = 0$$

in a three-dimensional region R, which has a boundary[1] sufficiently regular so that the divergence theorem applies for sufficiently well-behaved functions as integrands, subject to the boundary condition $\dfrac{d\psi}{dn} + \alpha\psi = 0$ on S, the boundary of R. We shall characterize the solutions of this boundary-value problem as solutions of any one of the following problems in the calculus of variations:

1. Among all functions f which are continuous and have piecewise continuous first derivatives in R (i.e., R can be subdivided into a finite number of subregions in each of which the first partial derivatives of f are continuous and have limits as the boundary is approached from the interior), minimize the ratio[2]

$$\frac{Q(f)}{N(f)} = \frac{\iiint\limits_{R} (\nabla f \cdot \nabla f)\, dV + \iint\limits_{S} \alpha f^2\, dS}{\iiint\limits_{R} f^2\, dV}$$

The minimum will be equal to the lowest eigenvalue λ_1, and the minimizing function will be the first eigenfunction ψ_1. Next minimize $Q(f)/N(f)$ subject to $\iiint\limits_{R} f\psi_1\, dV = 0$. This minimum will be equal to the next eigenvalue λ_2, and the minimizing function will be the second eigenfunction ψ_2. Since we have added a constraint to the first problem, λ_2 is at least as large as λ_1, and thus $\lambda_1 \le \lambda_2$. For the kth eigenvalue and eigenfunction we minimize $Q(f)/N(f)$ subject to $\iiint\limits_{R} f\psi_j\, dV = 0,\ j = 1, 2, \ldots, k - 1$. We therefore arrive at a

---

[1] For quite general conditions on the boundary see Oliver D. Kellogg, "Foundations of Potential Theory," Dover Publications, New York, 1953.

[2] α can be a function of position on the surface of R but must be nonnegative everywhere on S.

sequence of eigenvalues $\lambda_1 \leq \lambda_2 \leq \lambda_3 \leq \cdots$ and corresponding eigenfunctions $\psi_1, \psi_2, \psi_3, \ldots$. The eigenfunctions will constitute an orthogonal set but will not necessarily be normalized. However, one can construct from them an orthonormal set, since the problem is homogeneous.

2. Among all functions f which are continuous and have piecewise continuous first derivatives in R, minimize $Q(f)$ subject to $N(f) = 1$. The minimum will be equal to the first eigenvalue λ_1, and the minimizing function will be the first eigenfunction ψ_1, which will be normalized, i.e., $N(\psi_1) = 1$. The kth eigenvalue and eigenfunction are found by minimizing $Q(f)$ subject to

$$N(f) = 1 \text{ and } \iiint\limits_{R} f\psi_j \, dV = 0, j = 1, 2, \ldots, k - 1.$$ The solution of this

problem generates a sequence of eigenvalues $\lambda_1 \leq \lambda_2 \leq \lambda_3 \leq \cdots$ and an orthonormal set of eigenfunctions $\psi_1, \psi_2, \psi_3, \ldots$.

3. Among all functions f which are continuous and have piecewise continuous first derivatives in R, minimize $Q(f)$ subject to $N(f) = 1$ and

$$\iiint\limits_{R} fv_i \, dV = 0$$

where v_i, $i = 1, 2, \ldots, k - 1$, is *any* set of $k - 1$ linearly independent functions which are piecewise continuous in R. For all possible choices of the set v_i choose the maximum of the minima of $Q(f)$. This maximum will be the kth eigenvalue, and the function which produces the maximum will be the kth eigenfunction. This is the **minimax definition** of the kth eigenvalue and eigenfunction. It has the advantage that one can characterize the kth eigenvalue directly without going through $k - 1$ previous variational problems, as in the other two cases, and gives us the means to compare the eigenvalues of different problems.

We shall be content here to derive only necessary conditions for the solution of the variational problems. The sufficient conditions for the existence of a solution and the proof that the solution has continuous second partial derivatives in R are beyond the scope of this book.[1]

The solutions of problems 1 and 2 can be handled together. Assume that there exists a solution ψ_1 to the first minimum problem, in each case, with continuous second derivatives in R. Then

$$Q(\psi_1 + \epsilon\eta) \geq \lambda_1 N(\psi_1 + \epsilon\eta)$$

where ϵ is an arbitrary constant and η is an arbitrary function from the class of admissible functions, i.e., is continuous and has piecewise continuous first derivatives in R. Since ψ_1 is the solution to the minimum problem,

[1] See Richard Courant and David Hilbert, "Methoden der mathematischen Physik," Springer-Verlag, Berlin, 1937, vol. II, chap. 7.

$Q(\psi_1) = \lambda_1 N(\psi_1)$. Expanding the above inequality and using this fact, we have[1]

$$2\epsilon[Q(\psi_1,\eta) - \lambda_1 N(\psi_1,\eta)] + \epsilon^2[Q(\eta) - \lambda_1 N(\eta)] \geq 0$$

This must be true for arbitrary ϵ. Therefore

$$Q(\psi_1,\eta) - \lambda_1 N(\psi_1,\eta) = 0$$

for arbitrary η. Otherwise, given an η, we could choose an ϵ sufficiently small, and of the proper sign, so that

$$2\epsilon[Q(\psi_1,\eta) - \lambda_1 N(\psi_1,\eta)] + \epsilon^2[Q(\eta) - \lambda_1 N(\eta)] < 0$$

contradicting the above inequality. Consequently we have

$$\iiint_R \nabla\psi_1 \cdot \nabla\eta \, dV + \iint_S \alpha\psi_1\eta \, dS - \lambda_1 \iiint_R \psi_1\eta \, dV = 0$$

ψ_1 has continuous second derivatives in R, and η has piecewise continuous first derivatives in R; therefore we may use Green's identity, giving us

$$\iint_S \left(\frac{d\psi_1}{dn} + \alpha\psi_1\right)\eta \, dS - \iiint_R (\nabla^2\psi_1 + \lambda_1\psi_1)\eta \, dV = 0$$

for arbitrary η. Since η is arbitrary, we can first pick it to be zero on the boundary but otherwise arbitrary in the interior of R. The surface integral then must vanish, and we have

$$\iiint_R (\nabla^2\psi_1 + \lambda_1\psi_1)\eta \, dV = 0$$

implying that $\nabla^2\psi_1 + \lambda_1\psi_1 = 0$ in the interior of R. But this implies that the volume integral vanishes, and hence

$$\iint_S \left(\frac{d\psi_1}{dn} + \alpha\psi_1\right)\eta \, ds = 0$$

This implies that $\dfrac{d\psi_1}{dn} + \alpha\psi_1 = 0$ on S. Therefore, the solution to the first variational problem is also a solution of the boundary-value problem.

Notice that we arrived at the boundary condition $\dfrac{d\psi_1}{dn} + \alpha\psi_1 = 0$ as a necessary condition for the solution of the variational problem without requiring that this condition be satisfied by all the functions in the class of

---

[1] $Q(f,g)$ and $N(f,g)$ are the **associated bilinear forms**

$$Q(f,g) = \iiint_R \nabla f \cdot \nabla g \, dV + \iint_S \alpha fg \, dS \text{ and } N(f,g) = \iiint_R fg \, dV$$

admissible functions.   Such a boundary condition is called a **natural boundary condition.**   If $\alpha = 0$ everywhere on S, then $\dfrac{d\psi_1}{dn} = 0$ is the natural boundary condition.   On the other hand, if we want our solution to satisfy the boundary condition $\psi_1 = 0$ on S, we have to require that $f = 0$ on S for every function in the class of admissible functions.   In this case

$$Q(f) = \iiint\limits_R \nabla f \cdot \nabla f \, dV$$

and $\psi_1 = 0$ on S is a consequence of ψ_1 being in this class of functions.   This is then a **prescribed boundary condition,** as opposed to a natural boundary condition.

Next we solve the same minimum problem, but with the further condition that

$$N(\psi_1, f) = \iiint\limits_R \psi_1 f \, dV = 0$$

Let us assume that this problem has a solution ψ_2 with continuous second partial derivatives.   Then $Q(\psi_2) = \lambda_2 N(\psi_2)$, $N(\psi_1, \psi_2) = 0$, and

$$Q(\psi_2 + \epsilon\eta) \geq \lambda_2 N(\psi_2 + \epsilon\eta)$$

This time, however, η is not completely arbitrary, since $N(\psi_1, \eta) = 0$.   Therefore, starting with an arbitrary function ζ in the class of admissible functions, we can construct an η by subtracting out the part not orthogonal to ψ_1, i.e.,

$$\eta = \zeta - c\psi_1$$

where
$$c = \frac{N(\psi_1, \zeta)}{N(\psi_1)}$$

Then we have

$$Q(\psi_2 + \epsilon\zeta - \epsilon c\psi_1) \geq \lambda_2 N(\psi_2 + \epsilon\zeta - \epsilon c\psi_1)$$

or
$$Q(\psi_2, \zeta) - \lambda_2 N(\psi_2, \zeta) - c[Q(\psi_2, \psi_1) - \lambda_2 N(\psi_2, \psi_1)] = 0$$

by the same kind of argument as before.   Now we know that $N(\psi_2, \psi_1) = 0$ and that

$$Q(\psi_1, \zeta) - \lambda_1 N(\psi_1, \zeta) = 0$$

for arbitrary ζ, from the previous variational problem.   Letting $\zeta = \psi_2$, we have $Q(\psi_1, \psi_2) = 0$.   Therefore, $Q(\psi_2, \zeta) - \lambda_2 N(\psi_2, \zeta) = 0$ where ζ is arbitrary. Hence

$$\nabla^2 \psi_2 + \lambda_2 \psi_2 = 0 \qquad \text{in } R$$

$$\frac{d\psi_2}{dn} + \alpha\psi_2 = 0 \qquad \text{on } S$$

We continue in this way generating successive eigenvalues and eigenfunctions.

To establish the minimax definition of the kth eigenvalue and eigenfunction, we first note that the minimum of $Q(f) = \lambda_k$ when $v_i = \psi_i$, $i = 1, 2, \ldots,$ $k - 1$. Also, if $v_i \neq \psi_i$, the minimum of $Q(f) \leq \lambda_k$ for $f = \sum\limits_{j=1}^{k} c_j \psi_j$ produces a value

$$Q(f) = \sum_{j=1}^{k} c_j^2 \lambda_j \leq \lambda_k$$

because $N(f) = \sum\limits_{j=1}^{k} c_j^2 = 1$. The c's are uniquely determined by the $k - 1$ conditions $N(f, v_i) = 0$ plus $\sum\limits_{j=1}^{k} c_j^2 = 1$. We therefore know that for every choice of v_i, the minimum of Q is less than or equal to λ_k. Yet the minimum of Q is equal to λ_k for the particular choice $v_i = \psi_i$, from which it must follow that λ_k is equal to the maximum of the minima of Q, and this maximum is taken on when $f = \psi_k$.

The characterization of eigenvalues in terms of variational problems gives a powerful tool for comparing eigenvalues for different problems. The basis for these comparisons is in the following two theorems.

Theorem 1. Let λ_k be the kth eigenvalue of a variational problem in which $Q(f)$ is minimized over a certain class of admissible functions F. Let $\bar{\lambda}_k$ be the kth eigenvalue of a variational problem in which $Q(\bar{f})$ is minimized over a class of admissible functions $\bar{F}$ resulting from the addition of certain constraints to F. Then $\lambda_k \leq \bar{\lambda}_k$.

The proof of this theorem follows from the minimax definition of the eigenvalue. Since the v_i need only be piecewise continuous in R, the same sets can be chosen for either problem. Therefore, the minimum of $Q(f)$ is less than or equal to the minimum of $Q(\bar{f})$ for every choice of v_i. From this it follows that the maximum of the minima of $Q(f)$ is less than or equal to the maximum of the minima of $Q(\bar{f})$, or $\lambda_k \leq \bar{\lambda}_k$. Notice that this result is not obtainable from variational problems 1 or 2 because the eigenfunctions of one problem are not the same as for the other. Therefore, except for the lowest eigenvalue, the constraints in the two problems are not directly comparable.

Theorem 2. Let λ_k be the kth eigenvalue of a variational problem in which $Q(f)$ is minimized over a class of admissible functions F. Let $\bar{\lambda}_k$ be the kth eigenvalue of a variational problem in which $\bar{Q}(f)$ is minimized over the same class of functions, but $Q(f) \leq \bar{Q}(f)$ for every function in F. Then $\lambda_k \leq \bar{\lambda}_k$. The proof of this theorem will be left for the exercises.

To illustrate the use of these theorems, consider the following examples. Let $\nu_k = \sqrt{(\sigma/\rho)\lambda_k}$ be a natural frequency of an elastic membrane under tension σ and with density ρ. Suppose the membrane covers the region R in the xy plane and is clamped to the boundary curve C. Let us now take a smaller membrane over a region $\bar{R}$ contained in R and clamped on its boundary $\bar{C}$.

The natural frequency $\bar{\nu}_k = \sqrt{(\sigma/\rho)\bar{\lambda}_k}$ of the smaller membrane would tend to be larger, or at least not smaller, than ν_k. This follows from theorem 1. We get λ_k by minimizing

$$Q(f) = \iint_R \nabla f \cdot \nabla f \, dx \, dy$$

over a class of functions which vanish on C. By comparison, we get $\bar{\lambda}_k$ by minimizing Q over a class of functions which vanishes on C, $\bar{C}$, and the region between C and $\bar{C}$. But this class of functions has additional restrictions beyond those imposed on the first class of function. Hence, $\lambda_k \leq \bar{\lambda}_k$.

As another example, consider a membrane over the region R and attached to the boundary curve C by elastic supports. The boundary condition is $\dfrac{d\psi}{dn} + \alpha\psi = 0$ on C, where α is the modulus of elasticity. Suppose we now increase the modulus of elasticity on some part of the boundary. The natural frequencies will tend to increase, or at least not decrease. This follows from theorem 2. We get λ_k for the first problem by minimizing

$$Q(f) = \iint_R \nabla f \cdot \nabla f \, dx \, dy + \int_C \alpha f^2 \, ds$$

We get $\bar{\lambda}_k$ in the second problem by minimizing

$$Q(f) = \iint_R \nabla f \cdot \nabla f \, dx \, dy + \int_C \bar{\alpha} f^2 \, ds$$

over the same class of functions, where $\bar{\alpha} \geq \alpha$ on C. Therefore, $Q \leq \bar{Q}$ for every f, and hence $\lambda_k \leq \bar{\lambda}_k$.

Theorems 1 and 2 are also useful in telling us what the general behavior of the sequence of eigenvalues is. Consider the boundary-value problems for the same simply connected region R but under three different boundary conditions. Let λ_k, $\bar{\lambda}_k$, and $\tilde{\lambda}_k$ be the kth eigenvalues for the three problems corresponding to the boundary conditions $\psi = 0$, $\dfrac{d\psi}{dn} = 0$, and $\dfrac{d\psi}{dn} + \alpha\psi = 0$, respectively. By theorem 2 we know that $\bar{\lambda}_k \leq \tilde{\lambda}_k$, since we are minimizing functionals

$$\bar{Q}(f) = \iiint_R \nabla f \cdot \nabla f \, dV \leq \tilde{Q}(f) = \iiint_R \nabla f \cdot \nabla f \, dV + \iint_S \alpha f^2 \, dS$$

over the same class of admissible functions. By theorem 1 we know that $\tilde{\lambda}_k \leq \lambda_k$, since we are minimizing the same functional $\tilde{Q}$, but for λ_k we prescribe the condition $f = 0$ on S on the class of admissible functions. Therefore, we have

$$\bar{\lambda}_k \leq \tilde{\lambda}_k \leq \lambda_k$$

We shall show that $\lim_{k \to \infty} \lambda_k = \infty$ using theorem 1. Let R' be a rectangular parallelepiped containing R with dimensions a, b, and c and surface S'. Consider the eigenvalue problem

$$\frac{\partial^2 \psi}{\partial x^2} + \frac{\partial^2 \psi}{\partial y^2} + \frac{\partial^2 \psi}{\partial z^2} + \mu \psi = 0 \qquad \text{in } R'$$

with $\psi = 0$ on S'. By separating the variables, we obtain solutions

$$\psi_k = \sin \frac{m\pi x}{a} \sin \frac{n\pi y}{b} \sin \frac{p\pi z}{c}$$

with eigenvalues $\mu_k = \pi^2 \left(\frac{m^2}{a^2} + \frac{n^2}{b^2} + \frac{p^2}{c^2} \right)$, $m = 1, 2, 3, \ldots, n = 1, 2, 3, \ldots,$
$p = 1, 2, 3, \ldots$. Obviously $\lim_{k \to \infty} \mu_k = \infty$, and since the partial differential equation is the Euler equation for the variational problem

$$\min \iiint_{R'} \nabla f \cdot \nabla f \, dV \qquad f \equiv 0 \qquad \text{on } S'$$

there is a subsequence of the sequence $\{\mu_k\}$ whose members are respectively lower bounds for λ_k. Since every subsequence of $\{\mu_k\}$ is unbounded, $\lim_{k \to \infty} \lambda_k = \infty$.

Actually $\lim_{k \to \infty} \bar{\lambda}_k = \infty$ and $\lim_{k \to \infty} \tilde{\lambda}_k = \infty$, but we shall have to wait until Chap. 5, which deals with integral equations, to show this. The fact that the sequence of eigenvalues approaches infinity is important in the proof of the completeness of the set of eigenfunctions of the variational problem. It also implies that an eigenvalue of the variational problem can have only a finite degeneracy, i.e., if a single eigenvalue corresponds to more than one linearly independent eigenfunction, it can correspond to at most a finite number of them.

The analysis of this section is quite a bit more general than we have already indicated. The important features of the variational problem are the following:

1. $Q(f)$ and $N(f)$ must be real **quadratic functionals**. This means that

$$Q(f + g) + Q(f - g) = 2Q(f) + 2Q(g)$$
$$N(f + g) + N(f - g) = 2N(f) + 2N(g)$$

When this is the case, we can define **associated bilinear forms**

$$Q(f,g) = \tfrac{1}{2}[Q(f+g) - Q(f) - Q(g)]$$

$$= \tfrac{1}{4}[Q(f+g) - Q(f-g)]$$

$$N(f,g) = \tfrac{1}{2}[N(f+g) - N(f) - N(g)]$$

$$= \tfrac{1}{4}[N(f+g) - N(f-g)]$$

with the properties[1]

$$Q(f,g) = Q(g,f)$$

$$Q(c_1 f_1 + c_2 f_2, g) = c_1 Q(f_1,g) + c_2 Q(f_2,g)$$

and the corresponding properties for N.

2. $N(f)$ is positive-definite, i.e., $N(f) > 0$ unless $f \equiv 0$.

3. $Q(f)$ is bounded from below (or above).

Let us assume that $Q(f)$ is bounded from below.   In this case we minimize $Q(f)$ subject to $N(f) = 1$.   [If $Q(f)$ is bounded from above, we maximize $Q(f)$.] Assuming that there is a minimizing function ψ_1, for which Q takes on the value λ_1, we have

$$Q(\psi_1) = \lambda_1 N(\psi_1)$$

$$Q(\psi_1 + \epsilon\eta) \geq \lambda_1 N(\psi_1 + \epsilon\eta)$$

for arbitrary ϵ and η.   Then

$$2\epsilon[Q(\psi_1,\eta) - \lambda_1 N(\psi_1,\eta)] + \epsilon^2[Q(\eta) - \lambda_1 N(\eta)] \geq 0$$

from which it follows that[2]

$$Q(\psi_1,\eta) = \lambda_1 N(\psi_1,\eta)$$

for arbitrary η in the class of admissible functions.   Continuing in this way, we define a sequence of problems in the calculus of variations leading to a sequence of eigenvalues $\lambda_1 \leq \lambda_2 \leq \lambda_3 \leq \cdots$ and corresponding eigenfunctions $\psi_1, \psi_2, \psi_3, \ldots$ satisfying

$$Q(\psi_i,\eta) = \lambda_i N(\psi_i,\eta)$$

$$Q(\psi_i) = \lambda_i$$

$$N(\psi_i,\psi_j) = \delta_{ij}$$

In the next section, we shall discuss the completeness of the set of eigenfunctions and the expansion of arbitrary admissible functions in series of eigenfunctions.

[1] See exercise 5, Sec. 1.6.

[2] Compare with exercise 4, Sec. 2.1.

Exercises 2.7

1. Prove theorem 2 of this section.

*2. Prove directly from the differential equation $\nabla^2 \psi + \lambda \psi = 0$ and boundary condition $\dfrac{d\psi}{dn} + \alpha \psi = 0$, $\alpha > 0$, that if $\lambda_i \neq \lambda_j$, then

$$N(\psi_i, \psi_j) = 0$$

3. Show that the eigenvalues and eigenfunctions of the boundary-value problem $\nabla^4 \psi - \lambda \psi = 0$ in R, $\psi = \dfrac{d\psi}{dn} = 0$ on C, arising in the study of vibrations of a clamped elastic plate can be obtained from the solution of the following variational problem: to minimize

$$\frac{Q(f)}{N(f)} = \frac{\displaystyle\iint_R (\nabla^2 f)^2 \, dx \, dy}{\displaystyle\iint_R f^2 \, dx \, dy}$$

over the class of admissible functions f with piecewise continuous second derivatives which satisfy $f = \dfrac{df}{dn} = 0$ on C, subject to $N(f, \psi_i) = 0$, where ψ_i, $i = 1$, $2, \ldots, k - 1$, are the eigenfunctions already found. Assume that the solution of the variational problem exists and has continuous fourth derivatives in R.

4. An elastic membrane over the region R is clamped on its edge, the boundary curve C. Indicate with reasons whether the following will tend to increase or decrease the natural frequencies of the membrane:

  a. Part of the boundary is unclamped.

  b. An interior point is held down.

  c. The membrane is cut along an interior curve.

  d. A particle of mass m is attached to an interior point.

5. Consider the transverse vibrations of an elastic beam. The partial differential equation for small displacements is $\dfrac{\partial^4 \phi}{\partial x^4} + \dfrac{1}{a^2} \dfrac{\partial^2 \phi}{\partial t^2} = 0$. The boundary conditions for a built-in end are $\phi = \dfrac{\partial \phi}{\partial x} = 0$, for a hinged end are $\phi = \dfrac{\partial^2 \phi}{\partial x^2} = 0$, and for a completely free end are $\dfrac{\partial^2 \phi}{\partial x^2} = \dfrac{\partial^3 \phi}{\partial x^3} = 0$. Show that the natural frequencies can be derived from a variational principle based on the functional

$$Q(f) = \int_0^L \left(\frac{d^2 f}{dx^2} \right)^2 dx$$

Which boundary conditions are natural and which must be prescribed? If one end of the beam is built in, compare the natural frequencies for three conditions on the other end: free, hinged, and built in.

2.8 Eigenfunction Expansions

In the last section we showed that eigenvalues and eigenfunctions for certain boundary-value problems can be obtained from variational problems. We have yet to show that all the eigenvalues and eigenfunctions of a given problem can be so obtained. We can do this if we can show that the eigenfunctions of the appropriate variational problem form a complete set. If there exists an eigenfunction of the boundary-value problem corresponding to an eigenvalue not found by the variational problem, then it is orthogonal to every one of a complete set[1] and is therefore identically zero. If there exists an eigenfunction ψ of the boundary-value problem corresponding to an eigenvalue λ found by the variational problem, then a set of constants c_i, $i = 1, 2, \ldots, n$, where n is the multiplicity of this eigenvalue of the variational problem, can be found such that

$$g = \psi - c_i \psi_i \qquad i = 1, 2, \ldots, n$$

is orthogonal to every ψ_i, i.e., those eigenfunctions corresponding to the eigenvalue λ. This can be done with

$$c_i = N(\psi, \psi_i) \qquad i = 1, 2, \ldots, n$$

Then g is orthogonal not only to the eigenfunctions corresponding to λ, but to all the eigenfunctions of the variational problem corresponding to different eigenvalues. It is therefore orthogonal to every member of a complete set. It must therefore be identically zero, implying that ψ is a linear combination of the ψ_i. Consequently, the variational problem furnishes all the eigenfunctions. We have therefore to show that the eigenfunctions of the variational problem form a complete set.

Let f be an arbitrary function from the class of admissible functions in the variational problem. If we attempt to get an approximation for f in terms of a linear combination of eigenfunctions $c_i \psi_i$, $i = 1, 2, \ldots, m$, we know from Chap. 1 that we get the best approximation in the least-mean-square sense if we choose the c_i as

$$c_i = N(f, \psi_i)$$

Let
$$f_m = f - c_i \psi_i \qquad i = 1, 2, \ldots, m$$

where the c_i are defined in this way. Then f_m is an admissible function for the variational problem defining the $(m + 1)$st eigenvalue λ_{m+1}, for

$$N(f_m, \psi_j) = N(f, \psi_j) - c_i \delta_{ij} \qquad j = 1, 2, \ldots, m$$
$$= c_j - c_j = 0$$

Therefore,
$$Q(f_m) \geq \lambda_{m+1} N(f_m)$$

$Q(f_m)$ is bounded, since

$$Q(f) = Q(f_m) + Q(c_i \psi_i) + 2Q(c_i \psi_i, f_m)$$
$$= Q(f_m) + Q(c_i \psi_i)$$

<hr>

[1] See exercise 2, Sec. 2.7.

This follows from the relation $Q(\psi_i, \eta) - \lambda_i N(\psi_i, \eta) = 0$, which is true for ψ_i and an arbitrary admissible function η. If we let $\eta = f_m$, then

$$N(\psi_i, f_m) = Q(\psi_i, f_m) = 0$$

Therefore, we have

$$0 \leq Q(f_m) = Q(f) - Q(c_i \psi_i)$$
$$= Q(f) - \lambda_i c_i^2$$

$\lambda_i c_i^2$ is positive and nondecreasing with m. $Q(f)$ exists and is independent of m. Thus, $Q(f_m)$ is bounded as m increases. This implies, since $\lambda_{m+1} \to \infty$ as $m \to \infty$, that

$$N(f_m) \leq \frac{Q(f_m)}{\lambda_{m+1}} \to 0 \text{ as } m \to \infty$$

$$N(f_m) = N(f) - \sum_{i=1}^{m} c_i^2 \to 0 \text{ as } m \to \infty$$

or

$$N(f) = \sum_{i=1}^{\infty} c_i^2$$

which is the **completeness relation.** The ψ_i therefore are a complete set in the class of admissible functions.

By arguments similar to those given in Sec. 1.8, we get **Parseval's Equation**

$$N(f, g) = \sum_{i=1}^{\infty} c_i b_i$$

where $c_i = N(f, \psi_i)$ and $b_i = N(g, \psi_i)$ and f and g are any pair of functions from the class of admissible functions.

We must remember that completeness of a set of orthonormal functions, which is equivalent to convergence in mean of a series to an arbitrary function, is not the same as pointwise convergence. However, based on completeness, we can often establish pointwise or even uniform convergence. For example, consider the problem of the vibrating string stretched between $x = 0$ and $x = L$. The eigenvalues of the problem are $\lambda_k = k^2 \pi^2 / L^2$ and the eigenfunctions are $\psi_k = \left(\frac{2}{L}\right)^{\frac{1}{2}} \sin \frac{k\pi}{L} x$. From the variational problem we know then that the eigenfunctions are a complete set with respect to continuous functions which vanish at $x = 0$ and $x = L$ and have piecewise continuous first derivatives. Consider the series $\sum_{k=1}^{\infty} c_k \psi_k$, where

$$c_k = \int_0^L f \psi_k \, dx$$

By Schwarz's inequality,

$$\left(\sum_{k=n}^{p} c_k \psi_k \right)^2 \leq \sum_{k=n}^{p} c_k^2 \lambda_k \sum_{k=n}^{p} \frac{\psi_k^2}{\lambda_k} \leq \sum_{k=1}^{\infty} c_k^2 \lambda_k \sum_{k=n}^{\infty} \frac{\psi_k^2}{\lambda_k}$$

We have already shown that

$$0 \leq Q(f_m) = Q(f) - \sum_{k=1}^{m} c_k^2 \lambda_k$$

Therefore, the series $\sum\limits_{k=1}^{\infty} c_k^2 \lambda_k$ converges.   Also

$$\sum_{k=1}^{\infty} \frac{\psi_k^2}{\lambda_k} = \frac{2L}{\pi^2} \sum_{k=1}^{\infty} \frac{\sin^2(k\pi/L)x}{k^2}$$

converges uniformly, since $\sin^2 \dfrac{k\pi x}{L} \leq 1$ and the series $\sum\limits_{k=1}^{\infty} \dfrac{1}{k^2}$ converges. Therefore, $\sum\limits_{k=n}^{\infty} \dfrac{\psi_k^2}{\lambda_k}$ approaches zero as n approaches infinity uniformly in x. This implies that $\left(\sum\limits_{k=n}^{p} c_k \psi_k \right)^2$ approaches zero as n approaches infinity uniformly in x for every $p > n$, and by the Cauchy criterion for convergence the series $\sum\limits_{k=1}^{\infty} c_k \psi_k$ converges uniformly.   The series must therefore converge uniformly to f by the completeness of the eigenfunctions.[1]

The same argument would hold if we replaced $\left(\sum\limits_{k=n}^{p} c_k \psi_k \right)^2$ by $\left(\sum\limits_{k=n}^{p} |c_k| \, |\psi_k| \right)^2$. Therefore, we also have absolute convergence of the series $\sum\limits_{k=1}^{\infty} c_k \psi_k$.

Thus we have been able to show that every continuous function, with piecewise continuous first derivatives, which vanishes at $x = 0$ and $x = L$ can be expanded in a uniformly convergent series of sine functions, i.e., the eigenfunctions of the string with fixed ends.   This, however, depends on the completeness of the set of eigenfunctions, which in turn depends on the existence of the solution of the variational problem.[2]   However, if the completeness property has already been shown, then the expansion theorem can be proved directly.   We shall return to the problem of expanding arbitrary functions in terms of orthonormal sets of functions in Chap. 3, when we discuss the Sturm-Liouville problem.

Exercises 2.8

1. Obtain a uniformly convergent series of sine functions which converges to

$$f(x) = x \qquad 0 \leq x \leq \tfrac{1}{2}$$

$$f(x) = 1 - x \qquad \tfrac{1}{2} \leq x \leq 1$$

What does the series converge to for $-1 \leq x \leq 0$?

---

[1] See Sec. 1.8.

[2] See Sec. 1.9.

2. Consider the vibrating-string problem with free ends. What are the eigenvalues and eigenfunctions? With respect to what class of functions are the eigenfunctions a complete set? Obtain a uniformly convergent series of cosine functions which converges to the function of problem 1. What does the series converge to for $-1 \leq x \leq 0$?

2.9 Upper and Lower Bounds for Eigenvalues

The characterization of the eigenvalues of a boundary value by variational principles allows one to develop procedures for approximating eigenvalues when the corresponding eigenfunction is not known. For example, we know that λ_1 is the minimum of the ratio of two functionals in a certain function space. Therefore, if we take *any* function in the space and evaluate this ratio, we shall obtain an upper bound for λ_1. As an example, consider the string problem with fixed ends. The first eigenvalue λ_1 is the minimum of

$$\frac{Q(f)}{N(f)} = \frac{\int_0^1 (f')^2 \, dx}{\int_0^1 f^2 \, dx}$$

over the class of functions which are continuous,[1] vanish at $x = 0$ and $x = 1$, and have a piecewise continuous derivative. Such a function is

$$g_1(x) = x \qquad 0 \leq x \leq \tfrac{1}{2}$$
$$g_1(x) = 1 - x \qquad \tfrac{1}{2} \leq x \leq 1$$

An elementary calculation leads to

$$\frac{Q(g_1)}{N(g_1)} = 12 > \lambda_1 = \pi^2$$

As another example, we might take

$$g_2 = x(1 - x)$$

This function leads to an upper bound

$$\frac{Q(g_2)}{N(g_2)} = 10$$

which is a better approximation for π^2.

What is needed is a procedure for systematically improving the approximation afforded by the upper bound. Because the function space is a linear vector space, any linear combination of functions in the space is also in the space. Therefore, we may take a linear combination $c_1 g_1 + c_2 g_2$ to determine

---

[1] For convenience we have taken a string of unit length.

an upper bound for λ_1. However, now c_1 and c_2 are arbitrary and so can be chosen to give the smallest possible upper bound over the subspace spanned by g_1 and g_2. We have

$$\lambda_1 \leq \frac{Q(c_1g_1 + c_2g_2)}{N(c_1g_1 + c_2g_2)}$$

for any c_1 and c_2. Expanding, we have

$$\frac{Q(c_1g_1 + c_2g_2)}{N(c_1g_1 + c_2g_2)} = \frac{c_1^2 Q(g_1) + 2c_1c_2 Q(g_1,g_2) + c_2^2 Q(g_2)}{c_1^2 N(g_1) + 2c_1c_2 N(g_1,g_2) + c_2^2 N(g_2)}$$

The problem of minimizing the ratio of two quadratic forms where the denominator is positive-definite we have met before in exercise 3, Sec. 2.1. We are led to the characteristic equation

$$\begin{vmatrix} Q(g_1) - \lambda N(g_1) & Q(g_1,g_2) - \lambda N(g_1,g_2) \\ Q(g_1,g_2) - \lambda N(g_1,g_2) & Q(g_2) - \lambda N(g_2) \end{vmatrix} = 0$$

to solve for the stationary values of the ratio. In the present example, the characteristic equation becomes

$$3\lambda^2 - 416\lambda + 3{,}840 = 0$$

The smaller of the roots of this equation is approximately 9.944, as compared with π^2, which is approximately 9.870. The procedure outlined here is known as the **Rayleigh-Ritz method.** We shall now discuss it in a more general framework.

We wish to find an upper bound for the smallest eigenvalue of the boundary-value problem

$$\nabla^2 \psi + \lambda \psi = 0 \qquad \text{in } R$$

$$\frac{d\psi}{dn} + \alpha\psi = 0 \qquad \text{on } S$$

We know from the variational principle that

$$\lambda_1 \leq \frac{\displaystyle\iiint_R \nabla f \cdot \nabla f \, dV + \iint_S \alpha f^2 \, dS}{\displaystyle\iiint_R f^2 \, dV}$$

where f is any continuous function with piecewise continuous first derivatives in R. Let $f = c_i\varphi_i$, $i = 1, 2, \ldots, n$, where φ_i are any set of linearly independent functions in the space of admissible functions. Evaluating the functionals involved, we have

$$\lambda_1 \leq \frac{Q(c_i\varphi_i)}{N(c_i\varphi_i)} = \frac{a_{ij}c_ic_j}{b_{ij}c_ic_j}$$

where $a_{ij} = Q(\varphi_i, \varphi_j)$ and $b_{ij} = N(\varphi_i, \varphi_j)$. We note that the matrices A with elements a_{ij} and B with elements b_{ij} are both real and symmetric. $N(f)$ is never negative, and it is zero only if $f = c_i\varphi_i = 0$. But the φ_i are independent, so that $b_{ij}c_ic_j = 0$ only if $c_i = 0$ for all i. Therefore, $b_{ij}c_ic_j$ is a positive-definite quadratic form.

We now pick the c's to give us the "best" upper bound. This is the problem of minimizing the ratio of two quadratic forms, the denominator of which is positive-definite. The stationary values of this ratio are given by the solutions of the characteristic equation

$$|A - \mu B| = 0$$

There are n stationary values, all of which are real. The smallest of these will give us the best upper bound for λ_1 over the subspace spanned by the functions φ_i.

We next ask ourselves what is the relation between the other stationary values and eigenvalues of the boundary-value problem other than λ_1. Let C_α and C_β be eigenvectors of the problem

$$AC = \mu BC$$

corresponding to different eigenvalues μ_α and μ_β. Then

$$AC_\alpha = \mu_\alpha BC_\alpha$$

$$AC_\beta = \mu_\beta BC_\beta$$

$$C_\beta' AC_\alpha = \mu_\alpha C_\beta' BC_\alpha$$

$$C_\alpha' AC_\beta = \mu_\beta C_\alpha' BC_\beta$$

$$0 = (\mu_\alpha - \mu_\beta)C_\beta' BC_\alpha$$

Since $\mu_\alpha \neq \mu_\beta$, $C_\beta' BC_\alpha = 0$. Let $\theta_i = c_{ij}\varphi_j$, where c_{ij} is the jth component of the ith eigenvector. The θ_i are an orthogonal set for

$$N(\theta_i, \theta_j) = N(c_{ik}\varphi_k, c_{jm}\varphi_m) = c_{ik}c_{jm}N(\varphi_k, \varphi_m) = c_{ik}c_{jm}b_{km} = C_i' BC_j = 0$$

Even if there is a repeated eigenvalue, it will correspond to a finite-dimensional subspace in which we can construct an orthogonal basis, and we will have a set of n orthogonal eigenvectors.

We can go another step in the approximation procedure if we add another function to the set already used. Since the θ_i are an orthogonal set in the function space, let us use these and add a new function θ_{n+1}, which we assume is constructed orthogonal to the others. We shall also assume that the θ's are normalized. We then have

$$N(\theta_i, \theta_j) = \delta_{ij} \qquad i = 1, 2, \ldots, n+1$$

$$j = 1, 2, \ldots, n+1$$

Thus at each stage in the approximation the functions which produce stationary values are a linear combination of an orthonormal set. If we consider the kth stationary values in each of the successive approximations, we find that they form a nonincreasing sequence. This can be seen from a minimax definition of the stationary value.

$$\mu_k^{(n)} = \max \min \frac{Q(f)}{N(f)}$$

where f is in the subspace S spanned by $\theta_1, \theta_2, \ldots, \theta_n$, and $N(f,v_i) = 0$, $i = 1, 2, \ldots, k - 1$, and v_i are any set of $k - 1$ piecewise continuous functions.

$$\mu_k^{(n+1)} = \max \min \frac{Q(\bar{f})}{N(\bar{f})}$$

where $\bar{f}$ is in the subspace $\tilde{S}$ spanned by $\theta_1, \theta_2, \ldots, \theta_{n+1}$ and $N(\bar{f},v_i) = 0$, $i = 1, 2, \ldots, k - 1$. Now we know that S is contained in $\tilde{S}$, since any function in S can be written as a linear combination of $\theta_1, \theta_2, \ldots, \theta_{n+1}$ with $c_{n+1} = 0$. Therefore, $\mu_k^{(n+1)} \leq \mu_k^{(n)}$, $k = 1, 2, \ldots, n$. We know also that every stationary value is greater than or equal to λ_k, which is the maximum of the minima of Q/N in the whole space. Therefore, we have

$$\lambda_k \leq \cdots \leq \mu_k^{(n+2)} \leq \mu_k^{(n+1)} \leq \mu_k^{(n)}$$

and the set of kth stationary values forms a nonincreasing sequence bounded from below by the kth eigenvalue of the boundary-value problem. Such a sequence always has a limit. We have also shown that the function which produces the kth stationary value can be expressed as a linear combination of a set of orthonormal functions. If this is a complete set, then $\theta_k^{(n)}$ converges in mean to ψ_k, the kth eigenfunction of the boundary-value problem, i.e.,

$$\lim_{n \to \infty} N(\psi_k - \theta_k^{(n)}) = 0$$

It can be shown that this implies that

$$\lim_{n \to \infty} \mu_k^{(n)} = \lambda_k$$

but this involves some methods of functional analysis which are beyond the scope of this book. As a matter of fact, the Rayleigh-Ritz procedure has more than just a computational interest, for it can be used as a starting point for a proof of the existence of the solution of the variational problem. This is what Courant and Hilbert refer to as the "direct method" of the calculus of variations.[1] We shall not attempt to discuss these methods further here.

[1] See Richard Courant and David Hilbert, "Methods of Mathematical Physics," Interscience Publishers, Inc., New York, 1953, vol. I, pp. 174–176. See also Richard Courant and David Hilbert, "Methoden der mathematischen Physik," vol. II, chap. 7.

So far we have discussed only upper bounds for eigenvalues.   One can also get lower bounds.   Assume, for example, that

$$\nabla^2 f = g$$

where both f and g are admissible functions in the variational principle which defines the eigenvalues for the problem with boundary condition $\psi = 0$ on S. By Parseval's equation we have

$$N(f) = \sum_{k=1}^{\infty} c_k^2$$

$$N(f,g) = \sum_{k=1}^{\infty} c_k b_k$$

where $c_k = N(f,\psi_k)$ and $b_k = N(g,\psi_k)$.   From Green's theorem,

$$b_k = \iiint_R \psi_k \nabla^2 f \, dV = \iiint_R \nabla^2 \psi_k f \, dV + \iint_S \left(\psi_k \frac{df}{dn} - f \frac{d\psi_k}{dn} \right) dS$$

$$= -\lambda_k \iiint_R \psi_k f \, dV = -\lambda_k c_k$$

so that

$$N(f,g) = N(f,\nabla^2 f) = -Q(f) = -\sum_{k=1}^{\infty} \lambda_k c_k^2$$

Furthermore, $D(f) = N(\nabla^2 f, \nabla^2 f) = N(g,g) = \sum_{k=1}^{\infty} b_k^2 = \sum_{k=1}^{\infty} \lambda_k^2 c_k^2$

Let

$$\lambda = \frac{Q(f)}{N(f)} = \frac{\displaystyle\sum_{k=1}^{\infty} \lambda_k c_k^2}{\displaystyle\sum_{k=1}^{\infty} c_k^2}$$

Then

$$\frac{D(f)}{N(f)} - \lambda^2 = \frac{D}{N} - \lambda \frac{Q}{N} = \frac{D - \lambda Q}{N}$$

$$= \frac{D - 2\lambda Q + \lambda Q}{N} = \frac{D - 2\lambda Q + \lambda^2 N}{N}$$

$$= \frac{\displaystyle\sum_{k=1}^{\infty} c_k^2 (\lambda_k^2 - 2\lambda \lambda_k + \lambda^2)}{\displaystyle\sum_{k=1}^{\infty} c_k^2}$$

$$= \frac{\displaystyle\sum_{k=1}^{\infty} c_k^2 (\lambda_k - \lambda)^2}{\displaystyle\sum_{k=1}^{\infty} c_k^2} \geq (\lambda_i - \lambda)^2$$

where λ_i is the eigenvalue closest to λ. Then

$$\lambda - \sqrt{\frac{D}{N} - \frac{Q^2}{N^2}} \leq \lambda_i \leq \lambda + \sqrt{\frac{D}{N} - \frac{Q^2}{N^2}}$$

As an example, consider the function g_2, which gave us an approximation of 10 for $\lambda_1 = \pi^2$. We have $D(g_2) = 4$, $N(g_2) = \frac{1}{30}$, so that

$$10 - \sqrt{20} \leq \lambda_1 = \pi^2 \leq 10 + \sqrt{20}$$

These are not very good bounds in this case. For a procedure which leads to better bounds see Bernard Friedman, "Principles and Techniques of Applied Mathematics," page 212.

It may happen that the value of some functional is directly related to some physical quantity whose value is to be determined. Then finding upper and lower bounds for this functional is a good means of approximating that quantity. For example, in electrostatics, for a typical capacitor the electrostatic potential φ satisfies

$$\nabla^2 \varphi = 0 \qquad \text{in } R$$

$$\varphi = 1 \qquad \text{on } S_1$$

$$\varphi = 0 \qquad \text{on } S_0$$

where R is the region between two surfaces S_1 and S_0 which are perfect conductors and form the boundaries of R.[1] This is a Dirichlet problem, and its solution is the solution of the following minimum problem: to minimize

$$Q(f) = \iiint_R \nabla f \cdot \nabla f \, dV$$

over the class of functions continuous in R and on S, with piecewise continuous first derivatives in R, and taking on the given boundary values on S_0 and S_1. $Q(f)$ is positive-definite, for if $Q(f) = 0$, then $\dfrac{\partial f}{\partial x} = \dfrac{\partial f}{\partial y} = \dfrac{\partial f}{\partial z} = 0$ in R. This implies that f is constant in R and on S, but this is not possible if $f = 0$ on S_0 and $f = 1$ on S_1 and is continuous. Therefore,

$$\min Q(f) = \lambda > 0$$

Assume that the problem has a solution φ, and then $Q(\varphi) = \lambda$ and

$$Q(\varphi + \epsilon\eta) \geq \lambda$$

where ϵ and η are arbitrary, except that $\eta = 0$ on S. Hence

$$2\epsilon Q(\varphi,\eta) + \epsilon^2 Q(\eta) \geq 0$$

[1] Actually, to fit the present formulation of the problem, we have to think of these boundary values as an idealization of a continuous function which makes the transition from 0 to 1 in a small region of the boundary where S_0 and S_1 are joined.

This implies, since ϵ is arbitrary, that $Q(\varphi,\eta) = 0$. By Green's theorem,

$$Q(\varphi,\eta) = -\iiint_R \eta \nabla^2 \varphi \, dV + \iint_S \eta \frac{d\varphi}{dn} \, dS$$

$$= -\iiint_R \eta \nabla^2 \varphi \, dV = 0$$

Since η is arbitrary in R, $\nabla^2 \varphi = 0$ in R; and since φ is in the function space, it must satisfy the boundary conditions $\varphi = 1$ on S_1 and $\varphi = 0$ on S_0.

Now λ is not an eigenvalue of the differential equation, but in this case it is proportional to the capacity of the capacitor. Therefore, we are interested in its value, which we can approximate by getting upper and lower bounds. The Rayleigh-Ritz procedure for obtaining upper bounds is as follows. Let f_0 be any admissible function which satisfies the boundary conditions, and let $f_1, f_2, \ldots, f_n$ be any set of continuous functions with piecewise continuous first derivatives which satisfy the boundary condition $f_i = 0$ on S, $i = 1, 2, \ldots, n$. Then

$$f = f_0 + c_i f_i$$

is admissible, and $Q(f) \geq \lambda$. The c's are arbitrary and hence can be adjusted to give the smallest upper bound.

A method due to Trefftz for getting lower bounds is the following. Let g be any function satisfying the differential equation $\nabla^2 g = 0$ in R. By Schwarz's inequality,

$$[Q(\varphi,g)]^2 \leq Q(\varphi)Q(g)$$

By Green's theorem,

$$Q(\varphi,g) = -\iiint_R \varphi \nabla^2 g \, dV + \iint_S \varphi \frac{dg}{dn} \, dS$$

$$= \iint_{S_1} \frac{dg}{dn} \, dS$$

Therefore,

$$\frac{\left[\iint_{S_1} \frac{dg}{dn} \, dS \right]^2}{\iiint_R \nabla g \cdot \nabla g \, dV} \leq Q(\varphi) = \lambda$$

For a method of getting successively better lower bounds, see the paper by J. B. Diaz, "Upper and Lower Bounds for Quadratic Functionals," *Proceedings of the Symposium on Spectral Theory and Differential Problems*, Oklahoma A. & M., Stillwater, Okla., 1951.

Exercises 2.9

1. Find the best upper bound for the smallest eigenvalue of the string problem for one end $(x = 0)$ fixed and one end $(x = 1)$ free over the subspace spanned by the functions $g_1 = x$ and $g_2 = x^2$.

2. Prove that $N(\theta_i, \theta_j) = 0$ if $\lim_{n \to \infty} N(\theta_i^{(n)} - \theta_i) = 0$, $\lim_{n \to \infty} N(\theta_j^{(n)} - \theta_j) = 0$, and $N(\theta_i^{(n)}, \theta_j^{(n)}) = 0$ for all n.

3. If φ is the solution of the boundary-value problem $\nabla^2 \varphi = -\rho$, ρ a known function in R, and $\varphi = 0$ on S, the boundary of R, then show that

$$\frac{\left[\iiint_R \rho u \, dV \right]^2}{Q(u)} \leq Q(\varphi) \leq Q(v)$$

where $Q(f) = \iiint_R \nabla f \cdot \nabla f \, dV$, $f \not\equiv 0$ in R, and $\nabla^2 v = -\rho$ in R, and $u = 0$ on S.

HINT: Use Schwarz's inequality.

4. Under the conditions for the lower bound derived in this section, show that

$$\lambda_1 \geq \frac{\beta Q - D}{\beta N - Q}$$

where β is any number less than λ_2 and $\beta N - Q > 0$. Let $\beta = 39 < 4\pi^2 = \lambda_2$ and find a lower bound for $\lambda_1 = \pi^2$ in the string problem using $g_2 = x(1 - x)$ as the comparison function. HINT: $\sum_{k=1}^{\infty} (\lambda_k - \lambda_1)(\lambda_k - \beta)c_k^2 \geq 0$.

References

Courant, Richard, and David Hilbert: "Methods of Mathematical Physics," Interscience Publishers, Inc., New York, 1953, vol. I.

Friedman, Bernard: "Principles and Techniques of Applied Mathematics," John Wiley & Sons, Inc., New York, 1956.

Goldstein, Herbert: "Classical Mechanics," Addison-Wesley Publishing Company, Reading, Mass., 1950.

Hildebrand, F. B.: "Methods of Applied Mathematics," Prentice-Hall, Inc., Englewood Cliffs, N.J., 1952.

Temple, George F., and W. G. Brickley: "Rayleigh's Principle," Dover Publications, New York, 1956.

Weinstock, Robert: "Calculus of Variations," McGraw-Hill Book Company, Inc., New York, 1952.

Chapter 3. Boundary-value Problems.
Separation of Variables

3.1 Orthogonal Coordinate Systems. Separation of Variables

In the last chapter, we characterized the eigenfunctions of the Helmholtz equation as solutions of variational problems. Although this was very instructive and it led to several interesting theorems, as well as to approximation procedures, it is not very constructive as a method of finding explicit eigenfunctions. The method of **separation of variables** is one of the most important for finding explicit solutions of the Helmholtz and related partial differential equations. The Helmholtz equation separates into ordinary differential equations in eleven different **orthogonal coordinate systems**,[1] and these are sufficient to solve many problems of practical significance. Therefore, we shall restrict our discussion to orthogonal coordinates and avoid the difficulties of completely general coordinate transformations.

We shall assume that ours is a three-dimensional euclidean space, so that there exists a line element

$$(ds)^2 = (dx)^2 + (dy)^2 + (dz)^2$$

in terms of the usual orthogonal euclidean coordinates (x,y,z). We consider a coordinate transformation to new coordinates (u,v,w) by

$$u = u(x,y,z)$$

$$v = v(x,y,z)$$

$$w = w(x,y,z)$$

[1] See Chester H. Page, "Physical Mathematics," D. Van Nostrand Company, Inc., Princeton, N.J., 1955.

where u, v, w are single-valued, continuous, differentiable functions. At points where the Jacobian

$$J = \begin{vmatrix} \dfrac{\partial u}{\partial x} & \dfrac{\partial u}{\partial y} & \dfrac{\partial u}{\partial z} \\[2mm] \dfrac{\partial v}{\partial x} & \dfrac{\partial v}{\partial y} & \dfrac{\partial v}{\partial z} \\[2mm] \dfrac{\partial w}{\partial x} & \dfrac{\partial w}{\partial y} & \dfrac{\partial w}{\partial z} \end{vmatrix} \neq 0$$

the transformation has a unique inverse:

$$x = x(u,v,w)$$
$$y = y(u,v,w)$$
$$z = z(u,v,w)$$

A **coordinate surface** is a surface on which one of the coordinates is constant, so that $u = u_0$, $v = v_0$, and $w = w_0$ define three coordinate surfaces which intersect in the point (u_0,v_0,w_0).   A **coordinate curve** is a curve along which only one of the coordinates varies.   For example, if we set $v = v_0$ and $w = w_0$ we have the intersection of two coordinate surfaces, which is a coordinate curve along which only u varies.   We call this the u-coordinate curve.   At the point (u_0,v_0,w_0) we have the intersection of three coordinate curves (see Fig. 4).

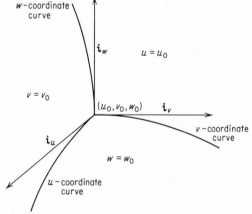

FIGURE 4

Let us draw unit tangent vectors to each of the coordinate curves at the point (u_0,v_0,w_0).   An **orthogonal coordinate system** is defined as one in which these three vectors are always mutually perpendicular, or equivalently, one in which the coordinate curves always meet at right angles.

The orthogonality of the coordinate system can be expressed in terms of the unit vectors $\mathbf{i}_u$, $\mathbf{i}_v$, $\mathbf{i}_w$ as follows:

$$\mathbf{i}_u \cdot \mathbf{i}_v = \mathbf{i}_u \cdot \mathbf{i}_w = \mathbf{i}_v \cdot \mathbf{i}_w = 0$$

This can be expressed analytically in at least two different ways. $\mathbf{i}_u$, $\mathbf{i}_v$, $\mathbf{i}_w$ are vectors normal to surfaces $u = u_0$, $v = v_0$, and $w = w_0$, respectively. Therefore, we have

$$\mathbf{i}_u = \frac{\nabla u}{\|\nabla u\|}$$

$$\mathbf{i}_v = \frac{\nabla v}{\|\nabla v\|}$$

$$\mathbf{i}_w = \frac{\nabla w}{\|\nabla w\|}$$

where these gradients are evaluated at (u_0, v_0, w_0). In terms of partial derivatives,

$$\nabla u \cdot \nabla v = \frac{\partial u}{\partial x}\frac{\partial v}{\partial x} + \frac{\partial u}{\partial y}\frac{\partial v}{\partial y} + \frac{\partial u}{\partial z}\frac{\partial v}{\partial z} = 0$$

$$\nabla u \cdot \nabla w = \frac{\partial u}{\partial x}\frac{\partial w}{\partial x} + \frac{\partial u}{\partial y}\frac{\partial w}{\partial y} + \frac{\partial u}{\partial z}\frac{\partial w}{\partial z} = 0$$

$$\nabla v \cdot \nabla w = \frac{\partial v}{\partial x}\frac{\partial w}{\partial x} + \frac{\partial v}{\partial y}\frac{\partial w}{\partial y} + \frac{\partial v}{\partial z}\frac{\partial w}{\partial z} = 0$$

Also, $\mathbf{i}_u$, $\mathbf{i}_v$, $\mathbf{i}_w$ are vectors tangent to the u-coordinate curve, v-coordinate curve, and w-coordinate curve, respectively. Along the u-coordinate curve, for example,

$$x = x(u, v_0, w_0)$$
$$y = y(u, v_0, w_0)$$
$$z = z(u, v_0, w_0)$$

are the parametric equations of the curve using u as the parameter. Hence, the unit tangent

$$\mathbf{i}_u = \left(\frac{\partial x}{\partial u}, \frac{\partial y}{\partial u}, \frac{\partial z}{\partial u}\right)\frac{du}{ds_u}$$

where

$$\frac{du}{ds_u} = \frac{1}{\left[\left(\frac{\partial x}{\partial u}\right)^2 + \left(\frac{\partial y}{\partial u}\right)^2 + \left(\frac{\partial z}{\partial u}\right)^2\right]^{\frac{1}{2}}}$$

and the partial derivatives are evaluated at (u_0, v_0, w_0). Similarly,

$$\mathbf{i}_v = \left(\frac{\partial x}{\partial v}, \frac{\partial y}{\partial v}, \frac{\partial z}{\partial v}\right)\frac{dv}{ds_v}$$

$$\mathbf{i}_w = \left(\frac{\partial x}{\partial w}, \frac{\partial y}{\partial w}, \frac{\partial z}{\partial w}\right)\frac{dw}{ds_w}$$

and we have

$$\frac{\partial x}{\partial u}\frac{\partial x}{\partial v} + \frac{\partial y}{\partial u}\frac{\partial y}{\partial v} + \frac{\partial z}{\partial u}\frac{\partial z}{\partial v} = 0$$

$$\frac{\partial x}{\partial u}\frac{\partial x}{\partial w} + \frac{\partial y}{\partial u}\frac{\partial y}{\partial w} + \frac{\partial z}{\partial u}\frac{\partial z}{\partial w} = 0$$

$$\frac{\partial x}{\partial v}\frac{\partial x}{\partial w} + \frac{\partial y}{\partial v}\frac{\partial y}{\partial w} + \frac{\partial z}{\partial v}\frac{\partial z}{\partial w} = 0$$

We are now in a position to express the line element in terms of the co-ordinates u, v, w. By the chain rule we have

$$dx = \frac{\partial x}{\partial u} du + \frac{\partial x}{\partial v} dv + \frac{\partial x}{\partial w} dw$$

$$dy = \frac{\partial y}{\partial u} du + \frac{\partial y}{\partial v} dv + \frac{\partial y}{\partial w} dw$$

$$dz = \frac{\partial z}{\partial u} du + \frac{\partial z}{\partial v} dv + \frac{\partial z}{\partial w} dw$$

Then

$$(ds)^2 = (dx)^2 + (dy)^2 + (dz)^2$$

$$= \left[\left(\frac{\partial x}{\partial u}\right)^2 + \left(\frac{\partial y}{\partial u}\right)^2 + \left(\frac{\partial z}{\partial u}\right)^2\right](du)^2 + \left[\left(\frac{\partial x}{\partial v}\right)^2 + \left(\frac{\partial y}{\partial v}\right)^2 + \left(\frac{\partial z}{\partial v}\right)^2\right](dv)^2$$

$$+ \left[\left(\frac{\partial x}{\partial w}\right)^2 + \left(\frac{\partial y}{\partial w}\right)^2 + \left(\frac{\partial z}{\partial w}\right)^2\right](dw)^2$$

$$= \left(\frac{ds_u}{du} du\right)^2 + \left(\frac{ds_v}{dv} dv\right)^2 + \left(\frac{ds_w}{dw} dw\right)^2$$

$$= (ds_u)^2 + (ds_v)^2 + (ds_w)^2$$

The cross product terms in $du\,dv$, $du\,dw$, and $dv\,dw$ have dropped out because of the orthogonality of the coordinate system. It is common to write the line element as

$$(ds)^2 = h_1^2(du)^2 + h_2^2(dv)^2 + h_3^2(dw)^2$$

where

$$h_1^2 = \left(\frac{\partial x}{\partial u}\right)^2 + \left(\frac{\partial y}{\partial u}\right)^2 + \left(\frac{\partial z}{\partial u}\right)^2$$

$$h_2^2 = \left(\frac{\partial x}{\partial v}\right)^2 + \left(\frac{\partial y}{\partial v}\right)^2 + \left(\frac{\partial z}{\partial v}\right)^2$$

$$h_3^2 = \left(\frac{\partial x}{\partial w}\right)^2 + \left(\frac{\partial y}{\partial w}\right)^2 + \left(\frac{\partial z}{\partial w}\right)^2$$

The magnitude of a gradient is equal to the directional derivative in a direction normal to a surface. Therefore,

$$\mathbf{i}_u = \frac{\nabla u}{\|\nabla u\|} = \frac{\nabla u}{\dfrac{du}{ds_u}} = h_1 \nabla u$$

$$\mathbf{i}_v = \frac{\nabla v}{\|\nabla v\|} = \frac{\nabla v}{\dfrac{dv}{ds_v}} = h_2 \nabla v$$

$$\mathbf{i}_w = \frac{\nabla w}{\|\nabla w\|} = \frac{\nabla w}{\dfrac{dw}{ds_w}} = h_3 \nabla w$$

We shall now express the gradient, divergence, and curl in terms of the coordinates u, v, w and unit vectors $\mathbf{i}_u$, $\mathbf{i}_v$, $\mathbf{i}_w$. Then the Laplacian can be expressed as the divergence of a gradient. By the chain rule we have

$$\frac{\partial \psi}{\partial x} = \frac{\partial \psi}{\partial u}\frac{\partial u}{\partial x} + \frac{\partial \psi}{\partial v}\frac{\partial v}{\partial x} + \frac{\partial \psi}{\partial w}\frac{\partial w}{\partial x}$$

$$\frac{\partial \psi}{\partial y} = \frac{\partial \psi}{\partial u}\frac{\partial u}{\partial y} + \frac{\partial \psi}{\partial v}\frac{\partial v}{\partial y} + \frac{\partial \psi}{\partial w}\frac{\partial w}{\partial y}$$

$$\frac{\partial \psi}{\partial z} = \frac{\partial \psi}{\partial u}\frac{\partial u}{\partial z} + \frac{\partial \psi}{\partial v}\frac{\partial v}{\partial z} + \frac{\partial \psi}{\partial w}\frac{\partial w}{\partial z}$$

Now $\nabla \psi = \dfrac{\partial \psi}{\partial x}\mathbf{i} + \dfrac{\partial \psi}{\partial y}\mathbf{j} + \dfrac{\partial \psi}{\partial z}\mathbf{k}$ in rectangular coordinates. Therefore,

$$\nabla \psi = \frac{\partial \psi}{\partial u}\left(\frac{\partial u}{\partial x}\mathbf{i} + \frac{\partial u}{\partial y}\mathbf{j} + \frac{\partial u}{\partial z}\mathbf{k}\right) + \frac{\partial \psi}{\partial v}\left(\frac{\partial v}{\partial x}\mathbf{i} + \frac{\partial v}{\partial y}\mathbf{j} + \frac{\partial v}{\partial z}\mathbf{k}\right)$$

$$+ \frac{\partial \psi}{\partial w}\left(\frac{\partial w}{\partial x}\mathbf{i} + \frac{\partial w}{\partial y}\mathbf{j} + \frac{\partial w}{\partial z}\mathbf{k}\right)$$

$$= \frac{\partial \psi}{\partial u}\nabla u + \frac{\partial \psi}{\partial v}\nabla v + \frac{\partial \psi}{\partial w}\nabla w$$

$$= \frac{1}{h_1}\frac{\partial \psi}{\partial u}\mathbf{i}_u + \frac{1}{h_2}\frac{\partial \psi}{\partial v}\mathbf{i}_v + \frac{1}{h_3}\frac{\partial \psi}{\partial w}\mathbf{i}_w$$

which expresses the gradient entirely in the new coordinate system.

Let $\mathbf{V}$ be a vector expressed in terms of the u, v, w coordinate system, i.e.,

$$\mathbf{V} = V_u\mathbf{i}_u + V_v\mathbf{i}_v + V_w\mathbf{i}_w$$

If $\mathbf{i}_u$, $\mathbf{i}_v$, $\mathbf{i}_w$ form a right-handed triad, then

$$\mathbf{i}_u = \mathbf{i}_v \times \mathbf{i}_w = h_2 h_3 (\nabla v \times \nabla w)$$

$$\mathbf{i}_v = \mathbf{i}_w \times \mathbf{i}_u = h_1 h_3 (\nabla w \times \nabla u)$$

$$\mathbf{i}_w = \mathbf{i}_u \times \mathbf{i}_v = h_1 h_2 (\nabla u \times \nabla v)$$

and $\mathbf{V} = h_2 h_3 V_u (\nabla v \times \nabla w) + h_1 h_3 V_v (\nabla w \times \nabla u) + h_1 h_2 V_w (\nabla u \times \nabla v)$

The divergence of $\mathbf{V}$ is

$$\begin{aligned}
\nabla \cdot \mathbf{V} &= \nabla \cdot [h_2 h_3 V_u (\nabla v \times \nabla w) + \nabla \cdot [h_1 h_3 V_v (\nabla w \times \nabla u)] \\
&\quad + \nabla \cdot [h_1 h_2 V_w (\nabla u \times \nabla v)] \\
&= \nabla (h_2 h_3 V_u) \cdot (\nabla v \times \nabla w) + \nabla (h_1 h_3 V_v) \cdot (\nabla w \times \nabla u) \\
&\quad + \nabla (h_1 h_2 V_w) \cdot (\nabla u \times \nabla v) + h_2 h_3 V_u \nabla \cdot (\nabla v \times \nabla w) \\
&\quad + h_1 h_3 V_v \nabla \cdot (\nabla w \times \nabla u) + h_1 h_2 V_w \nabla \cdot (\nabla u \times \nabla v)
\end{aligned}$$

The last three terms in this expression are zero because of the identity

$$\nabla \cdot (\nabla f \times \nabla g) = \nabla g \cdot (\nabla \times \nabla f) - \nabla f \cdot (\nabla \times \nabla g)$$

plus the fact that the curl of a gradient is zero.   Using the expression for the gradient, which we have already derived, and making use of the identity $\mathbf{A} \cdot (\mathbf{A} \times \mathbf{B}) = 0$ for any pair of vectors, we have

$$\begin{aligned}
\nabla \cdot \mathbf{V} &= \frac{\partial}{\partial u} (h_2 h_3 V_u) \nabla u \cdot (\nabla v \times \nabla w) + \frac{\partial}{\partial v} (h_1 h_3 V_v) \nabla v \cdot (\nabla w \times \nabla u) \\
&\quad + \frac{\partial}{\partial w} (h_1 h_2 V_w) \nabla w \cdot (\nabla u \times \nabla v)
\end{aligned}$$

Finally, we have

$$\begin{aligned}
1 &= \mathbf{i}_u \cdot (\mathbf{i}_v \times \mathbf{i}_w) = \mathbf{i}_v \cdot (\mathbf{i}_w \times \mathbf{i}_u) = \mathbf{i}_w \cdot (\mathbf{i}_u \times \mathbf{i}_v) \\
&= h_1 h_2 h_3 \nabla u \cdot (\nabla v \times \nabla w) = h_1 h_2 h_3 \nabla v \cdot (\nabla w \times \nabla u) \\
&= h_1 h_2 h_3 \nabla w \cdot (\nabla u \times \nabla v)
\end{aligned}$$

so that the divergence in the u, v, w coordinate system is

$$\nabla \cdot \mathbf{V} = \frac{1}{h_1 h_2 h_3} \left[\frac{\partial}{\partial u} (h_2 h_3 V_u) + \frac{\partial}{\partial v} (h_1 h_3 V_v) + \frac{\partial}{\partial w} (h_1 h_2 V_w) \right]$$

For completeness we shall derive the expression for the curl of a vector.   Let

$$\mathbf{V} = V_u \mathbf{i}_u + V_v \mathbf{i}_v + V_w \mathbf{i}_w = h_1 V_u \nabla u + h_2 V_v \nabla v + h_3 V_w \nabla w$$

Then $\nabla \times \mathbf{V} = \nabla (h_1 V_u) \times \nabla u + \nabla (h_2 V_v) \times \nabla v + \nabla (h_3 V_w) \times \nabla w$

where we have again made use of the fact that the curl of a gradient is zero.

Therefore,

$$\nabla \times \mathbf{V} = \frac{\partial}{\partial v}(h_1 V_u)(\nabla v \times \nabla u) + \frac{\partial}{\partial w}(h_1 V_u)(\nabla w \times \nabla u)$$

$$+ \frac{\partial}{\partial u}(h_2 V_v)(\nabla u \times \nabla v) + \frac{\partial}{\partial w}(h_2 V_v)(\nabla w \times \nabla v)$$

$$+ \frac{\partial}{\partial u}(h_3 V_w)(\nabla u \times \nabla w) + \frac{\partial}{\partial v}(h_3 V_w)(\nabla v \times \nabla w)$$

$$= \frac{1}{h_2 h_3}\left[\frac{\partial}{\partial v}(h_3 V_w) - \frac{\partial}{\partial w}(h_2 V_v)\right]\mathbf{i}_u$$

$$+ \frac{1}{h_1 h_3}\left[\frac{\partial}{\partial w}(h_1 V_u) - \frac{\partial}{\partial u}(h_3 V_w)\right]\mathbf{i}_v$$

$$+ \frac{1}{h_1 h_2}\left[\frac{\partial}{\partial u}(h_2 V_v) - \frac{\partial}{\partial v}(h_1 V_u)\right]\mathbf{i}_w$$

$$= \frac{1}{h_1 h_2 h_3}\begin{vmatrix} h_1\mathbf{i}_u & h_2\mathbf{i}_v & h_3\mathbf{i}_w \\ \dfrac{\partial}{\partial u} & \dfrac{\partial}{\partial v} & \dfrac{\partial}{\partial w} \\ h_1 V_u & h_2 V_v & h_3 V_w \end{vmatrix}$$

Our first interest here is in the expression for the Laplacian, $\nabla^2\psi$. We shall write this as $\nabla \cdot \nabla\psi$, and hence in the expression for the divergence we put $V_u = \dfrac{1}{h_1}\dfrac{\partial\psi}{\partial u}$, $V_v = \dfrac{1}{h_2}\dfrac{\partial\psi}{\partial v}$, and $V_w = \dfrac{1}{h_3}\dfrac{\partial\psi}{\partial w}$. Then

$$\nabla^2\psi = \frac{1}{h_1 h_2 h_3}\left[\frac{\partial}{\partial u}\left(\frac{h_2 h_3}{h_1}\frac{\partial\psi}{\partial u}\right) + \frac{\partial}{\partial v}\left(\frac{h_1 h_3}{h_2}\frac{\partial\psi}{\partial v}\right) + \frac{\partial}{\partial w}\left(\frac{h_1 h_2}{h_3}\frac{\partial\psi}{\partial w}\right)\right]$$

As an example, let us take spherical coordinates, one of the coordinate systems in which the Helmholtz equation is separable. The transformation to spherical coordinates is

$$x = r \sin\theta \cos\phi$$

$$y = r \sin\theta \sin\phi$$

$$z = r \cos\theta$$

with $0 \leq r$, $0 \leq \theta \leq \pi$, and $0 \leq \phi < 2\pi$, where r, θ, ϕ are the coordinates shown in Fig. 5.

The line element is

$$(ds)^2 = (dr)^2 + r^2(d\theta)^2 + r^2 \sin^2\theta(d\phi)^2$$

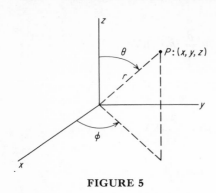

FIGURE 5

Hence, $h_1 = 1$, $h_2 = r$, and $h_3 = r \sin \theta$. The Laplacian is

$$\nabla^2 \psi = \frac{1}{r^2 \sin \theta} \left[\frac{\partial}{\partial r} \left(r^2 \sin \theta \frac{\partial \psi}{\partial r} \right) \right.$$

$$+ \frac{\partial}{\partial \theta} \left(\sin \theta \frac{\partial \psi}{\partial \theta} \right) + \frac{\partial}{\partial \phi} \left(\frac{1}{\sin \theta} \frac{\partial \psi}{\partial \phi} \right) \right]$$

$$= \frac{\partial^2 \psi}{\partial r^2} + \frac{2}{r} \frac{\partial \psi}{\partial r} + \frac{1}{r^2} \frac{\partial^2 \psi}{\partial \theta^2}$$

$$+ \frac{\cot \theta}{r^2} \frac{\partial \psi}{\partial \theta} + \frac{1}{r^2 \sin^2 \theta} \frac{\partial^2 \psi}{\partial \phi^2}$$

In Helmholtz's equation let us assume that $\psi(r,\theta,\phi) = U(r)V(\theta)W(\phi)$; then

$$\nabla^2 \psi + \lambda \psi = \frac{VW}{r^2} \frac{d}{dr} \left(r^2 \frac{dU}{dr} \right) + \frac{UW}{r^2 \sin \theta} \frac{d}{d\theta} \left(\sin \theta \frac{dV}{d\theta} \right)$$

$$+ \frac{UV}{r^2 \sin^2 \theta} \frac{d^2 W}{d\phi^2} + \lambda UVW = 0$$

Dividing through by UVW/r^2 and transposing, we have

$$\frac{1}{U} \frac{d}{dr} \left(r^2 \frac{dU}{dr} \right) + \lambda r^2 = - \frac{1}{V \sin \theta} \frac{d}{d\theta} \left(\sin \theta \frac{dV}{d\theta} \right) - \frac{1}{W \sin^2 \theta} \frac{d^2 W}{d\phi^2}$$

The left-hand side is a function of r only, whereas the right-hand side is a function of θ and ϕ only. The only way this can be an identity in r, θ, and ϕ is for both sides to be equal to a constant which we shall call α. Therefore, we have

$$\frac{d}{dr} \left(r^2 \frac{dU}{dr} \right) + \lambda r^2 U - \alpha U = 0$$

$$\frac{\sin \theta}{V} \frac{d}{d\theta} \left(\sin \theta \frac{dV}{d\theta} \right) + \alpha \sin^2 \theta = - \frac{1}{W} \frac{d^2 W}{d\phi^2}$$

In the last line the left-hand side is a function of θ only, and the right-hand side is a function of ϕ only. This can be an identity in θ and ϕ only if both sides are equal to a constant β. Then we have

$$\frac{d}{d\theta} \left(\sin \theta \frac{dV}{d\theta} \right) + \alpha V \sin \theta - \frac{\beta}{\sin \theta} V = 0$$

$$\frac{d^2 W}{d\phi^2} + \beta W = 0$$

Thus, the partial differential equation has been reduced to three ordinary differential equations to be solved. If there exist values of the separation constants α, β, and λ for which these ordinary differential equations have solutions, then

$$\psi(r,\theta,\phi) = U(r,\lambda,\alpha)V(\theta,\alpha,\beta)W(\phi,\beta)$$

is an eigenfunction of Helmholtz's equation in spherical coordinates. Of course the problem is not completely stated until boundary conditions and continuity conditions on the solution are specified. It is precisely these conditions which allow us to determine the admissible values of α, β, and λ. For example, if we were attempting to solve Helmholtz's equation on the interior of a sphere of radius a subject to one of the boundary conditions $\psi = 0$, $\dfrac{\partial \psi}{\partial r} = 0$, or $\dfrac{\partial \psi}{\partial r} + \sigma\psi = 0$ at $r = a$, then these become conditions on $U(r)$ at $r = a$, i.e., $U(a) = 0$, $U'(a) = 0$, or $U'(a) + \sigma U(a) = 0$. The requirement that ψ be continuous and have continuous first derivatives at $r = 0$ means that $U(0)$ and $U'(0)$ must be finite. If ψ is to be single-valued in the sphere and have a continuous derivative, then $W(0) = W(2\pi)$, $W'(0) = W'(2\pi)$, which means that $\beta = n^2$, n an integer. $V(0)$, $V'(0)$, $V(\pi)$, $V'(\pi)$ must all be finite if ψ is to be continuous and have continuous first derivatives on the polar axis of the sphere.

We notice that each of the separated equations can be written in the form

$$(py')' - qy + \lambda\rho y = 0$$

The solution of this equation subject to boundary conditions of the following types is known as the **Sturm-Liouville problem**:

1. $y(a) = 0$ or $y(b) = 0$

2. $y'(a) = 0$ or $y'(b) = 0$

3. $y'(a) - \sigma_1 y(a) = 0$ or $y'(b) + \sigma_2 y(b) = 0$, $\sigma_1 > 0$, $\sigma_2 > 0$

4. $y(a) = y(b)$ and $p(a)y'(a) = p(b)y'(b)$

5. $y(a)$ and $y'(a)$ finite, with $p(a) = 0$ or
   $y(b)$ and $y'(b)$ finite, with $p(b) = 0$

The first three are conditions imposed at physical boundaries; the fourth is a requirement of periodicity; the fifth is a requirement imposed to guarantee that ψ is sufficiently well-behaved in the interior of the region. We shall discuss this problem in detail in the next section, but first let us show that the solutions of a Sturm-Liouville problem form an orthonormal set of functions.

We first note that the Sturm-Liouville problem is homogeneous. Therefore, we can assume that any nontrivial solution has been normalized as follows:[1]

$$\int_a^b \rho y^2 \, dx = 1$$

[1] We assume that ρ is a nonnegative function. In actual practice this is the case.

Next assume that y_i is a solution corresponding to λ_i and that y_j is a solution corresponding to λ_j with $\lambda_i \neq \lambda_j$. Then

$$(py_i')' - qy_i + \lambda_i \rho y_i = 0$$

$$(py_j')' - qy_j + \lambda_j \rho y_j = 0$$

Multiplying the first equation by y_j and the second by y_i, subtracting, and integrating, we have

$$(\lambda_i - \lambda_j) \int_a^b \rho y_i y_j \, dx = \int_a^b [(py_j')'y_i - (py_i')'y_j] \, dx$$

$$= [py_j'y_i - py_i'y_j]_a^b$$

$$= 0$$

for any combination of the above boundary conditions.   Summarizing, we have

$$\int_a^b \rho y_i y_j \, dx = \delta_{ij}$$

which is to say that the solutions form an orthonormal set with respect to the **weighting function** $\rho(x)$.

We have stated that the technique of separation of variables leads to eigenfunctions of the Helmholtz equation under appropriate boundary conditions. It remains to show that it leads to all possible eigenfunctions of the boundary-value problem.   This can be established if we can show that the solutions obtained by separation of variables form a complete set.   Hence, any other solution of the boundary-value problem would be orthogonal to a complete set of functions and would, therefore, be identically zero.   We shall give the argument for a two-dimensional problem in which it is assumed that Helmholtz's equation separates into a pair of ordinary differential equations leading to two Sturm-Liouville problems:

$$(py')' - qy + \lambda ry = 0$$

$$(PY')' - QY + \mu RY = 0$$

We shall assume that there exists a denumerable set of solutions for each problem and that they are complete sets.[1]   We therefore have completeness relations

$$\int_a^b rfg \, dx = \sum_{i=1}^{\infty} a_i b_i$$

$$\int_c^d RFG \, dx = \sum_{i=1}^{\infty} A_i B_i$$

---

[1] These facts will be proved in the next section.

where
$$a_i = \int_a^b rfy_i \, dx$$

$$b_i = \int_a^b rgy_i \, dx$$

$$A_i = \int_c^d RFY_i \, dx$$

$$B_i = \int_c^d RGY_i \, dx$$

We shall prove that the functions $y_i(x)\,Y_j(t)$ are a complete set, i.e.,

$$\int_a^b \int_c^d r(x)R(t)f^2(x,t) \, dt \, dx = \sum_{i=1}^{\infty} \sum_{j=1}^{\infty} c_{ij}^2$$

where
$$c_{ij} = \int_a^b \int_c^d r(x)R(t)f(x,t)y_i(x)\,Y_j(t) \, dt \, dx$$

First we note that the functions $y_i(x)\,Y_j(t)$ are an orthonormal set, i.e.,

$$\int_a^b \int_c^d r(x)R(t)y_i(x)y_j(x)\,Y_k(t)\,Y_m(t) \, dt \, dx = \delta_{ij}\,\delta_{km}$$

For each t, such that $c \le t \le d$,

$$\int_a^b r(x)f^2(x,t) \, dx = \sum_{i=1}^{\infty} g_i^2(t)$$

where
$$g_i(t) = \int_a^b r(x)f(x,t)y_i(x) \, dx$$

The series $\sum_{i=1}^{\infty} g_i^2(t)$ converges uniformly. If this were not so, then there would exist a positive number ϵ, a sequence $\{n_k\}$, and a sequence $\{t_k\}$ such that

$$S_{n_k}(t_k) < S(t_k) - \epsilon$$

where
$$S(t) = \sum_{i=1}^{\infty} g_i^2(t) \quad \text{and} \quad S_n(t) = \sum_{i=1}^{n} g_i^2(t)$$

However, for a fixed N,
$$S_N(t_k) \le S_{n_k}(t_k)$$

for $n_k > N$. Therefore,
$$S_N(t_k) < S(t_k) - \epsilon$$

Also we know that the sequence $\{t_k\}$ must have a limit τ in the interval. Letting t_k pass to the limit and using the continuity of S_N and S, we have

$$S_N(\tau) < S(\tau) - \epsilon$$

But this is not possible, since we have convergence at $t = \tau$ and $S_N(\tau)$ can be made arbitrarily close to $S(\tau)$. Therefore, the series must converge uniformly.

We multiply the uniformly convergent series by a continuous function $R(t)$ and integrate term by term:

$$\int_a^b \int_c^d r(x)R(t)f^2(x,t)\,dt\,dx = \sum_{i=1}^\infty \int_c^d R(t)g_i^2(t)\,dt$$

Using the completeness relation for $R(t)\,g_i^2(t)$, we have

$$\int_a^b \int_c^d r(x)R(t)f^2(x,t)\,dt\,dx = \sum_{i=1}^\infty \sum_{j=1}^\infty c_{ij}^2$$

where $c_{ij} = \int_c^d R(t)g_i(t)\,Y_j(t)\,dt = \int_a^b \int_c^d r(x)R(t)f(x,t)y_i(x)\,Y_j(t)\,dt\,dx$

We know that any linear combination of solutions of the Helmholtz equation satisfying the physical boundary conditions will also satisfy the equation and the boundary.conditions. We are therefore led to seek the general solution of the boundary-value–initial-value problem as a finite or infinite linear combination of fundamental solutions. The exact solution will be determined when specific initial values are imposed. This will be possible if we can expand the functions representing the initial values in series of eigenfunctions. Therefore, we shall investigate the problem of expanding functions in series of solutions obtained by separation of variables, but, as we have seen, this ultimately depends on the completeness of the set of solutions of a Sturm-Liouville problem. Hence, we turn our attention in the next section to the Sturm-Liouville problem.

Exercises 3.1

*1. Discuss cylindrical coordinates. Describe the coordinate surfaces and curves. Separate the variables in the Helmholtz equation. Discuss the boundary conditions on the solutions of the separated equations, assuming the region is the interior of a cylinder of radius a and height h.

2. Discuss parabolic coordinates

$$x = \sqrt{uv}\,\cos w$$
$$y = \sqrt{uv}\,\sin w$$
$$z = \frac{u - v}{2}$$

$0 \le u$, $0 \le v$, $0 \le w < 2\pi$. Describe the coordinate surfaces and curves. Separate the variables in the Helmholtz equation.

*3. Assuming that $p(x)$, $q(x)$, and $\rho(x)$ are all greater than zero for $a \le x \le b$, prove that the eigenvalue λ in the Sturm-Liouville equation is positive under any of the boundary conditions 1 to 5.

*4. A circular membrane of radius 1 is in equilibrium with a displacement of $\phi(1,\theta) = a\theta(2\pi - \theta)$ on the boundary. Find the displacement at interior points.

3.2 Sturm-Liouville Problems. Fourier Series

As pointed out in the previous section, the Sturm-Liouville equation is

$$(py')' - qy + \lambda \rho y = 0$$

We shall assume that $p(x) \geq 0$ and $\rho(x) \geq 0$ over the interval $a \leq x \leq b$ in which the differential equation is to be satisfied. If either vanishes, this will occur at an end point or at an isolated point inside the interval. We sometimes write the equation

$$L(y) + \lambda \rho y = 0$$

where L is the linear operator $\dfrac{d}{dx}\left(p\,\dfrac{d}{dx}\right) - q$. The operator has the following property. If u and v are both functions which satisfy the same boundary conditions, then

$$\int_a^b [uL(v) - vL(u)]\,dx = \int_a^b [u(pv')' - v(pu')']\,dx$$

$$= [puv' - pvu']_a^b = 0$$

If we call the scalar product $(f,g) = \int_a^b fg\,dx$, then we can write

$$(u,Lv) = (Lu,v)$$

In general, when an operator has this property it is called **self-adjoint.**

The fact that L is self-adjoint has some interesting consequences. For example, let λ_i and λ_j be two different eigenvalues of the Sturm-Liouville equation, corresponding to solutions y_i and y_j; then

$$L(y_i) + \lambda_i \rho y_i = 0$$

$$L(y_j) + \lambda_j \rho y_j = 0$$

and $\qquad (\lambda_i - \lambda_j)\displaystyle\int_a^b \rho y_i y_j\,dx = (y_j,Ly_i) - (Ly_j,y_i) = 0$

Since $\lambda_i \neq \lambda_j$, $\displaystyle\int_a^b \rho y_i y_j\,dx = 0$. We say that solutions corresponding to different eigenvalues are orthogonal with respect to the weighting function ρ, or

$$(\sqrt{\rho}\,y_i, \sqrt{\rho}\,y_j) = 0$$

If there exist two different solutions u and v corresponding to the same eigenvalue λ, then

$$uL(v) - vL(u) = u(pv')' - v(pu')' = 0$$

$$= \frac{d}{dx}[p(uv' - vu')]$$

This implies that $p(uv' - vu')$ is constant. For every boundary condition except number 4, the condition for periodicity, the expression vanishes at the end points of the interval. However, p is not identically zero over any sub-interval; therefore, $uv' - vu' = 0$. Hence,

$$\frac{u'}{u} = \frac{v'}{v}$$

which implies that $u = cv$. This shows that λ cannot correspond to two linearly independent solutions except in the case of the boundary condition for periodicity. In the latter case we have, for example,

$$y'' + \lambda y = 0$$

and with $\lambda = n^2$ we have independent solutions $\cos n\theta$ and $\sin n\theta$ for the interval $0 \leq \theta \leq 2\pi$.

The solutions of the Sturm-Liouville problem can be characterized as solutions of problems in the calculus of variations. We shall begin by considering boundary conditions 1 to 3, corresponding to physical boundaries at the ends of the interval $a \leq x \leq b$. As we shall see in Sec. 3.3, if $p(x)$ vanishes at any points in the interval $a \leq x \leq b$ or if $q(x)$ or $\rho(x)$ become unbounded in the interval, the solution of the equation may become unbounded. We avoid this situation for now by making the following assumptions: $p(x)$, $q(x)$, and $p(x)$ are continuous functions in the interval $a \leq x \leq b$, and $p > 0$ and $\rho > 0$ in the interval. We shall call this the **regular case**. For boundary condition 3, the variational principle defining the kth eigenvalue and eigenfunction is

$$\lambda_k = \min \frac{Q(f)}{N(f)}$$

subject to $N(f,y_i) = 0$, $i = 1, 2, \ldots, k - 1$, where

$$Q(f) = \int_a^b [p(f')^2 + qf^2]\, dx + \sigma_1 p(a)[f(a)]^2 + \sigma_2 p(b)[f(b)]^2$$

$$N(f) = \int_a^b \rho f^2\, dx$$

and f is in the space of functions continuous and having a piecewise continuous derivative in the interval $a \leq x \leq b$.

We shall derive necessary conditions for the first eigenvalue and eigenfunction. The extension to the kth eigenvalue and eigenfunction is straightforward. We notice that Q and N are both quadratic functionals and that N is positive-definite since $\rho > 0$. Let y_1 be the first eigenfunction and λ_1 be the first eigenvalue; then

$$Q(y_1 + \epsilon\eta) \geq \lambda_1 N(y_1 + \epsilon\eta)$$

where ϵ is an arbitrary constant and η is an arbitrary function. Expanding, we have

$$Q(y_1) + 2\epsilon Q(y_1,\eta) + \epsilon^2 Q(\eta) \geq \lambda_1[N(y_1) + 2\epsilon N(y_1,\eta) + \epsilon^2 N(\eta)]$$

Since $Q(y_1) = \lambda_1 N(y_1)$,

$$2\epsilon[Q(y_1,\eta) - \lambda_1 N(y_1,\eta)] + \epsilon^2[Q(\eta) - \lambda_1 N(\eta)] \geq 0$$

This is to be true for arbitrary ϵ; therefore

$$Q(y_1,\eta) - \lambda_1 N(y_1,\eta) = 0$$

for arbitrary η. Integrating by parts, we have

$$\int_a^b [-(py_1')' + qy_1 - \lambda_1 \rho y_1]\eta \, dx + p(b)[y_1'(b) + \sigma_2 y_1(b)]\eta(b)$$
$$- p(a)[y_1'(a) - \sigma_1 y_1(a)]\eta(a) = 0$$

Since η is arbitrary, we have the following necessary conditions for the minimizing function:

$$(py_1')' - qy_1 + \lambda_1 \rho y_1 = 0 \qquad a \leq x \leq b$$
$$y_1'(b) + \sigma_2 y_1(b) = 0$$
$$y_1'(a) - \sigma_1 y_1(a) = 0$$

We see that the boundary conditions are natural boundary conditions. If we wanted the boundary conditions $y'(a) = y'(b) = 0$, we would merely set $\sigma_1 = \sigma_2 = 0$. The conditions $y(a) = y(b) = 0$ are not natural boundary conditions. In this case, we would prescribe $f(a) = f(b) = 0$. We could have one boundary condition satisfied at one end point and another at the other end point by properly specifying σ_1 and σ_2 and the conditions on the function space of admissible functions.

We recall from Sec. 2.8 that to show that all the solutions of the differential equation are obtained from the variational problem, we have to show that the eigenfunctions of the variational problem form a complete set. This is easily done if we can show that the eigenvalues increase without bound. Let λ_k, $\tilde{\lambda}_k$, and $\bar{\lambda}_k$ be the eigenvalues corresponding to the boundary conditions $y(a) = y(b) = 0$, $y'(a) - \sigma_1 y(a) = y'(b) + \sigma_2 y(b) = 0$, and $y'(a) = y'(b) = 0$, respectively. Then

$$\bar{\lambda}_k \leq \tilde{\lambda}_k \leq \lambda_k$$

This follows from theorems 1 and 2 of Sec. 2.7. The inequality on the left follows from theorem 2, for the minimum principles use the same class of functions, but the functionals differ in a predetermined sense for every function in the class. The inequality on the right follows from theorem 1, since, in this case, the functionals are the same, but the class of admissible functions is restricted for the prescribed boundary condition.   For mixed boundary conditions, the eigenvalues can be interspersed in this inequality.   However, $\bar{\lambda}_k$ will be the smallest and λ_k the largest for any choice of boundary conditions in the regular case.   Therefore, in this equality $\bar{\lambda}_k$ could be interpreted as the eigenvalue for any mixed set of boundary conditions as well.

We are assuming that p, q, and ρ are all continuous functions.   Hence,

$$0 < p_m \leq p(x) \leq p_M$$

$$0 < \rho_m \leq \rho(x) \leq \rho_M$$

$$q_m \leq q(x) \leq q_M$$

where p_m, ρ_m, q_m are the minimum values of p, ρ, and q, and p_M, ρ_M, and q_M are the maximum values of p, ρ, and q in the interval $a \leq x \leq b$.   Consider the following variational principle:

$$\mu_k = \min \frac{\displaystyle\int_a^b [p_m(f')^2 + q_m f^2]\, dx}{\displaystyle\int_a^b \rho_M f^2\, dx}$$

subject to $\displaystyle\int_a^b \rho_M f u_i\, dx = 0$, $i = 1, 2, \ldots, k - 1$, where $u_1, u_2, \ldots, u_{k-1}$ are the solutions of $k - 1$ preceding problems.   The necessary conditions for the minimizing function are

$$p_m u_k'' - q_m u_k + \mu_k \rho_M u_k = 0$$

$$u_k'(a) = u_k'(b) = 0$$

The differential equation can be written

$$u_k'' + \alpha_k^2 u_k = 0$$

with $\alpha_k^2 = (\rho_M \mu_k - q_m)/p_m$.   The solutions are

$$u_k = \cos \frac{(k - 1)\pi(x - a)}{(b - a)} \qquad k = 1, 2, \ldots$$

Thus, we have

$$\mu_k = \frac{p_m[(k - 1)^2\pi^2/(b - a)^2] + q_m}{\rho_M}$$

Also, from theorem 2, Sec. 2.7, we have $\mu_k \leq \bar{\lambda}_k$.

Next consider the variational principle

$$\gamma_k = \min \frac{\displaystyle\int_a^b [p_M(f')^2 + q_M f^2]\, dx}{\displaystyle\int_a^b \rho_m f^2\, dx}$$

subject to $f(a) = f(b) = 0$ and $\int_a^b \rho_m f v_i \, dx = 0$, $i = 1, 2, \ldots, k-1$, where $v_1, v_2, \ldots, v_{k-1}$ are the solutions of $k-1$ preceding minimum problems. The necessary conditions for the solution are

$$p_M v_k'' - q_M v_k + \gamma_k \rho_m v_k = 0$$

$$v_k(a) = v_k(b) = 0$$

The differential equation can be written

$$v_k'' + \beta_k^2 v_k = 0$$

with $\beta_k^2 = (\rho_m \gamma_k - q_M)/p_M$. The solutions are

$$v_k = \sin \frac{k\pi(x-a)}{b-a} \qquad k = 1, 2, \ldots$$

Thus, we have

$$\gamma_k = \frac{p_M[k^2\pi^2/(b-a)^2] + q_M}{\rho_m}$$

From theorem 2, Sec. 2.7, we have $\lambda_k \leq \gamma_k$. The following inequalities result:

$$\frac{p_m[(k-1)^2\pi^2/(b-a)^2] + q_m}{\rho_M} \leq \bar{\lambda}_k \leq \bar{\bar{\lambda}}_k \leq \lambda_k \leq \frac{p_M[k^2\pi^2/(b-a)^2] + q_M}{\rho_m}$$

This implies that the sequence of eigenvalues increases without bound regardless of what combination of boundary conditions 1 to 3 we take. It also implies that, although q may be negative and there may be negative eigenvalues, there are at most a finite number of them. Following the method of Sec. 2.8, we can show that the eigenfunctions of the successive variational problems are a complete set. This implies that eigenfunctions of the variational problem represent all the eigenfunctions of the Sturm-Liouville problem.

We can use the completeness of the set of eigenfunctions to prove an expansion theorem for arbitrary functions in the class of admissible functions for the variational principle. First, however, we must prove that the eigenfunctions are bounded independent of x and k. To do this we must transform the differential equations as follows. Let $v = fy$ and $t = \int_a^x \left(\frac{\rho}{p}\right)^{\frac{1}{2}} dx$, where $f = (\rho p)^{\frac{1}{4}}$. Then

$$y' = \frac{d}{dt}\left(\frac{v}{f}\right)\frac{dt}{dx} = \left(\frac{\dot{v}}{f} - \frac{v}{f^2}\dot{f}\right)\left(\frac{\rho}{p}\right)^{\frac{1}{2}}$$

$$py' = f\dot{v} - v\dot{f}$$

$$(py')' = (f\ddot{v} - v\ddot{f})\left(\frac{\rho}{p}\right)^{\frac{1}{2}} = \frac{\rho}{f}\ddot{v} - v\ddot{f}\frac{\rho}{f^2}$$

$$(py')' - qy + \lambda\rho y = \frac{\rho}{f}\left[\ddot{v} - \left(\frac{\ddot{f}}{f} + \frac{q}{\rho}\right)v + \lambda v\right] = 0$$

The equation satisfied by v is then

$$\ddot{v} - rv + \lambda v = 0$$

where $r = \dfrac{\ddot{f}}{f} + \dfrac{q}{\rho}$, which is a continuous function.   The equation is to hold in the interval $0 \leq t \leq T$ where $T = \displaystyle\int_a^b \left(\dfrac{\rho}{p}\right)^{\frac{1}{2}} dx$.

Multiplying by $\dot{v}$ and integrating from 0 to t, we have

$$[\dot{v}(t)]^2 + \lambda[v(t)]^2 - 2\int_0^t rv\dot{v}\, d\tau = [\dot{v}(0)]^2 + \lambda[v(0)]^2$$

We next integrate the equation from 0 to T to show that

$$T\{[\dot{v}(0)]^2 + \lambda[v(0)]^2\} = \int_0^T \dot{v}^2\, dt - 2\int_0^T \int_0^t rv\dot{v}\, d\tau\, dt + \lambda$$

We are assuming that the function has been normalized as follows:

$$\int_a^b \rho y^2\, dx = \int_0^T v^2\, dt = 1$$

As a result, we have

$$\lambda[v(t)]^2 \leq \lambda[v(t)]^2 + [\dot{v}(t)]^2 = 2\int_0^t rv\dot{v}\, d\tau + [\dot{v}(0)]^2 + \lambda[v(0)]^2$$

or $$\lambda[v(t)]^2 \leq \left|2\int_0^t rv\dot{v}\, d\tau\right| + \frac{\lambda}{T} + \frac{1}{T}\int_0^T \dot{v}^2\, dt + \frac{2}{T}\left|\int_0^T \int_0^t rv\dot{v}\, d\tau\, dt\right|$$

By Schwartz's inequality,

$$\left|2\int_0^t rv\dot{v}\, d\tau\right| \leq 2\left[\int_0^t r^2 v^2\, d\tau\right]^{\frac{1}{2}}\left[\int_0^t \dot{v}^2\, d\tau\right]^{\frac{1}{2}}$$

$$\leq C_1\left[\int_0^T v^2\, d\tau\right]^{\frac{1}{2}}\left[\int_0^T \dot{v}^2\, d\tau\right]^{\frac{1}{2}}$$

$$\leq C_1\left[\int_0^T \dot{v}^2\, d\tau\right]^{\frac{1}{2}}$$

where C_1 is a constant independent of t and λ.   Also

$$\left|\int_0^T \int_0^t rv\dot{v}\, d\tau\, dt\right| \leq \left[\int_0^T \int_0^t r^2 v^2\, d\tau\, dt\right]^{\frac{1}{2}}\left[\int_0^T \int_0^t \dot{v}^2\, d\tau\, dt\right]^{\frac{1}{2}}$$

$$\leq \left[\int_0^T \int_0^T r^2 v^2\, d\tau\, dt\right]^{\frac{1}{2}}\left[\int_0^T \int_0^T \dot{v}^2\, d\tau\, dt\right]^{\frac{1}{2}}$$

$$\leq T\left[\int_0^T r^2 v^2\, d\tau\right]^{\frac{1}{2}}\left[\int_0^T \dot{v}^2\, d\tau\right]^{\frac{1}{2}}$$

$$\leq C_2\left[\int_0^T \dot{v}^2\, d\tau\right]^{\frac{1}{2}}$$

Since $v = (\rho p)^{\frac{1}{2}} y = fy$ and $\dot{v} = (f'y + fy') \left(\dfrac{p}{\rho} \right)^{\frac{1}{2}}$,

$$\int_0^T \dot{v}^2 \, dt = \int_a^b \frac{(f')^2}{\rho} \left(\frac{p}{\rho} \right)^{\frac{1}{2}} \rho y^2 \, dx + 2 \int_a^b \frac{ff'}{\rho} \rho^{\frac{1}{2}} y p^{\frac{1}{2}} y' \, dx + \int_a^b p y'^2 \, dx$$

Therefore,

$$\int_0^T \dot{v}^2 \, dt \leq C_3 \int_a^b \rho y^2 \, dx + 2 \left[\int_a^b \left(\frac{ff'}{\rho} \right)^2 \rho y^2 \, dx \right]^{\frac{1}{2}} \left[\int_a^b p y'^2 \, dx \right]^{\frac{1}{2}} + \int_a^b p y'^2 \, dx$$

$$\leq C_3 + C_4 \left[\int_a^b p y'^2 \, dx \right]^{\frac{1}{2}} + \int_a^b p y'^2 \, dx$$

Starting from the Sturm-Liouville equation, we have

$$\int_a^b [(py')'y - qy^2 + \lambda \rho y^2] \, dx = 0$$

which implies that

$$\int_a^b p y'^2 \, dx + \sigma_2 p(b)[y(b)]^2 + \sigma_1 p(a)[y(a)]^2 = \lambda - \int_a^b q y^2 \, dx$$

Thus, $\displaystyle \int_a^b p y'^2 \, dx \leq \int_a^b p y'^2 \, dx + \sigma_2 p(b)[y(b)]^2 + \sigma_1 p(a)[y(a)]^2$

$$\leq \lambda + C_5$$

Combining this with the above,

$$\int_0^T \dot{v}^2 \, dt \leq C_6 + C_7 \sqrt{\lambda} + \lambda$$

and $\lambda[v(t)]^2 \leq C_8 + C_9 \sqrt{\lambda} + C_{10}\lambda$

$$[v(t)]^2 \leq C_{10} + \frac{C_9}{\sqrt{\lambda}} + \frac{C_8}{\lambda}$$

where the C's are all independent of t and λ. We have therefore shown that $v(t)$ is bounded independent of t and λ, which in turn implies that $y(x)$ is bounded independent of x and λ. We have assumed the third boundary condition, but it is clear that the same result holds for boundary conditions 1 and 2.

We are now ready to prove that any function in the class of admissible functions appropriate to the variational principle which defines the Sturm-Liouville functions for each of the three homogeneous boundary conditions can be expanded in a uniformly convergent series of the appropriate eigenfunctions. Consider the series $\displaystyle \sum_{i=1}^{\infty} c_k y_k$ where

$$c_k = \int_a^b \rho f y_k \, dx$$

and
$$\int_a^b \rho y_k^2 \, dx = 1$$

By Schwartz's inequality,

$$\left(\sum_{k=n}^p c_k y_k \right)^2 \leq \sum_{k=n}^p c_k^2 \lambda_k \sum_{k=n}^p \frac{y_k^2}{\lambda_k} \leq \sum_{k=1}^\infty c_k^2 \lambda_k \sum_{k=n}^\infty \frac{y_k^2}{\lambda_k}$$

We know from the proof of completeness of the eigenfunctions that for sufficiently large m

$$0 \leq Q(f_m) = Q(f) - \sum_{k=1}^m c_k^2 \lambda_k$$

where $f_m = f - \sum_{k=1}^m c_k y_k$. Therefore, the series $\sum_{k=1}^\infty c_k^2 \lambda_k$ converges. We have shown above that $y_k^2(x)$ is bounded independent of x and k. Therefore, the series $\sum_{k=1}^\infty \frac{y_k^2}{\lambda_k}$ converges uniformly. This follows because $\lambda_k \geq M(k-1)^2$ for k sufficiently large and $\sum_{k=2}^\infty \frac{1}{(k-1)^2}$ converges. Therefore, $\sum_{k=n}^\infty \frac{y_k^2}{\lambda_k}$ approaches zero as n approaches infinity uniformly in x. This implies that $\left(\sum_{k=n}^p c_k y_k \right)^2$ approaches zero uniformly in x for every $p > n$, and by the Cauchy criterion for convergence the series $\sum_{k=1}^\infty c_k y_k$ converges uniformly. The series must converge uniformly to $f(x)$ by the completeness of the eigenfunctions. The same result would hold if we use $\left(\sum_{k=n}^\infty |c_k y_k| \right)^2$ in the above argument. Therefore, we also have absolute convergence.

If we do not have the regular case considered above, certain modifications in the proof have to be made. For example, consider Bessel's equation, which occurs in the separation of the Helmholtz equation in cylindrical coordinates.[1] The equation has the form

$$(xy')' - \frac{m^2}{x} y + \lambda x y = 0$$

where m is commonly a nonnegative integer. We see that $p = x$ is zero at $x = 0$, $\rho = x$ is zero at $x = 0$, and $q = m^2/x$ is not continuous at $x = 0$. Therefore, if our independent variable lies in the interval $0 \leq x \leq b$, then we do not have the regular case. Let us take m, an integer greater than or equal to 1, and the boundary conditions $y(0)$ finite and $y(b) = 0$. We shall see later that Bessel's equation has two linearly independent solutions $J_m(\sqrt{\lambda} x)$, the Bessel function of the first kind of order m, and $Y_m(\sqrt{\lambda} x)$, the Bessel function

[1] See exercise 1, Sec. 3.1.

of the second kind of order m.   The second of these is not finite at $x = 0$; therefore, we discard it.   To find the eigenvalues λ_k we would then have to solve the equation $J_m(\sqrt{\lambda}b) = 0$.

We can get some idea of the behavior of the sequence of eigenvalues if we consider the problem from the point of view of the calculus of variations.   The solution of the above Sturm-Liouville problem can be characterized by the following variational principle.

$$\lambda_k = \min \frac{\displaystyle\int_0^b [x(f')^2 + (m^2/x)f^2]\, dx}{\displaystyle\int_0^b xf^2\, dx}$$

subject to $\displaystyle\int_0^b xf J_m(\sqrt{\lambda_j}x)\, dx = 0$ and $f(b) = 0$, where λ_j are the first $k - 1$ solutions of $J_m(\sqrt{\lambda}b) = 0$.   Before proceeding, we first transform the differential equation by introducing the new dependent variable $v = \sqrt{x}y$.   The equation then becomes

$$v'' - \frac{4m^2 - 1}{4x^2}\, v + \lambda v = 0$$

The variational principle corresponding to this differential equation is

$$\lambda_k = \min \frac{\displaystyle\int_0^b \{(f')^2 + [(4m^2 - 1)/4x^2]f^2\}\, dx}{\displaystyle\int_0^b f^2\, dx}$$

where $f(0) = f(b) = 0$, and $\displaystyle\int_a^b fv_i\, dx = 0$, $i = 1, 2, \ldots, k - 1$.   By theorem 2, Sec. 2.7,

$$\lambda_k \geq \mu_k = \min \frac{\displaystyle\int_0^b (f')^2\, dx}{\displaystyle\int_0^b f^2\, dx}$$

subject to $\displaystyle\int_0^b f \sin \sqrt{\mu_j}x\, dx = 0$ and $f(0) = f(b) = 0$, where

$$\mu_j = \frac{j^2\pi^2}{b^2} \qquad j = 1, 2, \ldots, k - 1$$

$\mu_k = k^2\pi^2/b^2$, and therefore we have the inequality $k^2\pi^2/b^2 \leq \lambda_k$.   There is, therefore, an infinite sequence of zeros of the Bessel function which increases without bound.   This immediately implies that the set of functions $J_m(\sqrt{\lambda_k}x)$

is a complete set. Also, if we exclude an arbitrarily small neighborhood of $x = 0$, we can prove that the eigenfunctions are bounded independent of x and λ_k. It is then possible to prove that $\sum_{k=1}^{\infty} c_k J_m(\sqrt{\lambda_k}x)$ converges uniformly to $f(x)$ in the interval $0 < \epsilon \leq x \leq b$ if f is a continuous function with a piecewise continuous first derivative and c_k is defined as follows:

$$c_k = \frac{\int_0^b xf J_m(\sqrt{\lambda_k}x)\, dx}{\int_0^b x J_m^2(\sqrt{\lambda_k}x)\, dx}$$

The denominator is easily evaluated. Multiplying the left-hand side of the differential equation by xJ'_m and integrating, we have

$$\int_0^x [(xJ'_m)'xJ'_m - m^2 J_m J'_m + \lambda_k x^2 J_m J'_m]\, dx = 0$$

$$[xJ'_m(\sqrt{\lambda_k}x)]^2 - m^2 J_m^2(\sqrt{\lambda_k}x) + \lambda_k x^2[J_m(\sqrt{\lambda_k}x)]^2$$

$$-\int_0^x xJ'_m\left[(xJ'_m)' - \frac{m^2}{x}J_m + \lambda_k x J_m\right]dx - 2\lambda_k \int_0^x xJ_m^2\, dx = 0$$

or, letting $x = b$ and making use of $J_m(\sqrt{\lambda_k}b) = 0$, we have

$$\int_0^b x J_m^2(\sqrt{\lambda_k}x)\, dx = \frac{b^2[J'_m(\sqrt{\lambda_k}b)]^2}{2\lambda_k}$$

If $m = 0$, we cannot use the same comparison procedure for the eigenvalues as above, so we must use a different means of showing that the sequence of zeros of $J_0(\sqrt{\lambda}b)$ increases without bound. Making the change of variable $z = \sqrt{\lambda}x$, we have

$$zJ_0''(z) + J_0'(z) + zJ_0(z) = 0$$

Differentiating this equation, we have

$$zJ_0''' + 2J_0'' + zJ_0' + J_0 = 0$$

$$zJ_0''' + J_0'' - \frac{J_0'}{z} + zJ_0' = 0$$

The latter equation satisfied by $J_0'(z)$ is the equation satisfied by $J_1(z)$. Therefore, $J_0'(z) = kJ_1(z)$. This means that the zeros of $J_1(z)$ are the zeros of $J_0'(z)$. We have already shown that the zeros of $J_1(z)$ form an unbounded sequence; therefore, the same is true of the zeros of $J_0'(z)$. We shall infer from this that the zeros of $J_0(z)$ increase without bound.

Let ξ be a zero of $J_0'(z)$; then $\xi J_0''(\xi) + \xi J_0(\xi) = 0$. This implies that $J_0''(\xi)$ and $J_0(\xi)$ are of opposite sign. Otherwise $J_0(\xi) = J_0'(\xi) = J_0''(\xi) = 0$, and the differential equation would imply that all higher derivatives of J_0 would vanish at ξ. Thus the power series expansion about ξ would vanish identically. Now let ξ_1 and ξ_2 be adjacent zeros of $J_0'(z)$. Hence, $J_0'(z)$ is all of one sign between ξ_1 and ξ_2. By Rolle's theorem $J_0''(z)$ must have an odd number of zeros between ξ_1 and ξ_2, where a zero of order n is counted n times. This implies that $J_0''(\xi_1)$ and $J_0''(\xi_2)$ are of opposite sign and, therefore, that $J_0(\xi_1)$ and $J_0(\xi_2)$ are of opposite sign. This implies that $J_0(z)$ has at least one zero between ξ_1 and ξ_2. It cannot have more than one zero, for if it did, Rolle's theorem would imply that $J_0'(z)$ has a zero between ξ_1 and ξ_2. We have thus shown that the zeros of $J_0'(z)$ bracket the zero of $J_0(z)$ and, therefore, the zeros of $J_0(z)$ increase without bound. The set of functions $J_0(\sqrt{\lambda_k}x)$, where the λ_k are the solutions of $J_0(\sqrt{\lambda}b) = 0$, are a complete set, and we have an expansion theorem in terms of Bessel functions of order zero.

The trigonometric functions $\sin nx$ and $\cos nx$ are special cases of Sturm-Liouville functions which come from the differential equation

$$y'' + \lambda y = 0$$

to be satisfied for $-\pi \leq x \leq \pi$, under periodic boundary conditions

$$y(\pi) = y(-\pi) \qquad \text{and} \qquad y'(\pi) = y'(-\pi)$$

The eigenvalues are $\lambda = n^2$, $n = 0, 1, 2, \ldots$. The expansion theorem leads to **Fourier series** expansions of functions which satisfy suitable continuity requirements. We can arrive at the expansion theorem by the following procedure.

Consider the solution of the following variational problem:

$$\lambda_k = \min \frac{\displaystyle\int_0^\pi (f')^2 \, dx}{\displaystyle\int_0^\pi f^2 \, dx}$$

over all continuous functions f which have a piecewise continuous derivative, vanish at the end points, and satisfy $\displaystyle\int_0^\pi f \sin jx \, dx = 0$, $j = 1, 2, 3, \ldots, k - 1$. This is a regular Sturm-Liouville problem with normalized solutions

$$\sqrt{2/\pi} \, \sin kx$$

We therefore know that any admissible function can be expanded in a uniformly convergent series

$$f(x) = \sum_{k=1}^\infty b_k \sin kx$$

where $b_k = \dfrac{2}{\pi} \displaystyle\int_0^{\pi} f \sin kx \, dx$.   Next consider the variational problem

$$\lambda_k = \min \frac{\displaystyle\int_0^{\pi} (f')^2 \, dx}{\displaystyle\int_0^{\pi} f^2 \, dx}$$

over all continuous functions f which have a piecewise continuous first deriva-

tive and satisfy $\displaystyle\int_0^{\pi} f \cos jx \, dx = 0$, $j = 0, 1, 2, \ldots, k - 1$.   This is also a

regular Sturm-Liouville problem with normalized solutions $\sqrt{\dfrac{1}{\pi}}, \sqrt{\dfrac{2}{\pi}} \cos kx$,

$k = 1, 2, 3, \ldots$.   We have an expansion theorem which states that any admissible function can be expanded in a uniformly convergent series

$$f(x) = \frac{a_0}{2} + \sum_{k=1}^{\infty} a_k \cos kx$$

where
$$a_k = \frac{2}{\pi} \int_0^{\pi} f \cos kx \, dx$$

Now consider any continuous function with a piecewise continuous deriva-tive which is periodic with period 2π.   Such a function can be written as follows:
$$f(x) = \tfrac{1}{2}[f(x) + f(-x)] + \tfrac{1}{2}[f(x) - f(-x)]$$

It is obvious that $\tfrac{1}{2}[f(x) + f(-x)]$ is even and $\tfrac{1}{2}[f(x) - f(-x)]$ is odd. Hence, we can write any such function as the sum of an odd and an even function, i.e.,
$$f(x) = f_e(x) + f_o(x)$$

$f_e(x)$ and $f_o(x)$ are continuous and have piecewise continuous first derivatives. Furthermore,
$$f_o(0) = \tfrac{1}{2}[(f0) - f(0)] = 0$$
$$f_o(\pi) = \tfrac{1}{2}[f(\pi) - f(-\pi)] = 0$$

since $f(x)$ is periodic.   Therefore, $f_o(x)$ is admissible in the first variational principle and $f_e(x)$ is admissible in the second variational principle.   Hence,

$$f_e(x) = \frac{a_0}{2} + \sum_{k=1}^{\infty} a_k \cos kx$$

$$f_o(x) = \sum_{k=1}^{\infty} b_k \sin kx$$

in the interval $0 \leq x \leq \pi$. These series also represent the functions in the interval $-\pi \leq x \leq 0$, for

$$f_e(-x) = f_e(x) = \frac{a_0}{2} + \sum_{k=1}^{\infty} a_k \cos kx$$

$$f_o(-x) = -f_o(x) = -\sum_{k=1}^{\infty} b_k \sin kx$$

Therefore, $f(x) = f_e(x) + f_o(x) = \frac{a_0}{2} + \sum_{k=1}^{\infty} (a_k \cos kx + b_k \sin kx)$

valid for $-\pi \leq x \leq \pi$, and the convergence is uniform. The expansion coefficients can be expressed in terms of $f(x)$ as follows:

$$a_k = \frac{2}{\pi} \int_0^{\pi} f_e \cos kx \, dx$$

$$= \frac{2}{\pi} \int_0^{\pi} \tfrac{1}{2}[f(x) + f(-x)] \cos kx \, dx$$

$$= \frac{1}{\pi} \left[\int_0^{\pi} f(x) \cos kx \, dx + \int_{-\pi}^0 f(x) \cos kx \, dx \right]$$

$$= \frac{1}{\pi} \int_{-\pi}^{\pi} f(x) \cos kx \, dx$$

$$b_k = \frac{2}{\pi} \int_0^{\pi} f_o \sin kx \, dx$$

$$= \frac{2}{\pi} \int_0^{\pi} \tfrac{1}{2}[f(x) - f(-x)] \sin kx \, dx$$

$$= \frac{1}{\pi} \left[\int_0^{\pi} f(x) \sin kx \, dx + \int_{-\pi}^0 f(x) \sin kx \, dx \right]$$

$$= \frac{1}{\pi} \int_{-\pi}^{\pi} f(x) \sin kx \, dx$$

We therefore have the following theorem: *Any continuous function which is periodic with period 2π and has a piecewise continuous first derivative can be expanded in a uniformly convergent Fourier series.*

$$f(x) = \frac{a_0}{2} + \sum_{k=1}^{\infty} (a_k \cos kx + b_k \sin kx)$$

where

$$a_k = \frac{1}{\pi} \int_{-\pi}^{\pi} f(x) \cos kx \, dx$$

$$b_k = \frac{1}{\pi} \int_{-\pi}^{\pi} f(x) \sin kx \, dx$$

This is the same as theorem 1 of Sec. 1.9.   Here the approach was from the point of view of the calculus of variations, as contrasted with the more algebraic approach of Sec. 1.9.   It also should be remembered that in Sec. 2.5 we showed the existence of the solutions of problem in the calculus of variations using the completeness of the set of trigonometric functions.   Hence, all these methods are intimately connected.   The present expansion theorem can be extended to the class of piecewise continuous functions, as was done in theorem 2 of Sec. 1.9.

Exercises 3.2

*1. Prove that the zeros of $J'_m(z)$ increase without bound and hence that

$$\phi_k(x) = J_m(\sqrt{\lambda_k}x)$$

where λ_k is a solution of $J'_m(\sqrt{\lambda}b) = 0$, forms a complete set of functions.

*2. Show that the Legendre polynomials $P_n(x)$, which are solutions of

$$[(1 - x^2)y']' + \lambda y = 0$$

$-1 \leq x \leq 1$, $y(-1)$, $y(1)$ finite, can be derived from the variational principle

$$\lambda_k = \min \frac{\int_{-1}^{1} (1 - x^2)(f')^2 \, dx}{\int_{-1}^{1} f^2 \, dx}$$

subject to $\int_{-1}^{1} fP_n(x) \, dx = 0$, $n = 1, 2, \ldots, k - 1$.

3. A tapered homogeneous elastic rod with density ρ, length L, and Young's modulus E has a circular cross section with diameter a at one end and b at the other.   It is built in at both ends.   Set up Hamilton's principle for small longitudinal vibrations of the cross sections; derive the Euler partial differential equation; and show that the method of separation of variables leads to a Sturm-Liouville problem.

3.3   Series Solutions of Ordinary Differential Equations

The general second-order linear homogeneous ordinary differential equation can be written

$$\frac{d^2w}{dz^2} + f(z)\frac{dw}{dz} + g(z)w = 0$$

We see that the Sturm-Liouville equation can be put in this form.   Although in the Sturm-Liouville problem we are usually concerned with a real independent variable, the present analysis can be readily carried through for a complex independent variable z, and therefore we shall do so.

We shall assume that the known functions $f(z)$ and $g(z)$ are analytic except possibly for poles.   If z_0 is a point where $f(z)$ and $g(z)$ are both analytic, then

z_0 is called an **ordinary point** of the differential equation.   In the neighborhood of an ordinary point, we can get a power series solution of the differential equation.   Without loss of generality we can assume that $z_0 = 0$.   If it is not, we can introduce a new independent variable $\xi = z - z_0$, and then the differential equation will have an ordinary point at the origin.   Since $f(z)$ and $g(z)$ are analytic at $z_0 = 0$, they have Taylor-series representations

$$f(z) = \sum_{k=0}^{\infty} a_k z^k \qquad g(z) = \sum_{k=0}^{\infty} b_k z^k$$

which converge in some neighborhood $|z| < R$ of the origin.   Let

$$w(z) = \sum_{k=0}^{\infty} c_k z^k$$

then

$$w'(z) = \sum_{k=1}^{\infty} k c_k z^{k-1}$$

$$w''(z) = \sum_{k=2}^{\infty} k(k-1) c_k z^{k-2}$$

Substituting in the differential equation and equating coefficients of various powers of z to zero, we have

$$2c_2 + a_0 c_1 + b_0 c_0 = 0$$

$$6c_3 + 2a_0 c_2 + a_1 c_1 + b_0 c_1 + b_1 c_0 = 0$$

$$12c_4 + 3a_0 c_3 + 2a_1 c_2 + a_2 c_1 + b_0 c_2 + b_1 c_1 + b_2 c_0 = 0$$

$$\dots\dots\dots\dots\dots\dots\dots\dots\dots\dots\dots\dots\dots\dots = 0$$

c_0 and c_1 can be assigned arbitrarily, giving us the two required arbitrary constants in the general solution of the second-order differential equation. The first equation then determines c_2 in terms of c_0 and c_1.   The next equation determines c_3 in terms of c_0, c_1, and c_2.   The next equation determines c_4, etc. We therefore have the general solution of the differential equation, provided we can justify the operations performed on the series, i.e., differentiation, multiplication, addition, etc.   This can be done provided we can find some circle of convergence for the assumed power series.   We can show that it will converge for $|z| < R$, which is the common region of convergence for the Taylor-series representations of $f(z)$ and $g(z)$.

Since $f(z)$ and $g(z)$ are analytic for $|z| < R$, Cauchy's inequalities tell us that

$$|a_k| \leq M r^{-k}$$

$$|b_k| \leq N r^{-k}$$

on any circle $|z| = r < R$, where $M = \max |f(z)|$ and $N = \max |g(z)|$ on the circle. Let K be the larger of M and Nr; then

$$|a_k| \le Kr^{-k}$$

$$|b_k| \le Kr^{-k-1}$$

If $|c_0| = \beta_0$ and $|c_1| = \beta_1$, then

$$2 |c_2| \le \beta_1 |a_0| + \beta_0 |b_0|$$

$$\le 2K\beta_1 + K\beta_0 r^{-1}$$

so that $|c_2| \le \beta_2$, where $2\beta_2 = K(2\beta_1 + \beta_0 r^{-1})$. Also

$$2 \cdot 3 |c_3| \le 2\beta_2 |a_0| + \beta_1 |a_1| + \beta_1 |b_0| + \beta_0 |b_1|$$

$$\le 3\beta_2 K + 2\beta_1 K r^{-1} + \beta_0 K r^{-2}$$

and $3 \cdot 4 |c_4| \le 3\beta_3 |a_0| + 2\beta_2 |a_1| + \beta_1 |a_2| + \beta_2 |b_0| + \beta_1 |b_1| + \beta_0 |b_2|$

$$\le 4\beta_3 K + 3\beta_2 K r^{-1} + 2\beta_1 K r^{-2} + \beta_0 K r^{-3}$$

Therefore, $|c_3| \le \beta_3$ and $|c_4| \le \beta_4$, where

$$2 \cdot 3\beta_3 = K(3\beta_2 + 2\beta_1 r^{-1} + \beta_0 r^{-2})$$

$$3 \cdot 4\beta_4 = K(4\beta_3 + 3\beta_2 r^{-1} + 2\beta_1 r^{-2} + \beta_0 r^{-3})$$

Continuing this way, we have $|c_k| \le \beta_k$, where

$$(k - 1)k\beta_k = K[k\beta_{k-1} + (k - 1)\beta_{k-2} r^{-1} + \cdots + 2\beta_1 r^{-k+2} + \beta_0 r^{-k+1}]$$

Next we write

$$(k - 2)(k - 1)\beta_{k-1} r^{-1} = K[(k - 1)\beta_{k-2} r^{-1} + \cdots + 2\beta_1 r^{-k+2} + \beta_0 r^{-k+1}]$$

and subtract. This gives us

$$(k - 1)k\beta_k - (k - 2)(k - 1)\beta_{k-1} r^{-1} = Kk\beta_{k-1}$$

from which it follows that

$$\frac{\beta_k}{\beta_{k-1}} = \frac{k - 2}{kr} + \frac{K}{k - 1}$$

Now consider the series $\sum_{k=0}^{\infty} \beta_k z^k$. Applying the ratio test, we see that this converges for $|z| < r$, for

$$\lim_{k \to \infty} \frac{\beta_k |z|}{\beta_{k-1}} = \frac{|z|}{r} < 1$$

implying convergence for $|z| < r$. By a comparison test, therefore, we have absolute convergence of $\sum_{k=0}^{\infty} c_k z^k$ in the same region, because $|c_k z^k| \le \beta_k |z|^k$.

But r is any positive number less than R. Therefore, we have convergence of

$$w(z) = \sum_{k=0}^{\infty} c_k z^k$$

for $|z| < R$.

If $f(z)$ or $g(z)$ has a pole at $z = z_0$, then z_0 is called a **singularity** of the differential equation. If $(z - z_0)f(z)$ and $(z - z_0)^2 g(z)$ are analytic at z_0, then we say that z_0 is a **regular singularity.** Otherwise it is an **irregular singularity.** In the neighborhood of a regular singularity we can always get a series solution of the differential equation as follows.[1]

We shall again assume that $z_0 = 0$. We first multiply the differential equation through by z^2. We then have to solve

$$z^2 w''(z) + [zf(z)][zw'(z)] + z^2 g(z)w(z) = 0$$

$zf(z)$ and $z^2 g(z)$ are analytic at $z = 0$. Therefore, we have the Taylor series

$$zf(z) = \sum_{k=0}^{\infty} a_k z^k$$

$$z^2 g(z) = \sum_{k=0}^{\infty} b_k z^k$$

valid for $|z| < R$. We assume a solution of the form

$$w(z) = \sum_{k=0}^{\infty} c_k z^{k+\alpha}$$

Then
$$z^2 w'' = \sum_{k=1}^{\infty} (k + \alpha)(k + \alpha - 1)c_k z^{k+\alpha}$$

$$zw' = \sum_{k=0}^{\infty} (k + \alpha)c_k z^{k+\alpha}$$

Substituting in the differential equations and equating coefficients of the various powers of z to zero, we have

$$c_0[\alpha(\alpha - 1) + \alpha a_0 + b_0] = 0$$

$$c_k[(\alpha + k)(\alpha + k - 1) + a_0(\alpha + k) + b_0]$$

$$+ \sum_{j=0}^{k-1} c_j[(\alpha + j)a_{k-j} + b_{k-j}] = 0 \qquad k = 1, 2, \ldots$$

The first equation indicates that c_0 is arbitrary and that α must be a solution of the **indicial equation**

$$\alpha(\alpha - 1) + \alpha a_0 + b_0 = 0$$

[1] This is usually referred to as **Frobenius's method.**

This equation is quadratic in α and therefore has two solutions, not necessarily distinct. Let α_1 and α_2 be the roots of the indicial equation. If $\alpha_1 \neq \alpha_2$ and $\alpha_2 - \alpha_1 \neq$ an integer, then the second equation yields the coefficients in each of two independent solutions, each of which contains an arbitrary constant. The sum of the two then gives us the general solution of the differential equation, provided the series can be shown to converge.

If $\alpha_1 = \alpha_2$ then the method yields only one solution. However, if we know one solution, we can always get another independent solution by a substitution which reduces the problem to the solution of a linear first-order equation. We shall return to this problem presently. If $\alpha_2 = \alpha_1 + n$, where n is a positive integer, then for $k = n$

$$(\alpha_1 + n)(\alpha_1 + n - 1) + a_0(\alpha_1 + n) + b_0 = 0$$

In this case, the solution corresponding to the root α_1 fails unless

$$\sum_{j=0}^{n-1} c_j[(\alpha_1 + j)a_{n-j} + b_{n-j}] = 0$$

In the latter case c_n is arbitrary. Otherwise the method fails to yield two solutions. We will, however, always get one series using the root α_2. The series $\sum_{k=0}^{\infty} c_k z^k$ can be shown to converge for $|z| < R$.

We can write

$$c_k I(\alpha + k) = -\sum_{j=0}^{k-1} c_j[(\alpha + j)a_{k-j} + b_{k-j}]$$

where $\qquad I(\alpha) = \alpha(\alpha - 1) + \alpha a_0 + b_0 = (\alpha - \alpha_1)(\alpha - \alpha_2)$

Then $\quad I(\alpha_1 + k) = k(k + \alpha_1 - \alpha_2) \quad$ and $\quad I(\alpha_2 + k) = k(k + \alpha_2 - \alpha_1)$

We can write the inequality

$$k(k - |\alpha_1 - \alpha_2|)\,|c_k| \leq |I(\alpha_2 + k)|\,|c_k| \leq \sum_{j=0}^{k-1} |c_j| \{(|\alpha_2| + j)\,|a_{k-j}| + |b_{k-j}|\},$$

for all $k \geq |\alpha_1 - \alpha_2|$. Let $|c_j| = \beta_j$ for $j < m$, where m is some integer greater than $|\alpha_1 - \alpha_2|$. Then

$$m(m - |\alpha_1 - \alpha_2|)\,|c_m| \leq \sum_{j=0}^{m-1} \beta_j \{(|\alpha_2| + j)\,|a_{m-j}| + |b_{m-j}|\}$$

By Cauchy's inequalities,

$$|a_k| \leq Mr^{-k} \leq Kr^{-k}$$

$$|b_k| \leq Nr^{-k} \leq Kr^{-k}$$

where $M = \max |zf(z)|$ and $N = \max |z^2 g(x)|$ on $|z| = r < R$, and K is the larger of M and N. Then

$$m(m - |\alpha_1 - \alpha_2|)\,|c_m| \leq K \sum_{j=0}^{m-1} \beta_j(|\alpha_2| + j + 1)r^{-m+j}$$

and $|c_m| \leq \beta_m$, where

$$m(m - |\alpha_1 - \alpha_2|)\beta_m = K \sum_{j=0}^{m-1} \beta_j(|\alpha_2| + j + 1)r^{-m+j}$$

Furthermore, for $n \geq m$,

$$n(n - |\alpha_1 - \alpha_2|)\,|c_n| \leq K \sum_{j=0}^{n-1} \beta_j(|\alpha_2| + j + 1)r^{-n+j}$$

and $|c_n| \leq \beta_n$, where

$$n(n - |\alpha_1 - \alpha_2|)\beta_n = K \sum_{j=0}^{n-1} \beta_j(|\alpha_2| + j + 1)r^{-n+j}$$

Replacing n by $n - 1$ and dividing by r, we have

$$(n - 1)(n - 1 - |\alpha_1 - \alpha_2|)\beta_{n-1}r^{-1} = K \sum_{j=0}^{n-2} \beta_j(|\alpha_2| + j + 1)r^{-n+j}$$

Subtracting,

$$n(n - |\alpha_1 - \alpha_2|)\beta_n - (n - 1)(n - 1 - |\alpha_1 - \alpha_2|)\beta_{n-1}r^{-1}$$
$$= K\beta_{n-1}(n + |\alpha_2|)r^{-1}$$

or

$$\frac{\beta_n}{\beta_{n-1}} = \frac{(n - 1)(n - 1 - |\alpha_1 - \alpha_2|)}{n(n - |\alpha_1 - \alpha_2|)r} + \frac{K(n + |\alpha_2|)}{n(n - |\alpha_1 - \alpha_2|)r}$$

Consider the series $\sum_{k=0}^{\infty} \beta_k z^k$. This series converges absolutely for $|z| < r$ by

the ratio test, since $\lim_{n \to \infty} \dfrac{\beta_n |z|}{\beta_{n-1}} = \dfrac{|z|}{r} < 1$ when $|z| < r$. By comparison $\sum_{k=0}^{\infty} c_k z^k$

converges absolutely in the same region, since $|c_k| \leq \beta_k$. If α_2 is zero or a

positive integer, then $w = z^{\alpha_2} \sum_{k=0}^{\infty} c_k z^k$ is analytic for $|z| < R$. If α_2 is a negative

integer, then w has a pole at $z = 0$. If α_2 is a fraction, is irrational, or is complex, w has a branch point at $z = 0$.

If $\alpha_2 - \alpha_1$ is not equal to zero or a positive integer, then we get a second independent solution using the root α_1, and the proof of convergence of the series is essentially the same as that for α_2. If the method fails to give two independent solutions, then we proceed as follows. Let $w(z) = u(z)\,v(z)$, where $u(z)$ is a known solution of the differential equation. The differential equation satisfied by v is

$$\frac{d^2v}{dz^2} + \left(\frac{2u'}{u} + f\right)\frac{dv}{dz} = 0$$

This is a first-order linear equation in v' with the solution

$$\frac{dv}{dz} = \frac{A}{u^2}\,e^{-\int f(z)\,dz}$$

Then
$$v = A \int [u^{-2} e^{-\int f(z)\,dz}]\,dz + B$$

$$w = uv = Au \int [u^{-2} e^{-\int f(z)\,dz}]\,dz + Bu$$

This is the complete solution.

To illustrate some of these ideas, let us consider the series solution of the **Legendre equation**

$$[(1 - z^2)w']' + \lambda w = 0$$

The equation can be written as

$$w'' - \frac{2z}{1 - z^2}\,w' + \frac{\lambda}{1 - z^2}\,w = 0$$

and we see that $z = 0$ is an ordinary point, while $z = \pm 1$ are regular singular points. The indicial equation at either of the singular points is $\alpha^2 = 0$, so that $\alpha_1 = \alpha_2 = 0$. Hence, we can get a power series solution valid in the neighborhood of either of the singularities. However, these solutions are not finite at the other singularity, unless λ has certain integer values. We can best determine these eigenvalues by seeking solutions valid near the origin as series in powers of z. Hence, we assume

$$w = \sum_{k=0}^{\infty} c_k z^k$$

Substituting in the differential equation, we have

$$(1 - z^2) \sum_{k=2}^{\infty} k(k-1)c_k z^{k-2} - 2z \sum_{k=1}^{\infty} kc_k z^{k-1} + \lambda \sum_{k=0}^{\infty} c_k z^k = 0$$

or
$$\sum_{m=0}^{\infty} [\lambda c_m + (m+2)(m+1)c_{m+2}]z^m - \sum_{m=1}^{\infty} 2mc_m z^m$$

$$- \sum_{m=2}^{\infty} m(m-1)c_m z^m = 0$$

Setting the coefficients of the various powers of z equal to zero, we have

$$c_{m+2} = \frac{m(m+1) - \lambda}{(m+2)(m+1)}\,c_m \qquad m = 0, 1, 2, \ldots$$

If we let $c_1 = 0$ while $c_0 \neq 0$, we obtain a series in even powers of z. If we let $c_0 = 0$ while $c_1 \neq 0$, we obtain a series in odd powers of z. These solutions are obviously linearly independent, and therefore a linear combination of them will be the complete solution of the differential equation. If $\lambda \neq n(n+1)$ for some nonnegative integer n, these solutions will be infinite series converging for $|z| < 1$. However, it can be shown that they diverge for $z = \pm 1$.[1] If we are seeking solutions finite at $z = \pm 1$, λ will have to equal $n(n + 1)$, where n is a nonnegative integer. In this case, either the series in even powers or odd powers terminates, depending on whether n is even or odd, giving us polynomial solutions. If c_0 or c_1 is adjusted so that the solution takes on the value 1 at $z = 1$, we have the **Legendre polynomials** $P_n(z)$. The first few of these are $P_0(z) = 1$, $P_1(z) = z$, $P_2(z) = \frac{1}{2}(3z^2 - 1)$, $P_3(z) = \frac{1}{2}(5z^3 - 3z)$, etc. More generally,

$$P_n(z) = \sum_{k=0}^{K} \frac{(-1)^k(2n - 2k)!}{2^n k! \, (n - k)! \, (n - 2k)!} z^{n-2k}$$

where $K = \frac{1}{2}n$ or $K = \frac{1}{2}(n - 1)$, depending on whether n is even or odd. We can rephrase the definition of $P_n(z)$ as follows:

$$P_n(z) = \sum_{k=0}^{K} \frac{(-1)^k}{2^n k! \, (n - k)!} \frac{d^n}{dz^n} z^{2n-2k}$$

$$= \frac{1}{2^n n!} \frac{d^n}{dz^n} \sum_{k=0}^{K} \frac{(-1)^k n!}{k! \, (n - k)!} z^{2n-2k}$$

$$= \frac{1}{2^n n!} \frac{d^n}{dz^n} \sum_{k=0}^{n} \frac{(-1)^k n!}{k! \, (n - k)!} z^{2n-2k}$$

$$= \frac{1}{2^n n!} \frac{d^n}{dz^n} (z^2 - 1)^n$$

The last line is known as **Rodrigues' formula.**

The Legendre polynomials are solutions of the Legendre equation

$$(1 - z^2)w'' - 2zw' + n(n + 1)w = 0$$

for $n = 0, 1, 2, \ldots$. Since they are polynomials, they are finite everywhere in the finite plane. They are, therefore, solutions of the Sturm-Liouville problem

$$[(1 - x^2)y']' + \lambda y = 0$$

with $y(1)$ and $y(-1)$ finite for $\lambda_n = n(n + 1)$. It follows from the differential equation that the Legendre polynomials are mutually orthogonal in the following sense:

$$\int_{-1}^{1} P_n(x)P_m(x) \, dx = 0$$

for $n \neq m$. That they are a complete set of functions follows from the fact that they are solutions of a variational problem[2] with an unbounded infinite

---

[1] See Richard Courant and David Hilbert, "Methods of Mathematical Physics," Interscience Publishers, Inc., New York, 1953, vol. I, pp. 325 and 326.

[2] See exercise 2, Sec. 3.2.

sequence of eigenvalues.   This tells us that the Legendre polynomials are the only solutions of the differential equation finite at $x = \pm 1$.

The Legendre polynomials are not normalized, but it can be shown, by use of Rodrigues' formula, that

$$\int_{-1}^{1} P_n^2(x)\, dx = \frac{2}{2n + 1}$$

The **associated Legendre equation** is

$$(1 - z^2)w'' - 2zw' + \left[\lambda - \frac{m^2}{1 - z^2}\right]w = 0$$

where in most applications m is an integer.   For example, in the separation of the Helmholtz equation in spherical coordinates,[1] m is a separation constant which must be an integer in order to make the ϕ-dependent part of the solution single-valued.   We shall consider only the case where m is an integer.   Let us perform the following transformation on the differential equation:

$$w = (1 - z^2)^{\frac{1}{2}m}v$$

Then
$$w' = (1 - z^2)^{\frac{1}{2}m}v' - zm(1 - z^2)^{\frac{1}{2}m-1}v$$

$$w'' = (1 - z^2)^{\frac{1}{2}m}v'' - 2zm(1 - z^2)^{\frac{1}{2}m-1}v'$$
$$-m(1 - z^2)^{\frac{1}{2}m-1}v + z^2 m(m - 2)(1 - z^2)^{\frac{1}{2}m-2}v$$

Substituting in the differential equation, we have

$$(1 - z^2)v'' - 2(m + 1)zv' + (\lambda - m - m^2)v = 0$$

We next let $v = \dfrac{d^m}{dz^m}\, u$.   Then the differential equation becomes

$$(1 - z^2)\frac{d^{m+2}u}{dz^{m+2}} - 2(m + 1)z\frac{d^{m+1}u}{dz^{m+1}} + (\lambda - m - m^2)\frac{d^m u}{dz^m} = 0$$

This can be written as follows:

$$\frac{d^m}{dz^m}\left[(1 - z^2)\frac{d^2 u}{dz^2} - 2z\frac{du}{dz} + \lambda u\right] = 0$$

for
$$\frac{d^m}{dz^m}\left[(1 - z^2)\frac{d^2 u}{dz^2}\right] = \sum_{k=0}^{m}\frac{m!}{(m - k)!\, k!}\frac{d^k}{dz^k}(1 - z^2)\frac{d^{m-k+2}u}{dz^{m-k+2}}$$

$$= (1 - z^2)\frac{d^{m+2}u}{dz^{m+2}} - 2zm\frac{d^{m+1}u}{dz^{m+1}} - m(m - 1)\frac{d^m u}{dz^m}$$

[1] See Sec. 3.1.

and

$$\frac{d^m}{dz^m}\left(-2z\frac{du}{dz}\right) = \sum_{k=0}^{m}\frac{m!}{(m-k)!\,k!}\frac{d^k(-2z)}{dz^k}\frac{d^{m-k+1}u}{dz^{m-k+1}}$$

$$= -2z\frac{d^{m+1}u}{dz^{m+1}} - 2m\frac{du^m}{dz^m}$$

We know that if $\lambda = n(n+1)$, with n a nonnegative integer, the equation

$$(1-z^2)u'' - 2zu' + n(n+1)u = 0$$

has a polynomial solution $P_n(z)$ which is finite at $z = \pm 1$. Therefore, the associated Legendre equation has solutions

$$P_n^m(z) = (1-z^2)^{\frac{1}{2}m}\frac{d^m}{dz^m}P_n(z)$$

$$= \frac{(1-z^2)^{\frac{1}{2}m}}{2^n n!}\frac{d^{n+m}}{dz^{n+m}}(z^2-1)^n$$

which are finite at $z = \pm 1$. These functions are called the **associated Legendre functions.** One can prove that for a given integer m these are the only solutions finite at $z = \pm 1$, by showing that these solutions are obtainable from a variational principle with eigenvalues $\lambda = n(n+1)$, $n = m$, $m+1$, $m+2$, ... $\rightarrow \infty$ and, therefore, are a complete set of functions satisfying the differential equation. It can be shown by direct integration that

$$\int_{-1}^{1}[P_n^m(x)]^2\,dx = \frac{2}{2n+1}\frac{(n+m)!}{(n-m)!}$$

In the separation of the Helmholtz equation in spherical coordinates we have the equation

$$\sin\theta\frac{\partial}{\partial\theta}\left(\sin\theta\frac{\partial S}{\partial\theta}\right) + \frac{\partial^2 S}{\partial\phi^2} + \alpha S\sin^2\theta = 0$$

where $S(\theta,\phi)$ is the angular dependent part of the eigenfunction. This equation also occurs in the solution of the steady-state Schrödinger equation in quantum mechanics when the potential $V(r)$ is spherically symmetric. We require that the solution be single-valued, and finite for $\theta = 0$ and π. A further separation of variables $S = V(\theta)W(\phi)$ yields

$$\frac{d^2 W}{d\phi^2} + \beta W = 0$$

with solutions $\sin\sqrt{\beta}\phi$, $\cos\sqrt{\beta}\phi$. $\beta = m^2$, with m an integer, is required to make W periodic with period 2π, and hence continuous. The other equation is then

$$\sin^2\theta\frac{d^2 V}{d\theta^2} + \sin\theta\cos\theta\frac{dV}{d\theta} + (\alpha\sin^2\theta - m^2)V = 0$$

We seek a solution of this equation which is finite for $\theta = 0$ and π.   Let $\cos \theta = x$, then

$$\frac{dV}{d\theta} = - \sin \theta \frac{dV}{dx}$$

$$\frac{d^2V}{d\theta^2} = \sin^2 \theta \frac{d^2V}{dx^2} - \cos \theta \frac{dV}{dx}$$

and the equation becomes

$$(1 - x^2) \frac{d^2V}{dx^2} - 2x \frac{dV}{dx} + \left(\alpha - \frac{m^2}{1 - x^2} \right) V = 0$$

This is the associated Legendre equation which has solutions $P_n^m(x)$ which are finite at $x = \pm 1$, or $\cos \theta = \pm 1$.   The solutions

$$S(\theta, \phi) = A P_n^m(\cos \theta) \sin m\phi + B P_n^m(\cos \theta) \cos m\phi$$

are called **spherical harmonics.**   The discussion at the end of Sec. 3.1 shows that they are a complete set of functions over the region $0 \le \theta \le \pi, 0 \le \phi < 2\pi$.

In the separation of the Helmholtz equation in spherical coordinates, the equation satisfied by the radial dependent part of the solution is

$$r^2 \frac{d^2U}{dr^2} + 2r \frac{dU}{dr} + \lambda r^2 U - n(n + 1)U = 0$$

Here the separation constant α is set equal to $n(n + 1)$ as required to make the angular dependent part of the solution finite at $\theta = 0$ and π.   We make the change of variables:

$$x = \lambda^{\frac{1}{2}} r$$

$$U = r^{-\frac{1}{2}} y$$

Then $$\frac{dU}{dr} = -\tfrac{1}{2} r^{-\frac{3}{2}} y + \lambda^{\frac{1}{2}} r^{-\frac{1}{2}} \frac{dy}{dx}$$

$$\frac{d^2U}{dr^2} = \tfrac{3}{4} r^{-\frac{5}{2}} y - r^{-\frac{3}{2}} \lambda^{\frac{1}{2}} \frac{dy}{dx} + \lambda r^{-\frac{1}{2}} \frac{d^2y}{dx^2}$$

The differential equation becomes

$$x^2 y'' + xy' + [x^2 - (n + \tfrac{1}{2})^2]y = 0$$

This is **Bessel's differential equation.**   It has a regular singular point at $z = 0$.   We shall consider the solution of the equation

$$z^2 w'' + zw' + (z^2 - \nu^2)w = 0$$

If we seek a series solution valid in the neighborhood of $z = 0$, the indicial equation is $\alpha^2 - \nu^2 = 0$. The roots are $\alpha_1 = -\nu$ and $\alpha_2 = \nu$. If ν is not an integer, we get the two independent solutions

$$w_1 = z^\nu \sum_{k=0}^{\infty} a_k z^k$$

$$w_2 = z^{-\nu} \sum_{k=0}^{\infty} b_k z^k$$

Substituting the first into the differential equation, we have

$$\sum_{k=0}^{\infty} k(k + 2\nu)a_k z^{k+\nu} + \sum_{k=0}^{\infty} a_k z^{k+\nu+2} = 0$$

The coefficient of $z^{\nu+1}$ is $(1 + 2\nu)a_1$. Since this must be zero, $a_1 = 0$ if $\nu \neq -\frac{1}{2}$. The other coefficients are determined by the recurrence relation

$$a_{k+2} = -\frac{a_k}{(k + 2)(k + 2 + 2\nu)}$$

Since $a_1 = 0$, all the coefficients with odd subscripts are also zero. a_0 is arbitrary, and the other coefficients are determined in terms of a_0 as follows:

$$a_{2n} = \frac{(-1)^n a_0}{2^{2n} n! \, (\nu + 1)(\nu + 2) \cdots (\nu + n)}$$

Recalling that $\Gamma(\nu + n + 1) = (\nu + n)(\nu + n - 1) \cdots (\nu + 1)\Gamma(\nu + 1)$, if we let $a_0 = 2^\nu \Gamma(\nu + 1)$, we can write

$$J_\nu(z) = \sum_{n=0}^{\infty} \frac{(-1)^n (\frac{1}{2}z)^{2n+\nu}}{n! \, \Gamma(\nu + n + 1)}$$

as a solution of the equation. This is the **Bessel function** of the first kind of order ν. A second solution is similarly

$$J_{-\nu}(z) = \sum_{n=0}^{\infty} \frac{(-1)^n (\frac{1}{2}z)^{2n-\nu}}{n! \, \Gamma(-\nu + n + 1)}$$

If ν is not an integer, these two solutions are independent, and the complete solution of the equation is

$$w = AJ_\nu(z) + BJ_{-\nu}(z)$$

If $\nu = 0$ then the two above solutions are obviously the same. If $\nu = m$, an integer, then

$$J_{-m}(z) = \sum_{n=m}^{\infty} \frac{(-1)^n (\frac{1}{2}z)^{2n-m}}{n! \, \Gamma(-m + n + 1)}$$

since $1/\Gamma(z) = 0$ for $z = 0, -1, -2, \dots$ This follows from the fact that $\Gamma(z)$ has simple poles at $z = 0, -1, -2, \dots$ We can thus write

$$J_{-m}(z) = \sum_{j=0}^{\infty} \frac{(-1)^{j+m}(\frac{1}{2}z)^{2j+m}}{(j+m)! \, \Gamma(j+1)}$$

$$= (-1)^m \sum_{j=0}^{\infty} \frac{(-1)^j(\frac{1}{2}z)^{2j+m}}{j! \, \Gamma(j+m+1)}$$

$$= (-1)^m J_m(z)$$

Therefore, if ν is an integer, we do not get independent solutions.   In this case, a second independent solution is given by

$$Y_m(z) = \frac{2}{\pi} J_m(z) \int \left\{ \frac{1}{[J_m(z)]^2} \, e^{-\int (1/z)\,dz} \right\} dz$$

$$= \frac{2}{\pi} J_m(z) \int \frac{1}{z[J_m(z)]^2} \, dz$$

We see that $J_m(z)$ has a zero of order m at the origin.   Therefore, $1/\{z[J_m(z)]^2\}$ has a pole of order $2m + 1$ and can be expanded as follows:

$$\frac{1}{z[J_m(z)]^2} = \frac{c_{2m+1}}{z^{2m+1}} + \frac{c_{2m}}{z^{2m}} + \cdots$$

where
$$c_{2m+1} = \lim_{z \to 0} \frac{z^{2m}}{[J_m(z)]^2} = 2^{2m}(m!)^2$$

The leading term in the expansion of $Y_m(z)$ is therefore $-\frac{1}{\pi}(m-1)! \left(\frac{z}{2}\right)^{-m}$.

This shows that $Y_m(z)$ is not bounded at $z = 0$.   If $m = 0$, the second solution is $Y_0(z)$, which has a logarithmic singularity at $z = 0$.

In the Sturm-Liouville problem

$$(xy')' - \frac{\nu^2}{x} y + \lambda xy = 0$$

with y finite at $z = 0$, we have the solution $J_\nu(\sqrt{\lambda}\,x)$, since the second solution is not finite at $x = 0$.   This is true whether ν is an integer or not.   The eigenvalue λ is determined by the requirement on the solution to satisfy the other boundary condition.   We have seen in the previous section that the Bessel functions form a complete set of functions.   In the above separation-of-variables problem in spherical coordinates the solution of

$$r^2 \frac{d^2U}{dr^2} + 2r \frac{dU}{dr} + \lambda r^2 U - n(n+1)U = 0$$

which is finite at $r = 0$, is $r^{-\frac{1}{2}}J_{n+\frac{1}{2}}(\sqrt{\lambda} r)$, and the eigenvalue λ is determined by the physical boundary condition at $r = a$.

Just as we have alternative forms

$$y = A \cos nx + B \sin nx$$

$$= Ce^{inx} + De^{-inx}$$

for the general solution of $y'' + n^2 y = 0$, we also have alternative forms for the general solution of Bessel's equation

$$xy'' + y' + \left(x - \frac{n^2}{x}\right)y = 0$$

The general solution can be expressed either as

$$y = AJ_n(x) + BY_n(x)$$

or as

$$y = CH_n^{(1)}(x) + DH_n^{(2)}(x)$$

where

$$H_n^{(1)}(x) = J_n(x) + iY_n(x)$$

$$H_n^{(2)}(x) = J_n(x) - iY_n(x)$$

$H_n^{(1)}(x)$ and $H_n^{(2)}(x)$ are called the **Hankel functions** of the first and second kind. They play an important role in the solution of the two-dimensional wave equation, as we shall see in Chap. 4.

Exercises 3.3

1. Find the analytic solution of the zeroth-order Bessel equation

$$w'' + (1/z)w' + w = 0$$

valid at the origin. Show that the other solution has a logarithmic singularity at the origin.

2. Show that the method of Frobenius yields two independent solutions of Bessel's equation of order $\frac{1}{2}$ valid near the origin, even though the roots of the indicial equation differ by an integer. Also show that the complete solution can be written as $w = A \dfrac{\sin z}{\sqrt{z}} + B \dfrac{\cos z}{\sqrt{z}}$.

3. Show that the method of Frobenius fails to give a solution of

$$z^3 w'' + z^2 w' + w = 0$$

valid near the origin. Note that the singularity at $z = 0$ is not a regular singularity.

4. Find the complete solution of Legendre's differential equation

$$(1 - z^2)w'' - 2zw' + n(n + 1)w = 0$$

with n an integer, and show that it has logarithmic singularities at $z = \pm 1$.

*5. Show that $\displaystyle\int_{-1}^{1} P_n^2(x)\, dx = \dfrac{2}{2n + 1}$.

6. Obtain Schläfli's integral formula for the Legendre polynomials

$$P_n(z_0) = \frac{2^{-n}}{2\pi i} \int_C \frac{(z^2 - 1)^n}{(z - z_0)^{n+1}} \, dz$$

where C is a simple closed contour surrounding z_0.

*7. Show that $\int_{-1}^{1} [P_n^m(x)]^2 \, dx = \frac{2}{2n+1} \frac{(n+m)!}{(n-m)!}$

8. Sometimes we are interested in solutions of $w'' + f(z)w' + g(z)w = 0$ for large values of z. Make the transformation $z = 1/\zeta$ and state criteria in terms of $f(z)$ and $g(z)$ for an ordinary point and a regular singular point at $z = \infty$. Develop a method of obtaining solutions of the form $w(z) = z^{-\alpha} \sum_{k=0}^{\infty} c_k z^{-k}$ valid for $|z| > R$ when there is a regular singular point at $z = \infty$.

9. The Bessel functions satisfy a great number of identities just as the trigonometric functions do. Prove, for example, the following recurrence relations:

$$J_{\nu-1}(z) + J_{\nu+1}(z) = \frac{2\nu}{z} J_\nu(z)$$

$$J_{\nu-1}(z) - J_{\nu+1}(z) = 2J_\nu'(z)$$

$$\frac{\nu}{z} J_\nu(z) + J_\nu'(z) = J_{\nu-1}(z)$$

$$\frac{\nu}{z} J_\nu(z) - J_\nu'(z) = J_{\nu+1}(z)$$

10. Prove the following recurrence relations for the Legendre polynomials:

$$nP_n(z) - (2n - 1)zP_{n-1}(z) + (n - 1)P_{n-2}(z) = 0$$
$$zP_n'(z) - P_{n-1}'(z) = nP_n(z)$$
$$P_n'(z) - zP_{n-1}'(z) = nP_{n-1}(z)$$
$$P_{n+1}'(z) - zP_{n-1}'(z) = (2n + 1)P_n(z)$$

3.4 Series Solutions of Boundary-value Problems

We conclude this chapter by solving some boundary-value problems which lend themselves nicely to the separation-of-variables technique and solution using eigenfunction expansions.

We consider first the vibrations of a circular membrane. Here we must solve the two-dimensional wave equation $\nabla^2 \phi = \frac{1}{a^2} \frac{\partial^2 \phi}{\partial t^2}$ in the interior of the membrane, i.e., $0 \leq r < b$, $0 \leq \theta < 2\pi$, subject to the boundary condition $\phi = 0$ on the edge, $r = b$. We shall specify an initial displacement

$$\phi(r,\theta,0) = f(r,\theta)$$

but no initial velocity, i.e., $\dot{\phi}(r,\theta,0) = 0$. With the introduction of polar coordinates, the wave equation becomes

$$\frac{\partial^2 \phi}{\partial r^2} + \frac{1}{r} \frac{\partial \phi}{\partial r} + \frac{1}{r^2} \frac{\partial^2 \phi}{\partial \theta^2} = \frac{1}{a^2} \frac{\partial^2 \phi}{\partial t^2}$$

Assuming a solution of this equation of the form

$$\phi(r,\theta,t) = \psi(r,\theta)F(t)$$

we obtain the separated equations

$$\ddot{F} + a^2\lambda F = 0$$

$$\frac{\partial^2\psi}{\partial r^2} + \frac{1}{r}\frac{\partial\psi}{\partial r} + \frac{1}{r^2}\frac{\partial^2\psi}{\partial\theta^2} + \lambda\psi = 0$$

The first of these has the solution $F = C \cos a\sqrt{\lambda}t$, since we are assuming no initial velocity. We next assume a separation of the space variable, i.e.,

$$\psi(r,\theta) = U(r)V(\theta)$$

giving us
$$r^2\frac{d^2U}{dr^2} + r\frac{dU}{dr} + (r^2\lambda - n^2)U = 0$$

$$\frac{d^2V}{d\theta^2} + n^2V = 0$$

The separation constant must be n^2 with $n = 0, 1, 2, 3, \ldots$ in order to guarantee that

$$V_n(\theta) = A_n \cos n\theta + B_n \sin n\theta$$

and its derivatives are continuous at $\theta = 0$. In the equation satisfied by U we make the substitution $x = \sqrt{\lambda}r$, and the equation becomes

$$x^2\frac{d^2U}{dx^2} + x\frac{dU}{dx} + (x^2 - n^2)U = 0$$

This is Bessel's equation of order n. The solution which is finite at $x = 0$ is $J_n(x)$. Therefore,

$$U_n(r) = J_n(\sqrt{\lambda}r)$$

To satisfy the boundary condition identically in θ, we set $J_n(\sqrt{\lambda}b) = 0$. We know that the Bessel function of order n has an infinite sequence of zeros increasing to infinity. Let these zeros be $\sqrt{\lambda_{nm}}b$, thus determining the eigenvalues λ_{nm}. The eigenfunctions are $J_n(\sqrt{\lambda_{nm}}r) \cos n\theta$ and $J_n(\sqrt{\lambda_{nm}}r) \sin n\theta$. A formal series solution of the problem is then

$$\phi(r,\theta,t) = \sum_{n=0}^{\infty} \sum_{m=1}^{\infty}(a_{nm} \cos n\theta + b_{nm} \sin n\theta)J_n(\sqrt{\lambda_{nm}}r) \cos a\sqrt{\lambda_{nm}}t$$

If this is to be a solution, the initial condition must be satisfied, i.e.,

$$\phi(r,\theta,0) = f(r,\theta) = \sum_{n=0}^{\infty} \sum_{m=1}^{\infty} (a_{nm} \cos n\theta + b_{nm} \sin n\theta) J_n(\sqrt{\lambda_{nm}}r)$$

The coefficients must therefore be

$$a_{om} = \frac{(1/2\pi)\int_0^{2\pi}\int_0^b rJ_0(\sqrt{\lambda_{om}}r)f(r,\theta)\,dr\,d\theta}{\int_0^b rJ_0^2(\sqrt{\lambda_{om}}r)\,dr}$$

$$a_{nm} = \frac{(1/\pi)\int_0^{2\pi}\int_0^b rJ_n(\sqrt{\lambda_{nm}}r)f(r,\theta)\cos n\theta\,dr\,d\theta}{\int_0^b rJ_n^2(\sqrt{\lambda_{nm}}r)\,dr}$$

$$b_{nm} = \frac{(1/\pi)\int_0^{2\pi}\int_0^b rJ_n(\sqrt{\lambda_{nm}}r)f(r,\theta)\sin n\theta\,dr\,d\theta}{\int_0^b rJ_n^2(\sqrt{\lambda_{nm}}r)\,dr}$$

The integral in the denominators can be evaluated simply as follows:

$$\int_0^b rJ_n^2(\sqrt{\lambda_{nm}}r)\,dr = \frac{b^2[J_n'(\sqrt{\lambda_{nm}}b)]^2}{2\lambda_{nm}}$$

$$= \frac{b^2}{2}\left[\frac{n}{\sqrt{\lambda_{nm}}b}J_n(\sqrt{\lambda_{nm}}b) - J_{n+1}(\sqrt{\lambda_{nm}}b)\right]^2$$

$$= \frac{b^2}{2}J_{n+1}^2(\sqrt{\lambda_{nm}}b)$$

We know that the eigenfunctions form a complete set of solutions of Helmholtz's equations. Thus, if $f(r,\theta)$ is continuous in the closed region and has piecewise continuous first partial derivatives, then the series converges in mean to the function. We shall later prove, in connection with our study of integral equations in Chap. 5, that if $f(r,\theta)$ is continuous along with its first and second partial derivatives, the series will converge absolutely and uniformly to the function.

We next turn our attention to a problem in heat conduction. Suppose a homogeneous hollow cylinder which occupies the region $a \leq r \leq b, 0 \leq \theta \leq 2\pi,$ $0 \leq z \leq h$ has its ends $z = 0$ and $z = h$ maintained at temperatures 0 and 100°C, respectively. The faces at $r = a$ and $r = b$ are insulated against the flow of heat. Assuming an initial temperature distribution $f(r,\theta,z)$, we have to solve the following boundary-value problem to determine the temperature $\phi(r,\theta,z,t)$ in the solid:

$$\frac{\partial^2\phi}{\partial r^2} + \frac{1}{r}\frac{\partial\phi}{\partial r} + \frac{1}{r^2}\frac{\partial^2\phi}{\partial\theta^2} + \frac{\partial^2\phi}{\partial z^2} = \frac{1}{c^2}\frac{\partial\phi}{\partial t}$$

for $a < r < b, 0 \leq \theta < 2\pi, 0 < z < h$, subject to

$$\phi(r,\theta,0,t) = 0$$

$$\phi(r,\theta,h,t) = 100$$

$$\phi_r(a,\theta,z,t) = \phi_r(b,\theta,z,t) = 0$$

$$\phi(r,\theta,z,0) = f(r,\theta,z)$$

Here we have a nonhomogeneous boundary condition at $z = h$. However, we can solve the problem by taking the following point of view. Let $\phi = \phi^{(S)} + \phi^{(T)}$, where $\phi^{(S)}$ is the **steady-state** solution, which does not depend on t, satisfying $\nabla^2\phi^{(S)} = 0$, subject to $\phi^{(S)}(r,\theta,0) = 0$, $\phi^{(S)}(r,\theta,h) = 100$, $\phi_r^{(S)}(a,\theta,z) = \phi_r^{(S)}(b,\theta,z) = 0$; and $\phi^{(T)}$ is the **transient solution** satisfying $\nabla^2\phi^{(T)} = \dfrac{1}{c^2}\dfrac{\partial\phi^{(T)}}{\partial t}$, subject to

$$\phi^{(T)}(r,\theta,0,t) = 0, \quad \phi^{(T)}(r,\theta,h,t) = 0, \quad \phi_r^{(T)}(a,\theta,z,t) = \phi_r^{(T)}(b,\theta,z,t) = 0$$

Obviously, the sum $\phi^{(S)} + \phi^{(T)}$ satisfies the differential equation and the boundary conditions. The initial condition for $\phi^{(T)}$ becomes

$$\phi^{(T)}(r,\theta,z,0) = f(r,\theta,z) - \phi^{(S)}(r,\theta,z)$$

Because of the symmetry of the problem and the boundary conditions on $\phi^{(S)}$, we see that the steady-state solution is just a uniform flow of heat from the high-temperature end to the low-temperature end, and hence

$$\phi^{(S)} = 100\,\frac{z}{h}$$

For the transient solution we attempt a separation of variables. Let $\phi^{(T)} = U(r)V(\theta)W(z)F(t)$. Then we have

$$\dot{F} + \lambda c^2 F = 0$$

$$\frac{d^2W}{dz^2} + (\lambda - \alpha)W = 0$$

$$\frac{d^2V}{d\theta^2} + n^2V = 0$$

$$r^2\frac{d^2U}{dr^2} + r\frac{dU}{dr} + (\alpha r^2 - n^2)U = 0$$

The solutions are

$$F = c_1 e^{-\lambda c^2 t}$$

$$W = c_2 \cos\sqrt{\lambda - \alpha}\,z + c_3 \sin\sqrt{\lambda - \alpha}\,z$$

$$V = c_4 \cos n\theta + c_5 \sin n\theta$$

$$U = c_6 J_n(\sqrt{\alpha}\,r) + c_7 Y_n(\sqrt{\alpha}\,r)$$

$W(0) = 0$ implies that $c_2 = 0$ and $W(h) = 0$ implies that $\lambda - \alpha = k^2\pi^2/h^2$, $k = 1, 2, 3, \ldots$ The boundary condition at $r = a$ and $r = b$ are to hold independently of θ and z. Therefore,

$$c_6 J'_n(\sqrt{\alpha}a) + c_7 Y'_n(\sqrt{\alpha}a) = 0$$

$$c_6 J'_n(\sqrt{\alpha}b) + c_7 Y'_n(\sqrt{\alpha}b) = 0$$

This requires that α be a solution of the equation

$$J'_n(\sqrt{\alpha}b) Y'_n(\sqrt{\alpha}a) - J'_n(\sqrt{\alpha}a) Y'_n(\sqrt{\alpha}b) = 0$$

We let

$$U_{mn}(r) = \frac{J_n(\sqrt{\alpha_{nm}}r) Y'_n(\sqrt{\alpha_{nm}}a) - Y_n(\sqrt{\alpha_{nm}}r) J'_n(\sqrt{\alpha_{nm}}a)}{Y'_n(\sqrt{\alpha_{nm}}a)}$$

where α_{nm} is the mth solution of the above equation corresponding to the subscript n. Our formal solution is then

$$\phi(r,\theta,z,t) = 100 \frac{z}{h}$$

$$+ \sum_{n=0}^{\infty} \sum_{m=1}^{\infty} \sum_{k=1}^{\infty} (a_{kmn} \cos n\theta + b_{kmn} \sin n\theta) \sin \frac{k\pi z}{h} U_{mn}(r) e^{-c^2 \lambda_{kmn} t}$$

where

$$\lambda_{kmn} = \frac{k^2\pi^2}{h^2} + \alpha_{nm}$$

To satisfy the initial condition we must have

$$f(r,\theta,z) - 100 \frac{z}{h} = \sum_{n=0}^{\infty} \sum_{m=1}^{\infty} \sum_{k=1}^{\infty} (a_{kmn} \cos n\theta + b_{kmn} \sin n\theta) \sin \frac{k\pi z}{h} U_{mn}(r)$$

The functions

$$\psi_{kmn}^{(1)} = \cos n\theta \sin (k\pi z/h) U_{mn}(r)$$

and

$$\psi_{kmn}^{(2)} = \sin n\theta \sin (k\pi z/h) U_{nm}(r)$$

form a complete orthogonal set. If $f(r,\theta,z)$ has continuous second partial derivatives, the series converges uniformly to the required function.

The steady-state solution of the heat-transfer problem just treated satisfies Laplace's equation. The solution in this case was particularly simple. To illustrate further the separation-of-variables technique, let us consider the following boundary value: $\nabla^2\psi = 0$ on the interior of the sphere $r = b$, i.e., in spherical coordinates,

$$\frac{\partial^2 \psi}{\partial r^2} + \frac{2}{r} \frac{\partial \psi}{\partial r} + \frac{1}{r^2} \frac{\partial^2 \psi}{\partial \theta^2} + \frac{\cot \theta}{r^2} \frac{\partial \psi}{\partial \theta} + \frac{1}{r^2 \sin^2 \theta} \frac{\partial^2 \psi}{\partial \phi^2} = 0$$

for $0 \leq r < b$, $0 \leq \theta \leq \pi$, $0 \leq \phi \leq 2\pi$, with $\psi(b,\theta,\phi) = f(\theta,\phi)$ prescribed. ψ may be regarded as the temperature in a steady-state heat-transfer problem, an electrostatic potential, the velocity potential in a homogeneous, incompressible, irrotational, nonviscous fluid, etc.

Let us assume that $\psi(r,\theta,\phi) = U(r)S(\theta,\phi)$. Then

$$\frac{r^2}{U}\frac{d^2U}{dr^2} + \frac{2r}{U}\frac{dU}{dr} = -\left(\frac{1}{S}\frac{\partial^2 S}{\partial\theta^2} + \frac{\cot\theta}{S}\frac{\partial S}{\partial\theta} + \frac{1}{S\sin^2\theta}\frac{\partial^2 S}{\partial\phi^2}\right) = n(n+1)$$

Hence,

$$r^2\frac{d^2U}{dr^2} + 2r\frac{dU}{dr} - n(n+1)U = 0$$

$$\sin^2\theta\frac{\partial^2 S}{\partial\theta^2} + \cos\theta\sin\theta\frac{\partial S}{\partial\theta} + \frac{\partial^2 S}{\partial\phi^2} + n(n+1)S = 0$$

Therefore, S is a spherical harmonic:

$$S = (A\cos m\phi + B\sin m\phi)P_n^m(\cos\theta)$$

The general solution for U is

$$U(r) = c_1 r^n + c_2 r^{-n-1}$$

However, our solution must be finite at $r = 0$, and we must therefore take $c_2 = 0$. Our formal series solution is then

$$\psi(r,\theta,\phi) = \sum_{n=0}^{\infty}\sum_{m=0}^{n}(A_{mn}\cos m\phi + B_{mn}\sin m\phi)P_n^m(\cos\theta)r^n$$

To satisfy the boundary condition, we must have

$$f(\theta,\phi) = \sum_{n=0}^{\infty}\sum_{m=0}^{n}(A_{mn}\cos m\phi + B_{mn}\sin m\phi)P_n^m(\cos\theta)b^n$$

The coefficients must therefore be

$$A_{on} = \frac{(2n+1)b^{-n}}{4\pi}\int_0^{2\pi}\int_0^{\pi}P_n(\cos\theta)f(\theta,\phi)\sin\theta\,d\theta\,d\phi$$

$$A_{mn} = \frac{(2n+1)(n-m)!\,b^{-n}}{2(n+m)!\,\pi}\int_0^{2\pi}\int_0^{\pi}P_n^m(\cos\theta)\cos m\phi\,f(\theta,\phi)\sin\theta\,d\theta\,d\phi$$

$$B_{mn} = \frac{(2n+1)(n-m)!\,b^{-n}}{2(n+m)!\,\pi}\int_0^{2\pi}\int_0^{\pi}P_n^m(\cos\theta)\sin m\phi\,f(\theta,\phi)\sin\theta\,d\theta\,d\phi$$

In the process of solving this problem we have obtained an expansion for a harmonic function which is finite at $r = 0$ and takes on prescribed values at $r = b$. In some situations which we shall meet in Chap. 4, we shall need expansions of functions not finite at $r = 0$ but decreasing to zero as r approaches infinity. In this case we shall obtain expansions using spherical harmonics and negative powers of r.

Finally, let us consider a problem in quantum mechanics. The hydrogen atom is pictured in terms of a single negatively charged electron orbiting around the positively charged nucleus. With the center of the nucleus as the origin of coordinates, the coulomb potential of the central force field in which the electron is moving is a function of radial distance r only. The steady-state Schödringer equation is then

$$\nabla^2 \psi + \frac{2m}{\hbar^2} [E - V(r)]\psi = 0$$

where $\psi(r,\theta,\phi)$ is the wave function for the electron.[1] Again using separation of variables, we assume a solution of the form $\psi(r,\theta,\phi) = U(r)S(\theta,\phi)$ in spherical coordinates and obtain

$$\frac{r^2}{U}\frac{d^2U}{dr^2} + \frac{2r}{U}\frac{dU}{dr} + \frac{2mr^2}{\hbar^2}[E - V(r)] = -\left[\frac{1}{S}\left(\frac{\partial^2 S}{\partial\theta^2} + \cot\theta\,\frac{\partial S}{\partial\theta} + \frac{1}{\sin^2\theta}\frac{\partial^2 S}{\partial\phi^2}\right)\right]$$

The separation constant must be of the form $n(n + 1)$ with $n = 0, 1, 2, \ldots$ to ensure finite solutions at $\theta = 0$ and π. The separated equations are then

$$r^2\frac{d^2U}{dr^2} + 2r\frac{dU}{dr} + \frac{2mr^2}{\hbar^2}[E - V(r)]U - n(n + 1)U = 0$$

$$\frac{\partial^2 S}{\partial\theta^2} + \cot\theta\,\frac{\partial S}{\partial\theta} + \frac{1}{\sin^2\theta}\frac{\partial^2 S}{\partial\phi^2} + n(n + 1)S = 0$$

Solution of the first equation subject to appropriate boundary conditions leads to a determination of the allowable quantum energy values E. The solution to the second equation leads to solutions in terms of spherical harmonics

$$S_{mn}(\theta,\phi) = A_{mn}\cos m\phi P_n^m(\cos\theta) + B_{mn}\sin m\phi P_n^m(\cos\theta)$$

with $m = 0, 1, 2, 3, \ldots, n$. The constants m and n are quantum numbers in the following sense. The allowable values of the z component of angular momentum are $\pm\hbar m$, and the allowable values of orbital angular momentum[2] are $\hbar\sqrt{n(n + 1)}$. Thus the eigenvalue problem is suggested in the very name of the subject of quantum mechanics.

We have tried to indicate that the method of separation of variables has wide application to the solution of boundary-value problems. There are other methods, such as the method of conformal mapping for two-dimensional problems in potential theory and finite difference equation methods, which we shall not develop here. In the next chapter, we shall develop methods based on the construction of Green's functions. In Chap. 5 we shall relate the

---

[1] Actually, the same equation holds in any central force field problem.
[2] This does not take into account the spin of the electron.

problem to the solution of integral equations, and in Chap. 6 we shall look at the problem again in terms of integral transform methods.

Exercises 3.4

1. Solve the following problem in the theory of heat conduction:

$$\frac{\partial^2 \phi}{\partial x^2} = \frac{1}{a^2} \frac{\partial \phi}{\partial t} \qquad 0 < x < L \qquad t > 0$$

$$\phi(0,t) = 0 \qquad \phi(L,t) = 100$$

$$\phi(x,0) = f(x)$$

2. Find the steady-state temperature in an infinitely long heat-conducting slab, $0 \leq x < \infty$, $0 \leq y \leq a$, which is insulated on the top and bottom faces so that the flow of heat is two-dimensional. The faces at $y = 0$ and $y = a$ are kept at temperature zero, while the face at $x = 0$ is heated so that the temperature is $100y(a - y)$.

3. Find the equilibrium displacement of a circular membrane of radius a when the boundary $r = a$ is displaced according to the prescription $\psi(a,\theta) = g(\theta)$. Find a series solution and show that it can be put in the closed form

$$\psi(r,\theta) = \frac{1}{2\pi} \int_0^{2\pi} \frac{(a^2 - r^2)g(\phi)}{a^2 + r^2 - 2ar \cos(\theta - \phi)} \, d\phi$$

HINT:
$$\sum_{n=0}^{\infty} \frac{2r^n}{a^n} \cos n(\theta - \phi) - 1 = \mathrm{Re}\left[\frac{\zeta + z}{\zeta - z}\right]$$

when $|z| < |\zeta|$ and $z = re^{i\theta}$, $\zeta = ae^{i\phi}$.

4. Find the natural frequencies and normal modes of vibration of a clamped membrane in the shape of a 60° sector of a circle of radius b.

References

Churchill, Ruel V.: "Fourier Series and Boundary Value Problems," McGraw-Hill Book Company, Inc., New York, 1941.

Copson, Edward T.: "Theory of Functions of a Complex Variable," Oxford University Press, New York, 1935.

Courant, Richard, and David Hilbert: "Methods of Mathematical Physics," Interscience Publishers, Inc., New York, 1953, vol. I.

Murnaghan, Francis D.: "Introduction to Applied Mathematics," John Wiley & Sons, Inc., New York, 1948.

Page, Chester H.: "Physical Mathematics," D. Van Nostrand Company, Inc., Princeton, N.J., 1955.

Sneddon, Ian N.: "Elements of Partial Differential Equations," McGraw-Hill Book Company, Inc., New York, 1957.

Chapter 4. Boundary-value Problems.
Green's Functions

4.1 Nonhomogeneous Boundary-value Problems

Up to now we have been concerned mainly with solving the homogeneous partial differential equation

$$\nabla^2 \phi = a\phi + b\frac{\partial \phi}{\partial t} + c\frac{\partial^2 \phi}{\partial t^2}$$

in a bounded three-dimensional region V, where a, b, and c are constants, subject to one of the three homogeneous boundary conditions

$$\phi = 0$$

$$\frac{d\phi}{dn} = 0$$

$$\frac{d\phi}{dn} + \alpha\phi = 0$$

on S, the boundary of V. If we specify the initial conditions

$$\phi(x,y,z,0) = g(x,y,z)$$

$$\left(\frac{\partial \phi}{\partial t}\right)_{t=0} = h(x,y,z)$$

the problem has a unique solution. Upon separating the variables, i.e., assuming $\phi = \psi(x,y,z)\,f(t)$, we find we have to solve the homogeneous partial differential equation

$$\nabla^2 \psi_i + \lambda_i \psi_i = 0$$

in V, subject to $\psi_i = 0$, or $\dfrac{d\psi_i}{dn} = 0$, or $\dfrac{d\psi_i}{dn} + \alpha\psi_i = 0$ on S, and the linear second-order ordinary differential equation

$$cf_i'' + bf_i' + (a + \lambda_i)f_i = 0$$

The latter equation has the solution

$$f_i = e^{-\gamma t}(A_i \cos \omega_i t + B_i \sin \omega_i t)$$

where $\gamma = b/2c$ and $\omega_i = (1/2c)\sqrt{|4c(a + \lambda_i) - b^2|}$.[1] The problem has a discrete spectrum of eigenvalues λ_i which increases without bound as $i \to \infty$, and a complete set of orthogonal eigenfunctions ψ_i, which we can assume are normalized as follows:

$$\iiint\limits_V \psi_i^2 \, dV = 1$$

The general solution is

$$\phi(x,y,z,t) = \sum_{i=1}^{\infty} f_i \psi_i$$

If the initial values g and h are sufficiently regular, g and h can be expanded in convergent series of the eigenfunctions, and the coefficients A_i and B_i are determined as follows:

$$g = \phi(x,y,z,0) = \sum_{i=1}^{\infty} A_i \psi_i$$

$$h = \dot{\phi}(x,y,z,0) = \sum_{i=1}^{\infty} (\omega_i B_i - \gamma A_i)\psi_i$$

where $\quad A_i = \iiint\limits_V g\psi_i \, dV \quad$ and $\quad B_i = \dfrac{1}{\omega_i}\left[\gamma A_i + \iiint\limits_V h\psi_i \, dV\right]$

The above problem becomes **nonhomogeneous** if the partial differential equation is nonhomogeneous or if the boundary condition is nonhomogeneous, or both. For example, in the membrane problem considered in Sec. 2.6, if we add a distributed force of density $f(x,y,t)$ per unit area, the partial differential equation satisfied by the displacement is

$$\nabla^2 \phi = \frac{\rho}{\sigma}\frac{\partial^2 \phi}{\partial t^2} - \frac{1}{\sigma}f(x,y,t)$$

If no external force is applied to the membrane, the partial differential equation remains homogeneous, but the problem may be nonhomogeneous if the boundary of the membrane is displaced in some prescribed way, i.e., $\phi = g(s,t)$ on the boundary curve, where s is a parameter which describes the boundary curve. Of course, one could also have both an applied external force and a

---

[1] If $4c(a + \lambda_i) - b^2 < 0$, sin and cos become sinh and cosh.

prescribed displacement of the boundary.   Then the boundary-value problem would become

$$\nabla^2\phi = \frac{\rho}{\sigma}\frac{\partial^2\phi}{\partial t^2} - \frac{1}{\sigma}f(x,y,t)$$

in R, with $\phi = g(s,t)$ on C.

One could enumerate countless other nonhomogeneous boundary-value problems, e.g., forced vibrations of an acoustic or electromagnetic cavity; forced vibrations of a string, an elastic rod, or a clamped plate; heat flow or diffusion problems with distributed sources or sources on the boundary; the transmission line with impressed voltages or currents; the Dirichlet, Neumann, or mixed boundary-value problems of potential theory; problems subject to Poisson's equation; etc.   As a rather general case, let us consider the following boundary-value problem:

$$\nabla^2\phi = a\phi + b\frac{\partial\phi}{\partial t} + c\frac{\partial^2\phi}{\partial t^2} - f(x,y,z,t)$$

to be satisfied in a region V, subject to

$$\frac{d\phi}{dn} + \alpha\phi = g(s,t)$$

on S, the boundary of V.   We note that we can split the problem up into three distinct problems and then combine the results to give us the desired solution. Let ϕ_0 be a solution of

$$\nabla^2\phi_0 = a\phi_0 + b\frac{\partial\phi_0}{\partial t} + c\frac{\partial^2\phi_0}{\partial t^2}$$

subject to $\dfrac{d\phi_0}{dn} + \alpha\phi_0 = 0$ on S, and let ϕ_1 be a solution of

$$\nabla^2\phi_1 = a\phi_1 + b\frac{\partial\phi_1}{\partial t} + c\frac{\partial^2\phi_1}{\partial t^2} - f(x,y,z,t)$$

subject to $\dfrac{d\phi_1}{dn} + \alpha\phi_1 = 0$ on S, and let ϕ_2 be a solution of

$$\nabla^2\phi_2 = a\phi_2 + b\frac{\partial\phi_2}{\partial t} + c\frac{\partial^2\phi_2}{\partial t^2}$$

subject to $\dfrac{d\phi_2}{dn} + \alpha\phi_2 = g(s,t)$ on S.   Then $\phi = \phi_0 + \phi_1 + \phi_2$ satisfies

$$\nabla^2\phi = a\phi + b\frac{\partial\phi}{\partial t} + c\frac{\partial^2\phi}{\partial t^2} - f(x,y,z,t)$$

subject to $\dfrac{d\phi}{dn} + \alpha\phi = g(s,t)$ on S.   The problem therefore reduces to solving a homogeneous problem and two nonhomogeneous problems, one of which has a nonhomogeneous differential equation and a homogeneous boundary condition, while the other has a homogeneous differential equation and a non-homogeneous boundary condition.

Let us first consider the problem defining ϕ_1. Suppose

$$f(x,y,z,t) = u(x,y,z)v(t)$$

In this case, the differential equation is separable, provided

$$\frac{av + b\dot{v} + c\ddot{v}}{v} = -\lambda$$

where λ is a known constant. We assume that $\phi_1 = \psi_1 v$. Then

$$\frac{\nabla^2 \psi_1}{\psi_1} + \frac{u}{\psi_1} = \frac{av + b\dot{v} + c\ddot{v}}{v} = -\lambda$$

and the problem is reduced to the solution of the nonhomogeneous boundary-value problem

$$\nabla^2 \psi_1 + \lambda \psi_1 = -u \qquad \text{in } V$$

$$\frac{d\psi_1}{dn} + \alpha \psi_1 = 0 \qquad \text{on } S$$

One of the important cases where this situation exists is when $a = b = 0$ and we have a sinusoidal forcing function. Even if the forcing function is only periodic, we may still be able to separate the equation with the help of Fourier series.[1]   In this case, $f(x,y,z;t) = u \sum_{i=0}^{\infty} c_i v_i$, where $c\ddot{v}_i = -\lambda_i v_i$ (no summation). In this case we seek a solution of the form $\phi_1 = \sum_{i=0}^{\infty} c_i \psi_i v_i$. Substituting in the differential equation, we have

$$\sum_{i=0}^{\infty} c_i \nabla^2 \psi_i v_i = \sum_{i=0}^{\infty} c c_i \psi_i \ddot{v}_i - \sum_{i=0}^{\infty} u c_i v_i$$

or

$$\sum_{i=0}^{\infty} c_i [\nabla^2 \psi_i + \lambda_i \psi_i + u] v_i = 0$$

We are thus led again to the nonhomogeneous problem

$$\nabla^2 \psi_i + \lambda_i \psi_i = -u \qquad \text{in } V$$

$$\frac{d\psi_i}{dn} + \alpha \psi_i = 0 \qquad \text{on } S$$

----

[1] If neither case holds, we may be able to resort to integral transform methods which will be discussed in Chap. 6.

For the problem with the nonhomogeneous boundary condition defining ϕ_2 we have similar considerations. Suppose $g(s,t) = u(s)v(t)$; then we seek a solution of the form $\phi_2 = \psi_2 v$. The differential equation becomes

$$\frac{\nabla^2 \psi_2}{\psi_2} = \frac{av + b\dot{v} + c\ddot{v}}{v} = -\lambda$$

and we have to solve $\nabla^2 \psi_2 + \lambda \psi_2 = 0$. The boundary condition becomes

$$v(t)\left(\frac{d\psi_2}{dn} + \alpha \psi_2\right) = u(s)v(t)$$

to be satisfied for all t. This implies that $\dfrac{d\psi_2}{dn} + \alpha \psi_2 = u(s)$. This will be possible, in particular, when we have a sinusoidal displacement of the boundary and $a = b = 0$. If g is periodic, we shall expand it in a Fourier series and seek a solution of the form

$$\phi_2 = \sum_{i=0}^{\infty} c_i \psi_i v_i$$

where $c\ddot{v}_i = -\lambda_i v_i$ (no summation). We shall then be led to the boundary-value problem

$$\nabla^2 \psi_i + \lambda_i \psi_i = 0$$

$$\frac{d\psi_i}{dn} + \alpha \psi_i = u$$

The boundary-value problem with the nonhomogeneous boundary condition is an essential equivalent to the problem with the nonhomogeneous differential equation, for if there exists a twice differentiable function F defined in V and on S such that

$$\frac{dF}{dn} + \alpha F = u$$

then we let $H = \psi_2 - F$. We then have

$$\frac{dH}{dn} + \alpha H = 0 \qquad \text{on } S$$

$$\nabla^2 H + \lambda H = \nabla^2 \psi_2 + \lambda \psi_2 - \nabla^2 F - \lambda F$$

$$\nabla^2 H + \lambda H = -f \qquad \text{in } V$$

and H satisfies a homogeneous boundary condition and a nonhomogeneous differential equation.

The nonhomogeneous problem

$$\nabla^2 \psi + \lambda \psi = -f \qquad \text{in } V$$

$$\frac{d\psi}{dn} + \alpha\psi = 0 \qquad \text{on } S$$

may be solvable in terms of the eigenfunctions of the homogeneous problem

$$\nabla^2 \psi_i + \lambda_i \psi_i = 0 \qquad \text{in } V$$

$$\frac{d\psi_i}{dn} + \alpha\psi_i = 0 \qquad \text{on } S$$

The coefficients in a "best" approximation to ψ by a linear combination $c_i\psi_i$ in the least-mean-square sense are

$$c_i = \iiint_V \psi\psi_i \, dV$$

Let

$$\gamma_i = \iiint_V f\psi_i \, dV$$

then

$$\gamma_i = -\iiint_V (\nabla^2 \psi + \lambda\psi)\psi_i \, dV$$

$$= -\iiint_V \psi\nabla^2 \psi_i \, dV + \iint_S \left(\psi_i \frac{d\psi}{dn} - \psi \frac{d\psi_i}{dn} \right) dS - \lambda c_i$$

$$= (\lambda_i - \lambda)c_i$$

Thus $c_i = \gamma_i/(\lambda_i - \lambda)$, provided $\lambda \neq \lambda_i$ for any i. The case where $\lambda = \lambda_i$ for some i is referred to as **resonance**. There may still be a solution in the case of resonance. Suppose that $\lambda = \lambda_k$ but $\gamma_k = \iiint_V f\psi_k \, dV = 0$. Then c_k is arbitrary, and there are an infinite number of solutions. Note the similarities between this discussion and the solution of nonhomogeneous linear equations in Sec. 1.10 and the problem of forced vibrations in Sec. 1.11.

Exercises 4.1

1. Solve for the forced vibrations of a clamped circular membrane of radius 1, if there is a distributed force of density $a(1 - r) \sin \omega t$ (a and ω are known constants), and the initial conditions are $\phi(r,\theta,0) = g(r,\theta)$ and $\dot{\phi}(r,\theta,0) = 0$.

2. Consider the Dirichlet problem, i.e.,

$$\nabla^2 \phi = 0 \qquad \text{in } V$$

$$\phi = f(x,y,z) \qquad \text{on } S$$

Describe a procedure for obtaining a series solution of the problem in terms of the eigenfunctions of the problem

$$\nabla^2 \psi_i + \lambda_i \psi_i = 0 \qquad \text{in } V$$

$$\psi_i = 0 \qquad \text{on } S$$

3. Prove the uniqueness of the solution of the nonhomogeneous boundary-value problem

$$\nabla^2 \psi + \lambda \psi = -f$$

$$\frac{d\psi}{dn} + \alpha \psi = g$$

if $\lambda \neq \lambda_i$, an eigenvalue of the homogeneous problem.   HINT: Consider the difference of two possible different solutions.

4.2   One-dimensional Green's Functions

Another approach to the solution of nonhomogeneous boundary-value problems is by means of the construction of auxiliary functions known as **Green's functions.**   To illustrate this method, let us consider the solution of the following boundary-value problem, which arises in the study of forced vibrations of a string with fixed ends.

$$\frac{d^2\psi}{dx^2} + k^2\psi = -f(x) \qquad 0 \leq x \leq a$$

$$\psi(0) = \psi(a) = 0$$

We shall first solve the problem by the method of variation of parameters. We assume a solution of the form $\psi = A(x) \sin kx + B(x) \cos kx$.   Then

$$\psi' = A' \sin kx + B' \cos kx + kA \cos kx - kB \sin kx$$

We assume $A' \sin kx + B' \cos kx = 0$ and then differentiate again.

$$\psi'' = -k^2 A \sin kx - k^2 B \cos kx + kA' \cos kx - kB' \sin kx$$

Substituting in the differential equation, we have

$$kA' \cos kx - kB' \sin kx = -f(x)$$

Therefore, we have two linear equations in A' and B' with the solution

$$A' = -\frac{1}{k} f(x) \cos kx$$

$$B' = \frac{1}{k} f(x) \sin kx$$

The solution is then

$$\psi = -\frac{\sin kx}{k}\int_{c_1}^{x} f(y)\cos ky\, dy + \frac{\cos kx}{k}\int_{c_2}^{x} f(y)\sin ky\, dy$$

where c_1 and c_2 are constants to be determined by the boundary conditions.

$$\psi(0) = \frac{1}{k}\int_{c_2}^{0} f(y)\sin ky\, dy = 0$$

implies that $c_2 = 0$.

$$\psi(a) = -\frac{\sin ka}{k}\int_{c_1}^{a} f(y)\cos ky\, dy + \frac{\cos ka}{k}\int_{0}^{a} f(y)\sin ky\, dy$$

$$0 = -\frac{\sin ka}{k}\int_{c_1}^{0} f(y)\cos ky\, dy + \frac{1}{k}\int_{0}^{a} f(y)\sin k(y-a)\, dy$$

We can therefore write the solution

$$\psi(x) = \frac{1}{k}\int_{0}^{x} f(y)\sin k(y-x)\, dy - \frac{\sin kx}{k\sin ka}\int_{0}^{a} f(y)\sin k(y-a)\, dy$$

$$= \frac{1}{k}\int_{0}^{x} f(y)\left[\frac{\sin k(y-x)\sin ka - \sin kx \sin k(y-a)}{\sin ka}\right] dy$$

$$+ \frac{1}{k}\int_{x}^{a} f(y)\frac{\sin kx \sin k(a-y)}{\sin ka}\, dy$$

$$= \int_{0}^{x} f(y)\frac{\sin ky \sin k(a-x)}{k\sin ka}\, dy$$

$$+ \int_{x}^{a} f(y)\frac{\sin kx \sin k(a-y)}{k\sin ka}\, dy$$

$$= \int_{0}^{a} f(y)G(x;y)\, dy$$

where

$$G(x;y) = \frac{\sin ky \sin k(a-x)}{k\sin ka}\qquad 0 \le y \le x$$

$$G(x;y) = \frac{\sin kx \sin k(a-y)}{k\sin ka}\qquad x \le y \le a$$

This function is called a **Green's function.** We note that it exists for this problem unless $\sin ka = 0$. In this case k^2 would be an eigenvalue of the homogeneous problem. Thus the Green's function exists unless k^2 is an eigenvalue of the homogeneous problem.

We have reduced the solution of the nonhomogeneous boundary-value problem to a simple formula:

$$\psi(x) = \int_0^a f(y)G(x;y)\, dy$$

The advantage of this formulation of the problem is that the Green's function is independent of f, i.e., it depends only on the form of the differential equation, k, and the boundary conditions.   Therefore, the solutions to all possible such problems with different functions f are known, provided the integral $\int_0^a f(y)G(x;y)\, dy$ exists.

Let us now look at the properties of the above Green's function so that we may use these properties to construct Green's functions for other problems. These properties are:

1. The Green's function satisfies the homogeneous differential equation $G'' + k^2 G = 0$ in each of the intervals $0 \leq y < x$ and $x < y \leq a$, but not at $y = x$.   This can be easily seen, because in each of these intervals G can be written in the form $C_1 \sin ky + C_2 \cos ky$.   The point $y = x$ must be excluded because, as we shall see, the second derivative of G does not exist there.

2. The Green's function is continuous at $y = x$, since

$$\lim_{y \to x-} G(x;y) = \frac{\sin kx \sin k(a - x)}{k \sin ka}$$

$$\lim_{y \to x+} G(x;y) = \frac{\sin kx \sin k(a - x)}{k \sin ka}$$

3. The derivative of the Green's function is discontinuous at $y = x$.

$$G'(x;x-) = \lim_{y \to x-} G'(x;y) = \frac{\cos kx \sin k(a - x)}{\sin ka}$$

$$G'(x;x+) = \lim_{y \to x+} G'(x;y) = -\frac{\sin kx \cos k(a - x)}{\sin ka}$$

and $G'(x;x+) - G'(x;x-) = -1$.   Because the derivative is discontinuous, the second derivative does not exist.

4. The Green's function satisfies the boundary condition of the problem. $G(x;0) = G(x;a) = 0$.

5. The Green's function is symmetric in the two arguments.   If we interchange x and y in the above definition, we do not change the definition, i.e.,

$$G(x;y) = G(y;x)$$

Let us now try to reconstruct the above Green's function by seeking a function with these properties.   Starting with property 1, we want a function

$$G(x;y) = A \sin ky + B \cos ky \qquad 0 \le y < x$$

$$G(x;y) = C \sin ky + D \cos ky \qquad x < y \le a$$

By property 4,
$$G(x;0) = B = 0$$

$$G(x;a) = C \sin ka + D \cos ka = 0$$

By property 2,
$$A \sin kx = C \sin kx + D \cos kx$$

By property 3,
$$kC \cos kx - kD \sin kx - kA \cos kx = -1$$

Solving these equations simultaneously, we have

$$A = \frac{\sin k(a - x)}{k \sin ka}$$

$$B = 0$$

$$C = -\frac{1}{k} \frac{\sin kx \cos ka}{\sin ka}$$

$$D = \frac{1}{k} \frac{\sin kx \sin ka}{\sin ka}$$

so that
$$G(x;y) = \frac{\sin ky \sin k(a - x)}{k \sin ka} \qquad a \le y \le x$$

$$G(x;y) = \frac{\sin kx \sin k(a - y)}{k \sin ka} \qquad x \le y \le a$$

Assuming a Green's function with the above properties, we can arrive at the solution of the boundary-value problem directly from the differential equation.

$$\int_0^a f(y)G(x;y)\, dy = -\int_0^a (\psi'' + k^2\psi)G(x;y)\, dy$$

The last integral could be evaluated by integration by parts except for the fact that G'' does not exist at $y = x$.   Therefore, we shall write

$$\int_0^a (\psi'' + k^2\psi)G(x;y)\, dy = \lim_{\xi \to x-} \int_0^\xi (\psi'' + k^2\psi)G\, dy + \lim_{\eta \to x+} \int_\eta^a (\psi'' + k^2\psi)G\, dy$$

We can then integrate by parts twice in each interval, i.e.,

$$\int_0^\xi (\psi'' + k^2\psi)G\,dy = [G\psi' - G'\psi]_0^\xi + \int_0^\xi \psi(G'' + k^2G)\,dy$$

$$= G(x;\xi)\psi'(\xi) - G'(x;\xi)\psi(\xi)$$

$$\int_\eta^a (\psi'' + k^2\psi)G\,dy = [G\psi' - G'\psi]_\eta^a + \int_\eta^a \psi(G'' + k^2G)\,dy$$

$$= G'(x;\eta)\psi(\eta) - G(x;\eta)\psi'(\eta)$$

Then

$$\int_0^a f(y)G(x;y)\,dy = -\psi(x)[G'(x;x+) - G'(x;x-)]$$

$$+ \psi'(x)[G(x;x+) - G(x;x-)] = \psi(x)$$

where we have used properties 1 to 4. It is now clear how we would modify the properties to obtain the Green's function for the problem

$$\nabla^2\psi + k^2\psi = -f(x)$$

$$\psi'(0) = \psi'(a) = 0$$

In this case, $G(x;y)$ would satisfy properties 1 to 3, and property 4 would be changed to $G'(x;0) = G'(x;a) = 0$.

Now let us consider the "function" $G'' + k^2G$. It is zero for $0 \le y < x$ and zero for $x < y \le a$, and yet if we write

$$-\psi(x) = -\int_0^a f(y)G(x;y)\,dy = \int_0^a (\psi'' + k^2\psi)G\,dy$$

and then formally integrate by parts and use the boundary conditions, we have

$$-\psi(x) = \int_0^a (G'' + k^2G)\psi\,dy$$

We indicate the behavior of $G'' + k^2G$ by writing

$$G'' + k^2G = -\delta(y - x)$$

where $\delta(t)$ is the **Dirac delta function.** It is zero everywhere except at $t = 0$, where it is undefined, and yet

$$\int_{-\infty}^\infty f(t)\,\delta(t)\,dt = f(0)$$

for any continuous function $f(t)$. In particular, if $f(t) = 1$, then

$$\int_{-\infty}^\infty \delta(t)\,dt = 1$$

The delta function is not a function in the usual sense.   It can be thought of as the "limit" of the function

$$d(t) = \frac{1}{a} \qquad \frac{-a}{2} \leq t \leq \frac{a}{2}$$

$$d(t) = 0 \qquad \text{elsewhere}$$

as a approaches zero.   The delta function is an example of a generalized function or distribution.[1]

In terms of the equation

$$G'' + k^2 G = -\delta(y - x)$$

we have an interesting physical interpretation of the Green's function. According to this equation, the *Green's function gives the displacement due to a force of density δ applied at the point $y = x$*.   This density would be achieved as the limit of a total force of one unit applied to a region containing the point $y = x$ as the region shrinks to a point keeping the total force equal to one unit. We also have an interpretation of the formula

$$\psi(x) = \int_0^a f(y) G(x;y) \, dy$$

If $G(x;y)$ is the displacement at y due to a unit force at x, then by the symmetry $G(x;y) = G(y;x)$ it also represents the displacement at x due to a unit force at y.   Now if we multiply $G(x;y)$ by a "weighing factor" of density $f(y)$ and integrate over all possible points, we get the total displacement at x due to a distributed force of density $f(y)$.

This physical interpretation actually affords a means of computing a certain Green's function.   Consider, for example, the equilibrium displacement of a string with fixed ends under a distributed force of density $f(x)$.   The differential equation for the displacement is

$$\phi'' = -\frac{f(x)}{\sigma}$$

where σ is the tension in the string.   Then the Green's function satisfies the equation

$$G'' = -\delta(y - x) = -\frac{\sigma \, \delta(y - x)}{\sigma}$$

Thus G represents the displacement at y due to a force of strength σ at x.

In equilibrium we have

$$\sigma = \sigma \sin \alpha + \sigma \sin \beta$$

$$= \sigma \tan \alpha + \sigma \tan \beta$$

[1] See C. Saltzer, "The Theory of Distributions," vol. 5, "Advances in Mechanics," Academic Press, Inc., New York, 1958.

assuming small displacements.   Also, we have

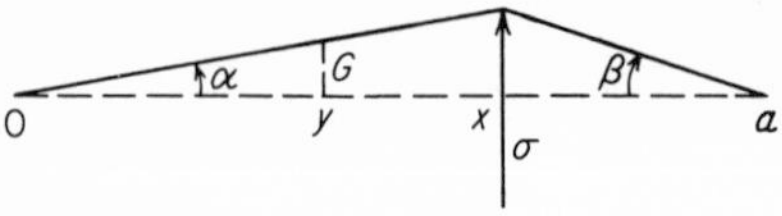

$$\tan \alpha = \frac{G}{y}$$

$$\tan \beta = \frac{x}{a - x} \tan \alpha$$

FIGURE 6

so that $\qquad\qquad G(x;y) = \dfrac{y(a - x)}{a} \qquad 0 \le y < x$

By symmetry $\qquad G(x;y) = \dfrac{x(a - y)}{a} \qquad x < y \le a$

Now let us consider the possibility of obtaining a Green's function for the nonhomogeneous Sturm-Liouville problem

$$(p\psi')' - q\psi + \lambda\rho\psi = -f(x) \qquad a \le x \le b$$

We seek a solution of the form

$$\psi(x) = \int_a^b f(y)G(x;y)\, dy$$

$$= -\int_a^b [(p\psi')' - q\psi + \lambda\rho\psi]G\, dy$$

$$= -\lim_{\xi \to x-} \int_a^\xi [(p\psi')' - q\psi + \lambda\rho\psi]G\, dy$$

$$\quad -\lim_{\eta \to x+} \int_\eta^b [(p\psi')' - q\psi + \lambda\rho\psi]G\, dy$$

Integrating by parts, we have

$$\int_a^\xi [(p\psi')' - q\psi + \lambda\rho\psi]G\, dy = [p(\psi'G - G'\psi)]_a^\xi + \int_a^\xi [(pG')' - qG + \lambda\rho G]\psi\, dy$$

$$\int_\eta^b [(p\psi')' - q\psi + \lambda\rho\psi]G\, dy = [p(\psi'G - G'\psi)]_\eta^b + \int_\eta^b [(pG')' - qG + \lambda\rho G]\,\psi\, dy$$

If we take as the first property of the Green's function that it satisfies the homogeneous equation

$$(pG')' - qG + \lambda\rho G = 0$$

in each of the intervals $a \le y < x$ and $x < y \le b$, then we can drop the integrals in each of the last two expressions.   Furthermore, if we take as another property that G satisfies the same boundary conditions as ψ at $y = a$ and $y = b$, i.e., one of the five homogeneous boundary conditions we considered for the homogeneous Sturm-Liouville problem, then $[p(\psi'G - G'\psi)]_a^b = 0$. Taking the limits as $\xi \to x-$ and $\eta \to x+$, we have

$$\psi(x) = -p(x)[G'(x;x+) - G'(x;x-)]\psi(x) + p(x)[G(x;x+) - G(x;x-)]\psi'(x)$$

This equation will be valid if G is continuous at $y = x$ and G' is discontinuous at $y = x$, with a discontinuity of

$$G'(x;x+) - G'(x;x-) = -\frac{1}{p(x)}$$

The four properties just described are sufficient to define the Green's function for the Sturm-Liouville problem, unless λ is an eigenvalue of the homogeneous problem. In this case, properties 1 to 3 determine the eigenfunction corresponding to the eigenvalue λ, which satisfies the homogeneous differential equation and the given boundary conditions and is continuous everywhere. But this solution has a continuous derivative, and therefore property 4 cannot be satisfied. A fifth property, namely, symmetry, i.e., $G(x;y) = G(y;x)$, can be proved from the other four. This proof will be left for the exercises. The symmetry results from the fact that the Sturm-Liouville operator is self-adjoint.

As an example, let us find the Green's function associated with the problem

$$(x\psi')' - \frac{n^2}{x}\psi + k^2 x\psi = -f(x) \qquad 0 \le x \le b$$

$$\psi(b) = 0$$

$$\psi(0) \text{ finite}$$

The Green's function should satisfy

$$(yG')' - \frac{n^2}{y}G + k^2 yG = 0$$

in the interval $0 \le y < x$, and be finite at $y = 0$. Hence,

$$G = AJ_n(ky) \qquad 0 \le y < x$$

In the interval $x < y \le b$, G should satisfy the same equation and $G(b) = 0$. Therefore,

$$G = BJ_n(ky) + CY_n(ky) \qquad x < y \le b$$

and

$$BJ_n(kb) + CY_n(kb) = 0$$

G is continuous at $y = x$, so that

$$AJ_n(kx) = BJ_n(kx) + CY_n(kx)$$

G' has a jump discontinuity equal to $-1/x$ at $y = x$, and therefore,

$$BJ'(kx) + CY'(kx) - AJ'(kx) = -\frac{1}{x}$$

Solving simultaneously for A, B, and C, we have

$$A = \frac{1}{x} \frac{J_n(kx)Y_n(kb) - J_n(kb)Y_n(kx)}{J_n(kb)[Y_n(kx)J'_n(kx) - J_n(kx)Y'_n(kx)]}$$

$$B = \frac{1}{x} \frac{J_n(kx)Y_n(kb)}{J_n(kb)[Y_n(kx)J'_n(kx) - J_n(kx)Y'_n(kx)]}$$

$$C = -\frac{1}{x} \frac{J_n(kx)}{Y_n(kx)J'_n(kx) - J_n(kx)Y'_n(kx)}$$

These expressions can be simplified somewhat by use of the Bessel differential equation. Since

$$J''_n + \frac{J'_n}{x} - \frac{n^2 J_n}{x^2} + k^2 J_n = 0$$

$$Y''_n + \frac{Y'_n}{x} - \frac{n^2 Y_n}{x^2} + k^2 Y_n = 0$$

we have $$x[J''_n Y_n - Y''_n J_n] + [J'_n Y_n - J_n Y'_n] = 0$$

or $$\frac{d}{dx}[x(J'_n Y_n - Y'_n J_n)] = 0$$

$$x(J'_n Y_n - Y'_n J_n) = K$$

where K can be evaluated by considering the limit of the expression as $x \to 0$.[1]
The Green's function is then

$$G(x;y) = \frac{J_n(ky)[J_n(kx)Y_n(kb) - Y_n(kx)J_n(kb)]}{KJ_n(kb)}$$

for $a \leq y \leq x$, and

$$G(x;y) = \frac{J_n(kx)[J_n(ky)Y_n(kb) - Y_n(ky)J_n(kb)]}{KJ_n(kb)}$$

for $x \leq y \leq b$, provided $J_n(kb) \neq 0$, i.e., provided k^2 is not an eigenvalue of the homogeneous equation.

We have seen that we get into difficulty when trying to determine the Green's function by the above procedure, if the constant λ in the nonhomogeneous Sturm-Liouville equation is an eigenvalue of the homogeneous problem. It is possible nevertheless to obtain a **generalized Green's function** for the nonhomogeneous problem if the function $f(x)$ on the right-hand side of the equation is orthogonal to the eigenfunction corresponding to the eigenvalue λ, i.e.,

$$(pu')' - qu + \lambda \rho u = 0$$

$$\int_a^b fu\, dx = 0$$

[1] $K = -2/\pi$.

We wish to solve, as before,

$$(p\psi')' - q\psi + \lambda\rho\psi = -f(x)$$

First, we note that $\int_a^b uf\,dx = 0$ is a necessary condition for a solution of the nonhomogeneous problem, for if there exists a solution,

$$\int_a^b uf\,dx = -\int_a^b u[L(\psi) + \lambda\rho\psi]\,dx$$

$$= -\int_a^b \psi[L(u) + \lambda\rho u]\,dx$$

$$= 0$$

Next we observe that, without loss of generality, we can seek a solution of the nonhomogeneous problem which is orthogonal to the solution of the homogeneous problem. This follows since for any solution ψ

$$L(\psi - cu) + \lambda\rho(\psi - cu) = L(\psi) + \lambda\rho\psi - c[L(u) + \lambda\rho u]$$

$$= -f$$

where c is arbitrary. Hence c may be chosen so that

$$\int_a^b \rho(\psi - cu)u\,dx = 0$$

i.e.,

$$c = \int_a^b \rho\psi u\,dx$$

assuming that u has been normalized. We also observe that if there exists a solution of the nonhomogeneous problem, there are actually infinitely many solutions, since any multiple of the solution of the nonhomogeneous problem may be added to the known solution.

In the present case, we seek a Green's function which satisfies

$$L(G) + \lambda\rho G - A\rho u = -\delta(x - y)$$

Then

$$\int_a^b f(y)G(x;y)\,dy = -\int_a^b G[L(\psi) + \lambda\rho\psi]\,dy$$

$$= -\int_a^b \psi[L(G) + \lambda\rho G]\,dy$$

$$= \int_a^b [\delta(x - y)\psi(y) - A\rho u(y)\psi(y)]\,dy$$

$$= \psi(x)$$

The constant A may be determined as follows:

$$A \int_a^b \rho u^2(y) \, dy = \int_a^b \delta(x - y) u(y) \, dy + \int_a^b u[L(G) + \lambda \rho G] \, dy$$

$$A = u(x) + \int_a^b G[L(u) + \lambda \rho u] \, dy$$

$$= u(x)$$

As an example, let us consider the problem

$$\psi'' + \psi = -f(x) \qquad 0 \le x \le \pi$$

$$\psi(0) = \psi(\pi) = 0$$

We see that $u'' + u = 0$, $u(0) = u(\pi) = 0$, has the normalized solution $u = \sqrt{2/\pi} \sin x$. Therefore, we seek a Green's function as a solution of

$$G'' + G = -\delta(x - y) + \frac{2}{\pi} \sin x \sin y$$

Hence, $G = A \cos y + B \sin y - \dfrac{1}{\pi} y \sin x \cos y \qquad 0 \le y < x$

$$G = C \cos y + D \sin y - \frac{1}{\pi} y \sin x \cos y \qquad x < y \le \pi$$

The boundary conditions imply that

$$G(0) = A = 0$$

$$G(\pi) = -C + \sin x = 0$$

Continuity at $y = x$ implies

$$B \sin x = \sin x \cos x + D \sin x$$

The Green's function must have a jump discontinuity of -1 at $y = x$; thus

$$-\sin^2 x + D \cos x - B \cos x = -1$$

The last two equations are satisfied if

$$B - D = \cos x$$

To have symmetry we choose

$$B = \cos x - \frac{x}{\pi} \cos x$$

$$D = -\frac{x}{\pi} \cos x$$

The appropriate Green's function is then

$$G = \cos x \sin y - \frac{x}{\pi} \cos x \sin y - \frac{y}{\pi} \sin x \cos y \qquad 0 \le y < x$$

$$G = \sin x \cos y - \frac{y}{\pi} \sin x \cos y - \frac{x}{\pi} \cos x \sin y \qquad x < y \le \pi$$

and the general solution of the problem is

$$\psi(x) = c \sin x + \int_a^b f(y)G(x;y)\, dy$$

In summary, we have the following: The nonhomogeneous Sturm-Liouville equation

$$(p\psi')' - q\psi + \lambda\rho\psi = -f(x) \qquad a \le x \le b$$

with appropriate homogeneous boundary conditions has a unique solution if λ is not an eigenvalue of the corresponding homogeneous problem. If λ is an eigenvalue of the homogeneous problem with solution u, the nonhomogeneous problem will have a solution if and only if $\int_a^b uf\, dx = 0$, in which case there are infinitely many solutions.

Exercises 4.2

1. Find the Green's function associated with the boundary-value problem $\psi'' + k^2\psi = -f(x)$, $0 \le x \le a$, $\psi'(0) = \psi'(a) = 0$.

2. Prove that the Green's function for the Sturm-Liouville problem is symmetric.

3. Find the Green's function associated with the boundary-value problem $(x\psi')' - (n^2/x)\psi = -f(x)$, $0 \le x \le 1$, $\psi(0)$ finite, $\psi(1) = 0$.

4. Find a generalized Green's function associated with the boundary-value problem

$$\psi'' + \psi = -f(x) \qquad 0 \le x \le \pi \qquad \psi'(0) = \psi'(\pi) = 0$$

if $\int_0^\pi f(x) \cos x\, dx = 0$. Show that the first method outlined in this section fails to yield a Green's function.

4.3　Green's Functions in Higher Dimensions

The use of Green's functions to solve boundary-value problems is not restricted to one-dimensional problems. Consider, for example, the two-dimensional boundary-value problem

$$\nabla^2\psi + \lambda\psi = -f(x,y) \qquad \text{in } R$$

subject to $\psi = 0$, or

$$\frac{d\psi}{dn} = 0 \qquad \text{or} \qquad \frac{d\psi}{dn} + \alpha\psi = 0 \qquad \text{on } C$$

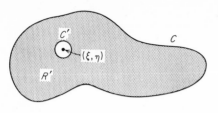

FIGURE 7

the boundary of R. We start by considering the following integral:

$$\iint\limits_{R} f(x,y)G(\xi,\eta\,;x,y)\,dx\,dy =$$

$$-\iint\limits_{R}(\nabla^2\psi + \lambda\psi)G\,dx\,dy$$

when G is the Green's function whose properties we wish to determine. We suspect, by analogy with the one-dimensional case, that the Green's function is not well-behaved at $x = \xi$, $y = \eta$. Therefore, we exclude this point from the region by deleting the interior of a small circle $(x - \xi)^2 + (y - \eta)^2 = \rho^2$, with radius ρ and center (ξ,η). We then treat the integral as an improper integral, i.e.,

$$\iint\limits_{R}(\nabla^2\psi + \lambda\psi)G\,dx\,dy = \lim_{\rho\to 0}\iint\limits_{R'}(\nabla^2\psi + \lambda\psi)G\,dx\,dy$$

where R' is the region between C and C'.

Using Green's theorem, we have

$$\iint\limits_{R'}(\nabla^2\psi + \lambda\psi)G\,dx\,dy = \iint\limits_{R'}(\nabla^2G + \lambda G)\psi\,dx\,dy$$

$$+ \int_{C}\left(G\frac{d\psi}{dn} - \psi\frac{dG}{dn}\right)ds$$

$$- \int_{C'}\left(G\frac{\partial\psi}{\partial r} - \psi\frac{\partial G}{\partial r}\right)ds$$

where $r = \sqrt{(x - \xi)^2 + (y - \eta)^2}$. On C', $ds = \rho\,d\theta$, where

$$\theta = \tan^{-1}\left[(y - \eta)/(x - \xi)\right]$$

and θ varies from 0 to 2π. Let us now assume that $\nabla^2G + \lambda G = 0$ in R, except at $x = \xi$, $y = \eta$. Then $\iint\limits_{R'}(\nabla^2G + \lambda G)\psi\,dx\,dy = 0$. If we also assume that G satisfies the same boundary condition on C as does ψ, then $\int_{C}\left(G\dfrac{d\psi}{dn} - \psi\dfrac{dG}{dn}\right)ds = 0$. Therefore,

$$\iint\limits_{R}f(x,y)G(\xi,\eta\,;x,y) = \lim_{\rho\to 0}\rho\int_{0}^{2\pi}\left(G\frac{\partial\psi}{\partial r} - \psi\frac{\partial G}{\partial r}\right)_{r=\rho}d\theta$$

This will yield the value $\psi(\xi,\eta)$ if G behaves in such a way that $\lim\limits_{\rho\to 0}\rho\left(\dfrac{\partial G}{\partial r}\right)_{r=\rho}$

is not zero and yet is finite, while $\lim\limits_{\rho \to 0} \rho G = 0$. This suggests that G should behave as $k \log r$ as $r \to 0$. Therefore, we take

$$G(\xi,\eta;x,y) = -\frac{1}{2\pi} \log r + H(\xi,\eta;x,y)$$

where H and its first and second partial derivatives with respect to x and y are continuous in R. H will have to be determined so that $\nabla^2 G + \lambda G = 0$ except at (ξ,η) and G satisfies the same boundary condition on C as ψ.

The same problem can be treated in three-dimensions, where this time we exclude the point (ξ,η,ζ) by deleting the interior of a small sphere with radius ρ and center (ξ,η,ζ). Then

$$\iiint\limits_{V} f(x,y,z) G(\xi,\eta,\zeta;x,y,z) \, dx \, dy \, dz = \psi(\xi,\eta,\zeta)$$

$$= -\iiint\limits_{V} (\nabla^2 \psi + \lambda \psi) G \, dx \, dy \, dz$$

$$= -\lim_{\rho \to 0} \iiint\limits_{V'} (\nabla^2 \psi + \lambda \psi) G \, dx \, dy \, dz$$

$$= -\lim_{\rho \to 0} \iiint\limits_{V'} (\nabla^2 G + \lambda G) \psi \, dx \, dy \, dz$$

$$+ \iint\limits_{S} \left(\psi \frac{dG}{dn} - G \frac{d\psi}{dn} \right) dS$$

$$+ \lim_{\rho \to 0} \rho^2 \int_0^\pi \int_0^{2\pi} \left(G \frac{\partial \psi}{\partial r} - \psi \frac{\partial G}{\partial r} \right)_{r=\rho} \sin \theta \, d\theta \, d\phi$$

We wish $\lim\limits_{\rho \to 0} \rho^2 \left(\dfrac{\partial G}{\partial r} \right)_{r=\rho}$ to be nonzero and finite and $\lim\limits_{\rho \to 0} \rho^2 G = 0$. This suggests a behavior like kr^{-1} as $r \to 0$. Therefore, we take

$$G(\xi,\eta,\zeta;x,y,z) = \frac{1}{4\pi r} + H(\xi,\eta,\zeta;x,y,z)$$

where H and its first and second partial derivatives are continuous in V. H is determined so that $\nabla^2 G + \lambda G = 0$ in V except at (ξ,η,ζ) and G satisfies the same boundary conditions as ψ on S.

In each of the above cases, the function H is unique, provided λ is not an eigenvalue of the homogeneous problem. Assume that there are two Green's functions in the three-dimensional case.[1]

$$G_1 = \frac{1}{4\pi r} + H_1$$

$$G_2 = \frac{1}{4\pi r} + H_2$$

Let $w = G_1 - G_2 = H_1 - H_2$. Then

$$\nabla^2 w + \lambda w = 0$$

except possibly at (ξ,η,ζ). Actually, this equation is satisfied also at (ξ,η,ζ), since w is continuous and has continuous second partial derivatives in V. Furthermore, w satisfies the boundary conditions of the homogeneous boundary-value problem. Therefore, w is a continuous function with continuous first and second partial derivatives, which is a solution of the homogeneous boundary-value problem. But the homogeneous boundary-value problem has no nontrivial solutions except for a certain set of eigenvalues of which λ is not a member. Therefore, $w \equiv 0$, which implies that $H_1 \equiv H_2$.

Now let us see how we would use Green's functions to solve other types of boundary-value problems. Consider the **Dirichlet problem,** i.e., to find a function ψ with continuous second partial derivatives in a two-dimensional region R of the xy plane which satisfies Laplace's equation in R and takes on prescribed boundary values f on C, the boundary of R. Let $F(x,y)$ be a function with continuous second partial derivatives in R which takes on the values f on C; then

$$g = \psi - F = 0$$

on C. In R,

$$\nabla^2 g = \nabla^2 \psi - \nabla^2 F = -\nabla^2 F$$

Now if we let $G(\xi,\eta;x,y) = -\dfrac{1}{2\pi} \log \sqrt{(x-\xi)^2 + (y-\eta)^2} + H(\xi,\eta;x,y)$

with $\nabla^2 H = 0$ in R and $G = 0$ on C, then[2]

$$g(\xi,\eta) = \iint\limits_{R} G\nabla^2 F \, dx \, dy$$

$$\psi(\xi,\eta) - F(\xi,\eta) = \iint\limits_{R} F\nabla^2 G \, dx \, dy + \int_C \left(G\frac{dF}{dn} - F\frac{dG}{dn} \right) ds$$

$$= -\iint\limits_{R} F \, \delta(x-\xi) \, \delta(y-\eta) \, dx \, dy - \int_C f\frac{dG}{dn} \, ds$$

$$= -F(\xi,\eta) - \int_C f\frac{dG}{dn} \, ds$$

---

[1] The other case is quite similar.

[2] The delta function is used here to indicate the argument only. It can be made rigorous by the use of limits as in the above treatment of two-dimensional Green's functions.

Therefore,

$$\psi(\xi,\eta) = -\int_C f \frac{dG}{dn}\, ds$$

Suppose that R is the interior of a unit circle with center at the origin. Let the point (ξ,η) be an interior point. Then the point $\left(\dfrac{\xi}{\xi^2 + \eta^2}, \dfrac{\eta}{\xi^2 + \eta^2}\right)$ is an exterior point.

The locus of points the ratio of whose distances from these two points is $\sqrt{\xi^2 + \eta^2}$ is the unit circle. This is easily verified. Let $\rho = \sqrt{\xi^2 + \eta^2}$; then if (x,y) is on the locus,

$$(x - \xi)^2 + (y - \eta)^2 = \rho^2\left[\left(x - \frac{\xi}{\rho^2}\right)^2 + \left(y - \frac{\eta}{\rho^2}\right)^2\right]$$

$$\rho^2(x^2 + y^2 - 2x\xi - 2y\eta + \rho^2) = \rho^4(x^2 + y^2) - 2\rho^2 x\xi - 2\rho^2 y\eta + \rho^2$$

$$(x^2 + y^2)(1 - \rho^2) = 1 - \rho^2$$

$$x^2 + y^2 = 1$$

We take

$$G(\xi,\eta;x,y) = -\frac{1}{2\pi} \log \sqrt{(x - \xi)^2 + (y - \eta)^2}$$

$$+ \frac{1}{2\pi} \log \sqrt{\left(x - \frac{\xi}{\rho^2}\right)^2 + \left(y - \frac{\eta}{\rho^2}\right)^2} + \frac{1}{2\pi} \log \sqrt{\xi^2 + \eta^2}$$

This has the desired properties, for

$$H = \frac{1}{2\pi} \log \sqrt{\left(x - \frac{\xi}{\rho^2}\right)^2 + \left(y - \frac{\eta}{\rho^2}\right)^2} + \frac{1}{2\pi} \log \sqrt{\xi^2 + \eta^2}$$

is harmonic inside the unit circle, and when $x^2 + y^2 = 1$,

$$\log \sqrt{(x - \xi)^2 + (y - \eta)^2} - \log \sqrt{\left(x - \frac{\xi}{\rho^2}\right)^2 + \left(y - \frac{\eta}{\rho^2}\right)^2} = \log \sqrt{\xi^2 + \eta^2}$$

On the unit circle $ds = d\theta$ and $\dfrac{dG}{dn} = \dfrac{\partial G}{\partial r}$, where $r = \sqrt{x^2 + y^2}$. Let $x = r \cos\theta,\ y = r \sin\theta,\ \xi = \rho \cos\phi,\ \eta = \rho \sin\phi$; then

$$\frac{\partial G}{\partial r} = -\frac{1}{2\pi} \frac{(r\cos\theta - \rho\cos\phi)\cos\theta + (r\sin\theta - \rho\sin\phi)\sin\theta}{(r\cos\theta - \rho\cos\phi)^2 + (r\sin\theta - \rho\sin\phi)^2}$$

$$+ \frac{1}{2\pi} \frac{(r\cos\theta - \cos\phi/\rho)\cos\theta + (r\sin\theta - \sin\phi/\rho)\sin\theta}{(r\cos\theta - \cos\phi/\rho)^2 + (r\sin\theta - \sin\phi/\rho)^2}$$

$$\left(\frac{\partial G}{\partial r}\right)_{r=1} = -\frac{1}{2\pi} \frac{1 - \rho\cos(\theta - \phi)}{1 + \rho^2 - 2\rho\cos(\theta - \phi)} + \frac{1}{2\pi} \frac{\rho^2 - \rho\cos(\theta - \phi)}{1 + \rho^2 - 2\rho\cos(\theta - \phi)}$$

$$= -\frac{1}{2\pi} \frac{1 - \rho^2}{1 + \rho^2 - 2\rho\cos(\theta - \phi)}$$

Therefore,
$$\psi(\xi,\eta) = \frac{1}{2\pi} \int_0^{2\pi} \frac{(1 - \rho^2)f(\theta)\, d\theta}{1 + \rho^2 - 2\rho \cos(\theta - \phi)}$$

This is known as **Poisson's integral formula.**[1]   By means of it we can solve the Dirichlet problem for any region which can be mapped conformally onto the interior of the unit circle.

There is actually a closer connection between conformal mapping and Green's functions.   Suppose $w = f(z)$ is a conformal mapping which maps the simply connected region R bounded by a simple closed curve C onto the interior of the unit circle so that C maps onto the unit circle and the point $\zeta = \xi + i\eta$ maps into the origin.   Then

$$G(\xi,\eta;x,y) = -\frac{1}{2\pi} \log |f(z)|$$

is the Green's function appropriate for the solution of the Dirichlet problem in R at the point (ξ,η).   This follows since

$$G = \mathrm{Re}\left\{-\frac{1}{2\pi} \log f(z)\right\}$$

and is therefore the real part of a function which is analytic except at (ξ,η), where $f(z)$ is zero.   Therefore, G is harmonic except at (ξ,η).   It has the right type of singularity at (ξ,η), since

$$f(z) = f(\zeta) + a_1(z - \zeta) + a_2(z - \zeta)^2 + \cdots$$
$$= a_1(z - \zeta) + a_2(z - \zeta)^2 + \cdots$$
$$= (z - \zeta)g(z)$$

where $g(\zeta) = f'(\zeta) \neq 0$.   Otherwise the mapping would not be conformal at $z = \zeta$.   Now

$$-\frac{1}{2\pi} \log |f(z)| = -\frac{1}{2\pi} \log |z - \zeta| - \frac{1}{2\pi} \log |g(z)|$$

$$= -\frac{1}{2\pi} \log \sqrt{(x - \xi)^2 + (y - \eta)^2} + H(\xi,\eta;x,y)$$

where H is regular at (ξ,η).   Finally, the boundary condition is satisfied on C, for

$$\lim_{z \to C} G = \lim_{z \to C}\left\{-\frac{1}{2\pi} \log |f(z)|\right\}$$

$$= -\frac{1}{2\pi} \log 1 = 0$$

---

[1] Compare with exercise 3, Sec. 3.4.

The **Riemann mapping theorem** states that any simply connected region bounded by a simple closed curve can be mapped conformally onto the unit circle so that a given point ζ in R maps into the origin. This ensures the existence of the mapping, which in turn implies the existence of the Green's function, from which one can deduce the existence of the solution of the Dirichlet problem for reasonably well-behaved boundary conditions.

Exercises 4.3

1. Derive the Poisson integral formula for the solution of the Dirichlet problem in the unit sphere

$$\psi(\xi,\eta,\zeta) = \frac{1}{4\pi} \int_0^\pi \int_0^{2\pi} \frac{(\rho^2 - 1) f(\theta,\phi) \sin\theta \, d\theta \, d\phi}{(1 + \rho^2 - 2\rho Q)^{\frac{3}{2}}}$$

where $Q = \sin\theta \sin\alpha \cos(\phi - \beta) + \cos\theta \cos\alpha$ with

$$x = r \sin\theta \cos\phi$$
$$y = r \sin\theta \sin\phi$$
$$z = r \cos\theta$$
$$\xi = \rho \sin\alpha \cos\beta$$
$$\eta = \rho \sin\alpha \sin\beta$$
$$\zeta = \rho \cos\alpha$$

2. What are properties required for the Green's function associated with the problem

$$\nabla^2 \psi = -f(x,y,z) \qquad \text{in } V$$

$$\frac{d\psi}{dn} = g(x,y,z) \qquad \text{on } S$$

Give a formal expression for the solution in terms of this Green's function.

3. If $w = f(z)$ is any conformal mapping which maps R onto the interior of the unit circle and ζ is a point in R, show that the Green's function for the Dirichlet problem in R is

$$G(\xi,\eta;x,y) = -\frac{1}{2\pi} \log \left| \frac{f(z) - f(\zeta)}{\overline{f(\zeta)}f(z) - 1} \right|$$

where $\zeta = \xi + i\eta$. Here $\bar{f} = f^*$.

4.4 Problems in Unbounded Regions

Up to this point we have considered problems in bounded regions only. In the homogeneous problem the separation-of-variables technique led to a boundary-value problem with a discrete spectrum of eigenvalues which could be formed by finding solutions of a certain homogeneous partial differential equation subject to a homogeneous boundary condition on the surface of a bounded region V. The nonhomogeneous problem could then be formulated in terms of a series in the solutions of the homogeneous problem or in terms of

Green's functions.   When the problem involves an unbounded region, not only do we have to specify conditions on boundaries in the finite region but we must also specify the behavior of the solution at very large distances from the origin in order to ensure a unique solution of the problem.   Part of our investigation will be to determine what these conditions should be.   We shall again be able to formulate the solution of nonhomogeneous problems in terms of Green's functions, provided we impose proper conditions on the Green's function at large distances from the origin.   The homogeneous problem, however, now has only the trivial solution and this guarantees the uniqueness of the solution of the nonhomogeneous problem.

Consider the solution of the following partial differential equation in the unbounded three-dimensional region outside of the finite volume V bounded by the surface S:

$$\nabla^2 \phi = a\phi + b\frac{\partial \phi}{\partial t} + c\frac{\partial^2 \phi}{\partial t^2} - f(x,y,z,t)$$

where $f \equiv 0$ outside of a finite volume and a, b, and c are real constants.   We shall assume a boundary condition of the form

$$\frac{d\phi}{dn} + \alpha\phi = g(x,y,z,t)$$

on S, and leave open for the moment the condition to be satisfied at large distances from V.   The problem is linear, so that we may write the solution as $\phi = \phi_0 + \phi_1 + \phi_2$, where ϕ_0 is the solution of the homogeneous problem

$$\nabla^2 \phi_0 = a\phi_0 + b\frac{\partial \phi_0}{\partial t} + c\frac{\partial^2 \phi_0}{\partial t^2}$$ outside V, subject to $\frac{d\phi_0}{dn} + \alpha\phi_0 = 0$ on S; ϕ_1

is a solution of the nonhomogeneous problem $\nabla^2 \phi_1 = a\phi_1 + b\frac{\partial \phi_1}{\partial t} + c\frac{\partial^2 \phi_1}{\partial t^2} - f$,

subject to $\frac{d\phi_1}{dn} + \alpha\phi_1 = 0$ on S; and ϕ_2 is a solution of

$$\nabla^2 \phi_2 = a\phi_2 + b\frac{\partial \phi_2}{\partial t} + c\frac{\partial^2 \phi_2}{\partial t^2}$$

subject to $\frac{d\phi_2}{dn} + \alpha\phi_2 = g$ on S.

Let us first consider the homogeneous problem.   As in the problem for the bounded region, we attempt a separation of variables:

$$\phi_0 = \psi_0(x,y,z)F(t)$$

Then
$$\frac{\nabla^2 \psi_0}{\psi_0} = \frac{aF + b\dot{F} + c\ddot{F}}{F} = -\lambda$$

and therefore the equation separates into

$$c\ddot{F} + b\dot{F} + (a + \lambda)F = 0$$

$$\nabla^2 \psi_0 + \lambda\psi_0 = 0$$

In the bounded problem we next showed that $\lambda \geq 0$ using Green's identity.

$$\lambda \iiint_{V'} \psi_0^2 \, dV = -\iiint_{V'} \psi_0 \nabla^2 \psi_0 \, dV$$

$$= \iiint_{V'} \nabla \psi_0 \cdot \nabla \psi_0 \, dV + \iint_S \alpha \psi_0^2 \, dS$$

$$- \lim_{R \to \infty} \iint_{S'} \psi_0 \frac{d\psi_0}{dn} \, dS$$

where V' is the region outside V and S' is a large sphere of radius R. The proof fails this time because we have not specified the behavior of ψ_0 at large distances from V.

Before proceeding further, let us consider some elementary solutions of

$$\nabla^2 \psi + k^2 \psi = 0$$

and by so doing we may gain some insight into the nature of the conditions we must specify on our solution at large distances from the origin. Let us first look for solutions with spherical symmetry, i.e., solutions which depend on r only in the usual spherical coordinate system. In spherical coordinates the equation becomes

$$\frac{1}{r^2} \frac{d}{dr} [r^2 \psi(r)] + k^2 \psi = 0$$

Let $\psi(r) = \dfrac{h(r)}{r}$, then $\psi' = \dfrac{h'}{r} - \dfrac{h}{r^2}$, $r^2 \psi' = rh' - h$, and the equation becomes

$$h'' + k^2 h = 0$$

This equation has the following solutions: $\sin kr$, $\cos kr$, e^{ikr}, e^{-ikr}. If in the original problem $a = b = 0$, then we can write $F = e^{-i\omega t}$, where $\omega = k/\sqrt{c}$. We would then have the wave equation with a periodic time dependence. This is the case which will be of primary interest to us. It will be convenient to write the time dependence as $e^{-i\omega t}$ with the agreement that the final solution will be the real or imaginary part of the complex solution. Combining this time dependence with the above spherically symmetric solution, we have

solutions of the form $\dfrac{\sin kr}{r} \cos \omega t$, $\dfrac{\sin kr}{r} \sin \omega t$, $\dfrac{\cos kr}{r} \cos \omega t$, $\dfrac{\cos kr}{r} \sin \omega t$,

$\dfrac{\cos (kr + \omega t)}{r}$, $\dfrac{\sin (kr + \omega t)}{r}$, $\dfrac{\cos (kr - \omega t)}{r}$, $\dfrac{\sin (kr - \omega t)}{r}$. The first four of these represent standing waves, the next two inward traveling waves, and the last two outward traveling waves.[1]   We shall take it as a basic assumption that a disturbance in the finite region should produce only outward traveling waves.   The choice of a spherically symmetric solution satisfying this requirement would have to be $\psi = e^{ikr}/r$.   It is easily shown that for this solution

$$\lim_{r \to \infty} r\left[\frac{\partial \psi}{\partial r} - ik\psi\right] = 0$$

This is called the **radiation condition.**   We shall take this as the required behavior of the solution of the boundary-value problem for large values of r. We shall see that this implies that the solution of the homogeneous boundary-value problem is identically zero, which in turn implies that the solution of the nonhomogeneous problem is unique.

The basic theorem of this section is the following: Let ψ be a complex-valued function with continuous second partial derivatives outside of a bounded volume V bounded by S, which satisfies $\nabla^2\psi + k^2\psi = 0$ outside V, $\dfrac{d\psi}{dn} + \alpha\psi = 0$ on S, with k and α both real, and let $\lim\limits_{r \to \infty} r\left[\dfrac{\partial \psi}{\partial r} - ik\psi\right] = 0$; then $\psi \equiv 0$ outside V.   We begin the proof by considering the solution expanded in a series of spherical harmonics, i.e.,

$$\psi(r,\theta,\phi) = \sum_{n=0}^{\infty} v_n(r)S_n(\theta,\phi)$$

where $$S_n(\theta,\phi) = \sum_{m=0}^{n} A_m P_n^m(\cos\theta)\cos m\phi + B_m P_n^m(\cos\theta)\sin m\phi$$

and $$\int_0^\pi \int_0^{2\pi} S_n S_p \sin\theta\, d\theta\, d\phi = 0$$

for $n \neq p$.   We shall assume that these functions have been normalized, i.e.,

$$\int_0^\pi \int_0^{2\pi} S_n^2 \sin\theta\, d\theta\, d\phi = 1$$

By Bessel's inequality we have

$$\sum_{n=0}^{\infty} |v_n|^2 \leq \int_0^\pi \int_0^{2\pi} |\psi|^2 \sin\theta\, d\theta\, d\phi$$

Either $v_n \equiv 0$ for all n, in which case $\psi \equiv 0$, or $v_N \not\equiv 0$ for some N.   In the latter case,

$$|v_N|^2 \leq \sum_{n=0}^{\infty} |v_n|^2 \leq \int_0^\pi \int_0^{2\pi} |\psi|^2 \sin\theta\, d\theta\, d\phi$$

---

[1] This can be seen by considering the location of the nodes as determined by the equation $\psi(r)e^{-i\omega t} = 0$.

Now we know that $\psi_N = v_N(r)S_N(\theta,\phi)$ is a solution of the differential equation. Hence,

$$\nabla^2\psi_N + k^2\psi_N = 0$$

or

$$\frac{r^2v_N'' + 2rv_N'}{v_N} + k^2r^2 = -\frac{1}{S_N}\left[\frac{1}{\sin\theta}\frac{\partial}{\partial\theta}\left(\sin\theta\frac{\partial S_N}{\partial\theta}\right)\right.$$

$$\left.+ \frac{1}{\sin^2\theta}\frac{\partial^2 S_N}{\partial\phi^2}\right] = N(N+1)$$

Therefore, v_N satisfies the equation

$$r^2v_N'' + 2rv_N' + [k^2r^2 - N(N+1)]v_N = 0$$

To solve this we first make the substitution $v_N = e^{ikr}h(r)$. Then

$$v_N' = e^{ikr}h' + ike^{ikr}h$$

$$v_N'' = e^{ikr}h'' + 2ike^{ikr}h' - k^2e^{ikr}h$$

Substituting in the equation for v_N, we have

$$r^2h'' + (2ikr + 2)rh' + [2ikr - N(N+1)]h = 0$$

When we assume a solution of the form

$$h = r^\beta\sum_{j=0}^{\infty}c_jr^j$$

the indicial equation is $(\beta - N)(\beta + N + 1)$. If we take the root $\beta_2 = N$, the solution will contain positive powers of r which are not consistent with the radiation condition. By use of $\beta_1 = -N - 1$ the equation becomes

$$\sum_{j=0}^{\infty} j(j - 2N - 1)c_jr^{j-N-1} + 2ik\sum_{j=0}^{\infty}(j - N)c_jr^{j-N} = 0$$

from which we get the recurrence relation

$$c_j = \frac{2ik(N + 1 - j)}{j(j - 2N - 1)}c_{j-1}$$

Thus we see that $c_{N+1} = c_{N+2} = \cdots = 0$. Therefore,

$$v_N = \frac{e^{ikr}}{r}\sum_{j=0}^{N}c_{N-j}r^{-j}$$

Now

$$\int_{R_0}^{R}|v_N|^2r^2\,dr \geq KR$$

where K is a constant, and

$$\int_{R_0}^{R}\int_0^{\pi}\int_0^{2\pi}|\psi|^2r^2\sin\theta\,dr\,d\theta\,d\phi \geq \int_{R_0}^{R}|v_N|^2r^2\,dr \geq KR$$

Therefore, either $\psi \equiv 0$ or $\int_{R_0}^{R} \int_0^{\pi} \int_0^{2\pi} |\psi|^2 r^2 \sin \theta \, dr \, d\theta \, d\phi$ becomes large at least as fast as KR as $R \to \infty$.

Applying Green's identity, we have

$$0 = \iiint_{V'} (\psi \nabla^2 \psi^* - \psi^* \nabla^2 \psi) \, dV = \iint_{S} \left(\psi \frac{d\psi^*}{dn} - \psi^* \frac{d\psi}{dn} \right) dS$$

$$+ \iint_{S'} \left(\psi \frac{d\psi^*}{dn} - \psi^* \frac{d\psi}{dn} \right) dS$$

where S' is an arbitrary surface completely surrounding S.   But the surface integral over S vanishes by the boundary condition, and therefore the integral over S' must also vanish.

Using the radiation condition, we have

$$0 = \lim_{r \to \infty} \int_0^{\pi} \int_0^{2\pi} r^2 \left(\frac{\partial \psi}{\partial r} - ik\psi \right) \left(\frac{\partial \psi^*}{\partial r} + ik\psi^* \right) \sin \theta \, d\theta \, d\phi$$

$$= \lim_{r \to \infty} \int_0^{\pi} \int_0^{2\pi} r^2 \left\{ \left| \frac{\partial \psi}{\partial r} \right|^2 + k^2 |\psi|^2 + ik \left(\psi^* \frac{\partial \psi}{\partial r} - \psi \frac{\partial \psi^*}{\partial r} \right) \right\} \sin \theta \, d\theta \, d\phi$$

$$= \lim_{r \to \infty} \int_0^{\pi} \int_0^{2\pi} r^2 \left\{ \left| \frac{\partial \psi}{\partial r} \right|^2 + k^2 |\psi|^2 \right\} \sin \theta \, d\theta \, d\phi$$

But this implies that

$$\lim_{r \to \infty} \int_0^{\pi} \int_0^{2\pi} r^2 |\psi|^2 \sin \theta \, d\theta \, d\phi = 0$$

However, this is impossible unless $\psi \equiv 0$; for if it is not, then

$$\int_{R_0}^{R} \int_0^{\pi} \int_0^{2\pi} r^2 |\psi|^2 \sin \theta \, d\theta \, d\phi \geq KR$$

But $\lim_{r \to \infty} F(r) = 0$ implies that $\lim_{R \to \infty} \frac{1}{R} \int_{R_0}^{R} F(r) \, dr = 0$.   To show this, let ρ be sufficiently large that $|F(r)| < \epsilon$ for all r such that $R_0 < \rho < r < R$. Then

$$\left| \frac{1}{R} \int_{R_0}^{R} F(r) \, dr \right| \leq \frac{1}{R} \int_{R_0}^{\rho} |F(r)| \, dr + \frac{1}{R} \int_{\rho}^{R} \epsilon \, dr$$

$$\leq \frac{M}{R} (\rho - R_0) + \frac{\epsilon}{R} (R - \rho)$$

$$\leq 2\epsilon$$

by taking R sufficiently large that $M(\rho - R_0)/R < \epsilon$.　Letting

$$F(r) = \int_0^\pi \int_0^{2\pi} r^2 |\psi|^2 \sin \theta \, d\theta \, d\phi$$

we see clearly that we cannot have at the same time

$$\frac{1}{R} \int_{R_0}^R \int_0^\pi \int_0^{2\pi} r^2 |\psi|^2 \sin \theta \, d\theta \, d\phi \geq K$$

and

$$\lim_{r \to \infty} \int_0^\pi \int_0^{2\pi} r^2 |\psi|^2 \sin \theta \, d\theta \, d\phi = 0$$

This completes the proof.

Now let us consider one of the nonhomogeneous problems.　Assuming that $a = b = 0$ and that $f(x,y,z,t) = \text{Re} \{F(x,y,z)e^{-i\omega t}\}$, we take

$$\phi_1 = \psi_1 e^{-i\omega t}$$

Then we write

$$\nabla^2 \psi_1 e^{-i\omega t} = -\omega^2 c \psi_1 e^{-i\omega t} - F(x,y,z)e^{-i\omega t}$$

and we have the separated equation

$$\nabla^2 \psi_1 + k^2 \psi_1 = -F(x,y,z)$$

with $k^2 = \omega^2 c$.　The boundary condition for ψ_1 is

$$\frac{d\psi_1}{dn} + \alpha \psi_1 = 0$$

on S.　This problem has a unique solution, for if

$$w = \psi_1 - \bar{\psi}_1$$

the difference of two possibly different solutions, then

$$\nabla^2 w + k^2 w = 0 \qquad \text{outside } V$$

$$\frac{dw}{dn} + \alpha w = 0 \qquad \text{on } S$$

and w satisfies the radiation condition

$$\lim_{r \to \infty} r\left(\frac{\partial w}{\partial r} - ikw\right) = 0$$

But by the theorem just proved $w \equiv 0$, and therefore $\psi_1 \equiv \bar{\psi}_1$.

The other nonhomogeneous problem is

$$\nabla^2 \psi_2 + k^2 \psi_2 = 0 \qquad \text{outside } V$$

$$\frac{d\psi_2}{dn} + \alpha \psi_2 = g(x,y,z) \qquad \text{on } S$$

This also has a unique solution by the theorem proved above.

Now let us turn to the representation of the solution of these nonhomogeneous problems in terms of Green's functions. For the first problem we would want to construct a Green's function with the following properties:

1. $\nabla^2 G + k^2 G = 0$ outside V except at (ξ, η, ζ)

2. $G \sim \dfrac{1}{4\pi} \dfrac{1}{R}$ as $R \to 0$ with $R = \sqrt{(x - \xi)^2 + (y - \eta)^2 + (z - \zeta)^2}$

3. $\dfrac{dG}{dn} + \alpha G = 0$ on S

4. $\lim\limits_{r \to \infty} r\left(\dfrac{\partial G}{\partial r} - ikG\right) = 0$ uniformly in θ and ϕ

We see how properties 1, 2, and 3 carry over from the corresponding problem for bounded regions. Property 4, the radiation condition, is appended on the grounds that the Green's function should physically have the interpretation of outward traveling spherical waves originating from the point (ξ, η, ζ). Also we find that this condition is needed to assure uniqueness of the Green's function.

In this case it is somewhat more convenient to let

$$G(\xi, \eta, \zeta; x, y, z) = \frac{e^{ikR}}{4\pi R} + H(\xi, \eta, \zeta; x, y, z)$$

Then since $e^{ikR}/4\pi R$ satisfies the differential equation except at (ξ, η, ζ) and behaves properly as $R \to 0$, we can take H as a solution of the differential equation regular everywhere outside V. H satisfies the nonhomogeneous boundary condition

$$\frac{dH}{dn} + \alpha H = -\left(\frac{d}{dn} + \alpha\right) \frac{1}{4\pi} \frac{e^{ikR}}{R}$$

on S. $e^{ikR}/4\pi R$ satisfies the radiation condition, since

$$R = \sqrt{(x - \xi)^2 + (y - \eta)^2 + (z - \zeta)^2}$$

$$= r\sqrt{1 + \frac{\rho^2}{r^2} - \frac{2\rho}{r} Q}$$

where $Q = \sin\theta \sin\gamma \cos(\phi - \beta) + \cos\theta \cos\gamma$, with

$$x = r \sin\theta \cos\phi$$

$$y = r \sin\theta \sin\phi$$

$$z = r \cos\theta$$

$$\xi = \rho \sin\gamma \cos\beta$$

$$\eta = \rho \sin\gamma \sin\beta$$

$$\zeta = \rho \cos\gamma$$

Then $\dfrac{e^{ikR}}{4\pi R} = \dfrac{\exp\{ikr[1 - (2\rho/r)Q + (\rho^2/r^2)]^{\frac{1}{2}}\}}{4\pi r}\left(1 - \dfrac{2\rho Q}{r} + \dfrac{\rho^2}{r^2}\right)^{-\frac{1}{2}}$

$$= \frac{e^{ikr}}{4\pi r} h(\theta,\phi) + O\left(\frac{1}{r^2}\right)^{\dagger}$$

Since the Green's function satisfies the radiation condition and $e^{ikR}/4\pi R$ also does, then H must as well. Therefore, H is the solution of a nonhomogeneous boundary-value problem and satisfies the radiation condition and hence is unique.

As for the solution of the original nonhomogeneous boundary-value problem, this can be formulated as follows:

$$-\iiint_V FG\,dV = \iiint_{V'} [G(\nabla^2\psi_1 + k^2\psi_1) - \psi_1(\nabla^2 G + k^2 G)]\,dV$$

$$= \iint_S \left[G\left(\frac{d\psi_1}{dn} + \alpha\psi_1\right) - \psi_1\left(\frac{dG}{dn} + \alpha G\right)\right]dS$$

$$-\iint_\Sigma \left(G\frac{\partial\psi_1}{\partial R} - \psi_1\frac{\partial G}{\partial R}\right)dS + \iint_{\Sigma'}\left(G\frac{\partial\psi_1}{\partial r} - \psi_1\frac{\partial G}{\partial r}\right)dS$$

where V' is a volume bounded by S; Σ, a small sphere of radius δ about (ξ,η,ζ); and Σ', a large sphere of radius D with center at the origin. The nature of the singularity of G at (ξ,η,ζ) ensures that the surface integral on Σ will approach $-\psi(\xi,\eta,\zeta)$ as $\delta \to 0$. The surface integral on S will vanish by the boundary conditions on ψ_1 and G, while the surface integral on Σ' approaches zero as $D \to \infty$ by the radiation conditions on G and ψ_1. Indeed

$$\psi_1 = \frac{e^{ikr}}{r}f(\theta,\phi) + O\left(\frac{1}{r^2}\right)$$

$$G = \frac{1}{4\pi}\frac{e^{ikr}}{r}h(\theta,\phi) + O\left(\frac{1}{r^2}\right)$$

as $r \to \infty$. Therefore,

$$\lim_{D\to\infty}\iint_{\Sigma'}\left(G\frac{\partial\psi_1}{\partial r} - \psi_1\frac{\partial G}{\partial r}\right)_{r=D} D^2 \sin\theta\,d\theta\,d\phi$$

$$= \lim_{D\to\infty}\iint_{\Sigma'}\frac{1}{4\pi}\left\{\frac{e^{ikr}}{r}h\left[\frac{ike^{ikr}}{r}f + O\left(\frac{1}{r^2}\right)\right]\right.$$

$$\left.- \frac{e^{ikr}}{r}f\left[\frac{ik}{4\pi}\frac{e^{ikr}}{r}h + O\left(\frac{1}{r^2}\right)\right]\right\}_{r=D} D^2 \sin\theta\,d\theta\,d\phi$$

$$= 0$$

$\dagger f(r) = O(1/r^2)$ as $r \to \infty$ implies that $|r^2 f(r)|$ is bounded as $r \to \infty$.

Therefore, we have an integral representation for the solution

$$\psi_1(\xi,\eta,\zeta) = \iiint\limits_{\bar{V}} F(x,y,z) G(\xi,\eta,\zeta\,;x,y,z) \; dx \; dy \; dz$$

where $\bar{V}$ is that part of the volume outside V where $F \not\equiv 0$.

The same Green's function can be used to formulate the solution of the other nonhomogeneous problem.   In this case, the solution becomes

$$\psi_2(\xi,\eta,\zeta) = \iint\limits_{S} g(x,y,z) G(\xi,\eta,\zeta\,;x,y,z) \; dS$$

One could argue that the Green's-function formulation of the problem just substitutes for the original problem the equally difficult problem of finding the Green's function.   In a few cases, the Green's function can be found without too much difficulty, and then we have an explicit representation of the solution. Another approach is to pick a Green's function which does not satisfy all the conditions and is thus simpler to find.   However, then we lose the explicit representation of the solution.   On the other hand, we get an **integral equation** which may be solvable by other techniques.   For example, in the first nonhomogeneous boundary-value problem above, if we take what is called the **free-space Green's function**

$$G = \frac{1}{4\pi} \frac{e^{ikR}}{R}$$

the Green's function no longer satisfies the boundary condition.   We then have

$$\psi_1(\xi,\eta,\zeta) = \iiint\limits_{\bar{V}} FG \; dV - \iint\limits_{S} \psi_1 \left(\frac{dG}{dn} + \alpha G \right) dS$$

If (ξ,η,ζ) is a point on S, then this becomes an integral equation for the boundary values of ψ_1 on S.   Having determined the values of ψ_1 on S, we can then substitute back into the above equation to obtain values of ψ_1 at points not on S.   We shall explore this avenue of approach in the next chapter.

Now let us turn to the solution of some particular problems in terms of Green's functions.   In electrostatics we are sometimes interested in the potential due to a continuous distribution of charge over a finite volume $\bar{V}$. In this case, we must solve **Poisson's equation**[1] $\nabla^2 \psi = -f(x,y,z)$ in $\bar{V}$ and Laplace's equation outside $\bar{V}$.   This is the first nonhomogeneous boundary-value problem treated above if we take $k = 0$ and let S shrink to a point.

---

[1] Here f is proportional to the charge density.

Then we want the Green's function to satisfy the following properties:

1. $\nabla^2 G = 0$ except at (ξ,η,ζ)

2. $G \sim \dfrac{1}{4\pi R}$ as $R \to 0$

3. $G \sim \dfrac{C}{r}$ as $r \to \infty$ (C a constant)

In this case we can find G explicitly as $1/4\pi R$.   Then the solution is

$$\psi(\xi,\eta,\zeta) = \frac{1}{4\pi} \iiint\limits_{V} \frac{f(x,y,z)}{\sqrt{(x-\xi)^2 + (y-\eta)^2 + (z-\zeta)^2}}\, dx\, dy\, dz$$

It is a problem in potential theory to determine general conditions on f which will assure that ψ is a solution of the problem.[1]

Next, let us consider the Dirichlet problem for unbounded regions, i.e.,

$$\nabla^2 \psi = 0 \qquad \text{outside } V$$
$$\psi = g(x,y,z) \qquad \text{on } S$$

The Green's function should satisfy

1. $\nabla^2 G = 0$ except at (ξ,η,ζ)

2. $G \sim \dfrac{1}{4\pi R}$ as $R \to 0$

3. $G \sim \dfrac{C}{r}$ as $r \to \infty$ (C a constant)

4. $G = 0$ on S

The solution is then

$$\psi(\xi,\eta,\zeta) = -\iint\limits_{S} g(x,y,z)\,\frac{dG}{dn}\, dS$$

For example, suppose we wish to solve Laplace's equation in the upper half space, $z > 0$, with $\psi(x,y,0) = g(x,y)$ on the xy plane.   The Green's function can be written explicitly as

$$G = \frac{1}{4\pi}\frac{1}{\sqrt{(x-\xi)^2 + (y-\eta)^2 + (z-\zeta)^2}}$$
$$-\frac{1}{4\pi}\frac{1}{\sqrt{(x-\xi)^2 + (y-\eta)^2 + (z+\zeta)^2}}$$

[1] See O. D. Kellogg, "Foundations of Potential Theory," Dover Publications, New York, 1953.

The first term has the proper singularity at (ξ,η,ζ) and satisfies Laplace's equation except at that point.   The second term is obtained by reflecting the singularity in the xy plane.   It therefore satisfies Laplace's equation everywhere in the upper half space.   When $z = 0$, $G = 0$, so that the boundary condition is satisfied.

$$\left(\frac{dG}{dn}\right)_{z=0} = -\left(\frac{\partial G}{\partial z}\right)_{z=0}$$

$$= -\frac{1}{2\pi} \frac{\zeta}{[(x - \xi)^2 + (y - \eta)^2 + \zeta^2]^{\frac{3}{2}}}$$

so that

$$\psi(\xi,\eta,\zeta) = \frac{1}{2\pi} \int_{-\infty}^{\infty}\int_{-\infty}^{\infty} g(x,y) \frac{\zeta}{[(x - \xi)^2 + (y - \eta)^2 + \zeta^2]^{\frac{3}{2}}}\, dx\, dy$$

In this case, since the surface S is unbounded, to verify the Green's-function representation of the solution, we would have to integrate over a large circle of radius D in the xy plane and over the surface of a large hemisphere of radius D in the upper half space, take the limit at $D \to \infty$, and show that the integral over the surface of the hemisphere approaches zero as $D \to \infty$.   This is not hard to do, since $G \sim C/r$ and $\psi \sim B/r$ as $r \to \infty$, and therefore

$$r^2\left(G\frac{\partial \psi}{\partial r} - \psi\frac{\partial G}{\partial r}\right) \sim \frac{K}{r}$$

as $r \to \infty$.

Exercises 4.4

1. Find the Green's function associated with the problem

$$\psi''(x) - k^2\psi(x) = -f(x) \qquad 0 \leq x < \infty$$
$$\psi(0) = 0$$
$$\psi \to 0 \quad \text{as} \quad x \to \infty$$

which will give the integral representation of the solution

$$\psi(x) = \int_0^{\infty} G(x;\xi)\, f(\xi)\, d\xi$$

2. Solve the exterior Dirichlet problem for the unit sphere, i.e., $\nabla^2\psi = 0$ for $x^2 + y^2 + z^2 > 1$, with $\psi = g(1,\theta,\phi)$ on S: $x^2 + y^2 + z^2 = 1$.   Find an explicit integral representation.

3. Find an integral representation for the solution of the following problem: $\nabla^2\psi = 0$ for $z > 0$, $y > 0$, with $\psi(x,y,0) = g(x,y)$, $\psi(x,0,z) = h(x,z)$, $\psi = O(1/r)$ as $r = \sqrt{x^2 + y^2 + z^2} \to \infty$.

4. A square membrane is vibrating in its fundamental mode.   Formulate an integral equation whose solution will give approximately the acoustic field produced by the membrane.   List the assumptions which you make to make this formulation possible.

4.5   A Problem in Diffraction Theory

In some problems the source of excitation is at a large distance from the volume V. For example, in diffraction theory we are often interested in the interaction between a passive surface S and a plane wave. In this case, the source of excitation of the field is a plane wave. The plane wave itself does not satisfy the boundary condition on S. The effect of the surface is then to produce a scattered field which together with the plane wave will satisfy the boundary condition. Consider a plane wave

$$\phi_p = e^{i(ku - \omega t)}$$

where $u = x \cos \alpha + y \cos \beta + z \cos \gamma$, a coordinate with axis in a direction making angles α, β, and γ with the x, y, and z coordinate axes. It is easily shown that ϕ_p satisfies the wave equation

$$\nabla^2 \phi_p = \frac{k^2}{\omega^2} \frac{\partial^2 \phi_p}{\partial t^2}$$

and is a plane wave proceeding in the direction of the u-coordinate axis. Now we let the whole field be

$$\phi = \phi_p + \phi_s$$

where ϕ_s represents the scattered field. ϕ must satisfy the wave equation

$$\nabla^2 \phi = \frac{1}{a^2} \frac{\partial^2 \phi}{\partial t^2}$$

Then letting $\phi = \psi e^{-i\omega t}$, we have the result that ψ satisfies

$$\nabla^2 \psi + k^2 \psi = 0$$

with $k^2 = \omega^2/a^2$. We can write

$$\psi = \psi_p + \psi_s$$
$$= e^{iku} + \psi_s$$

In the acoustic case, if S is a rigid boundary, there cannot be a normal component of velocity across it. Therefore, $\dfrac{d\phi}{dn} = 0$ and $\dfrac{d\psi}{dn} = 0$ on S. We see that ψ satisfies a homogeneous boundary-value problem. This does not, however, imply that $\psi \equiv 0$, for it contains a plane wave which does not satisfy the radiation condition. We will require, however, that ψ_s satisfy the radiation condition. ψ_s will satisfy then the following nonhomogeneous boundary-value problem:

$$\nabla^2 \psi_s + k^2 \psi_s = 0 \qquad \text{outside } V$$

$$\frac{d\psi_s}{dn} = -\frac{d\psi_p}{dn} \qquad \text{on } S$$

$$\lim_{r \to \infty} r \left[\frac{\partial \psi_s}{\partial r} - ik\psi_s \right] = 0$$

ψ_s is therefore unique, and the problem can be formulated in terms of Green's functions.

To be a little more specific, let us consider a classical diffraction theory problem, the diffraction of a plane wave by a rigid semi-infinite plane sheet.

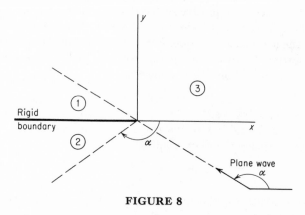

FIGURE 8

We shall assume a plane wave with perpendicular incidence striking the edge (z axis) of the rigid plane sheet (xz plane, $x \leq 0$). From the geometry we see that the solution will not depend on the z coordinate. The velocity potential $\phi(x,y,t)$ will satisfy the wave equation except on the xz plane, $x \leq 0$, where it must satisfy the boundary condition $\dfrac{d\phi}{dn} = 0$. We write

$$\phi(x,y,t) = \phi_p + \phi_s$$
$$= [e^{ikr\cos(\theta-\alpha)} + \psi_s(x,y)]e^{-i\omega t}$$

In this case, geometrical optics tells us to expect a shadow (no plane wave) in region 1 and a reflected plane wave in region 2. Therefore, we write $\psi_s = \bar{\psi}_s$ for $-\alpha < \theta < \alpha$, $\psi_s = \bar{\psi}_s - e^{ikr\cos(\theta-\alpha)}$ for $\alpha < \theta < \pi$, and $\psi_s = \bar{\psi}_s + e^{ikr\cos(\theta+\alpha)}$ for $\pi < \theta < 2\pi - \alpha$. In this problem we have reflection and diffraction, and the diffraction effect is entirely contained in the function $\bar{\psi}_s$. The reflected plane wave does not satisfy the radiation condition, but we shall require that $\bar{\psi}_s$ do so.

Our procedure will be to introduce a Green's function for the purpose of formulating an integral equation whose solution will allow us to find the acoustic field. To determine the appropriate Green's function we shall consider axially symmetric solutions of the two-dimensional Helmholtz equation. These solutions must satisfy the zeroth-order Bessel equation

$$\psi'' + \frac{1}{r}\psi' + k^2\psi = 0$$

which has solutions

$$J_0(kr) \qquad Y_0(kr) \qquad H_0^{(1)}(kr) = J_0(kr) + iY_0(kr)$$

and
$$H_0^{(2)}(kr) = J_0(kr) - iY_0(kr)$$

It can be shown that these functions behave as

$$\frac{\cos kr}{\sqrt{r}} \qquad \frac{\sin kr}{\sqrt{r}} \qquad \frac{e^{ikr}}{\sqrt{r}} \qquad \text{and} \qquad \frac{e^{-ikr}}{\sqrt{r}}$$

respectively, as $r \to \infty$. Therefore, we take the solution $H_0^{(1)}(kr)$ as the one representing outward traveling cylindrical waves. To have the proper behavior as (x,y) approaches (ξ,η), the Green's function must be asymptotic to $(i/4)H_0^{(1)}(kR)$ where $R = \sqrt{(x-\xi)^2 + (y-\eta)^2}$. That the constant must be $i/4$ follows from the fact that $J_0(kR) \sim 1$ and $Y_0(kR) \sim (2/\pi) \log R$ as $R \to 0$. In the two-dimensional problem the radiation condition takes the form

$$\lim_{r \to \infty} \sqrt{r}\left[\frac{\partial \psi}{\partial r} - ik\psi\right] = 0$$

Getting back to the diffraction problem, for the purpose of formulating the integral equation, we shall use the following Green's function:

$$G(\xi,\eta\,;x,y) = \frac{i}{4}\left[H_0^{(1)}(k\sqrt{(x-\xi)^2 + (y-\eta)^2}) + H_0^{(1)}(k\sqrt{(x-\xi)^2 + (y+\eta)^2})\right]$$

This function satisfies the conditions $\left(\dfrac{\partial G}{\partial y}\right)_{y=0} = 0$, and

$$G = \frac{e^{ikr}}{\sqrt{r}} g(\theta) + O(r^{-\frac{3}{2}})$$

as $r \to \infty$.

Consider the regions R_1 and R_2 bounded by the contours C_1 and C_2 (see Fig. 9). We apply the Green's identity to $\psi^{(1)} = \psi_s^{(1)} + e^{ikr \cos(\theta - \alpha)}$, which is the whole field in the upper half plane, in the region R_1, i.e.,

$$\psi^{(1)}(\xi,\eta) = \int_{C_1} \left(G\frac{d\psi^{(1)}}{dn} - \psi^{(1)}\frac{dG}{dn}\right) ds$$

$$= -\int_{-\infty}^{\infty} G\left(\frac{\partial \psi}{\partial y}\right)_{y=0+} dx$$

provided we can show that the contributions of the small and large semicircles approach zero as the radii approach zero and infinity, respectively. We also apply the Green's identity to $\psi^{(2)} - e^{ikr \cos(\theta-\alpha)} - e^{ikr \cos(\theta+\alpha)}$, which is the whole field with the plane wave and reflected wave subtracted out, in the region R_2, i.e.,

$$\psi^{(2)}(\xi,\eta) - e^{ik(\xi \cos \alpha + \eta \sin \alpha)} - e^{ik(\xi \cos \alpha - \eta \sin \alpha)}$$

$$= \int_{-\infty}^{\infty} G \left(\frac{\partial \psi}{\partial y} \right)_{y = 0-} dx$$

provided again that we can show that the contributions of the small and large semicircles approach zero.   Here we have also made use of the fact that

$$\frac{\partial}{\partial y} [e^{ikr \cos (\theta - \alpha)} + e^{ikr \cos (\theta + \alpha)}]_{y = 0} = 0$$

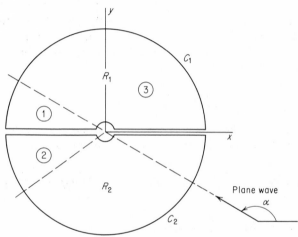

FIGURE 9

To complete the derivation of the integral equation we proceed as follows. Noting that for $x > 0$, $y = 0$, ψ and $\dfrac{\partial \psi}{\partial y}$ are continuous, we have

$$-2e^{ik\xi \cos \alpha} = 2\int_{-\infty}^{\infty} G \left(\frac{\partial \psi}{\partial y} \right)_{y=0} dx$$

$$-2e^{ik\xi \cos \alpha} = i\int_{-\infty}^{\infty} H_0^{(1)}(k |x - \xi|)I(x) \, dx$$

where $I(x) = \left(\dfrac{\partial \psi}{\partial y} \right)_{y=0}$.   For $x < 0$

$$\psi(\xi,0-) - \psi(\xi,0+) - 2e^{ik\xi \cos \alpha} = i\int_{-\infty}^{\infty} H_0^{(1)}(k |x - \xi|)I(x) \, dx$$

Hence, we have

$$i \int_{-\infty}^{\infty} H_0^{(1)}(k |x - \xi|) I(x) \, dx = g(\xi)$$

where $g(\xi) = -2e^{ik\xi \cos \alpha} \qquad x > 0$

$$g(\xi) = \psi(\xi, 0-) - \psi(\xi, 0+) - 2e^{ik\xi \cos \alpha} \qquad x < 0$$

The integral equation we have just derived is known as the **Wiener-Hopf integral equation.** It also occurs in the theory of stochastic processes. The function $g(\xi)$ is not completely known, but this does not turn out to be serious. We shall find that the equation can be solved by the **Wiener-Hopf technique,** which will be discussed in Chap. 6 in connection with the study of Fourier transforms.

To complete the discussion we must show that the integrals over the small and large semicircles approach zero as their radii approach zero and infinity, respectively. Let us take the radius of the small semicircle as δ. If the edge of the rigid sheet ($r = 0$) were a source point, then $\psi = O(\log r)$ as $r \to 0$. In this case

$$\int_0^{2\pi} \left(G \frac{\partial \psi}{\partial r} - \psi \frac{\partial G}{\partial r} \right)_{r=\delta} \delta \, d\theta = O(1)$$

as $\delta \to 0$, and the integrals over the small semicircles would not vanish as $\delta \to 0$. Therefore, we must assume that $\psi = o(\log r)$ as $r \to 0$,[1] which means physically that $r = 0$ is not a source point. Under this assumption,

$$\lim_{\delta \to 0} \int_0^{\pi} \left(G \frac{\partial \psi^{(1)}}{\partial r} - \psi^{(1)} \frac{\partial G}{\partial r} \right)_{r=\delta} \delta \, d\theta = 0$$

$$\lim_{\delta \to 0} \int_{\pi}^{2\pi} \left(G \frac{\partial \psi^{(2)}}{\partial r} - \psi^{(2)} \frac{\partial G}{\partial r} \right)_{r=\delta} \delta \, d\theta = 0$$

As far as the large semicircles are concerned, we note that for $\alpha < \theta < 2\pi - \alpha$ we have, in effect, applied Green's identity to $\bar{\psi}_s$, which satisfies the radiation condition, and hence

$$\bar{\psi}_s = \frac{e^{ikr}}{\sqrt{r}} h(\theta) + O(r^{-\frac{3}{2}})$$

Clearly $\int_0^{2\pi} \left(G \frac{\partial \bar{\psi}_s}{\partial r} - \bar{\psi}_s \frac{\partial G}{\partial r} \right)_{r=D} D \, d\theta = O\left(\frac{1}{D}\right)$

as $D \to \infty$, where D is the radius of the large semicircle. Therefore,

$$\lim_{D \to \infty} \int_0^{2\pi} \left(G \frac{\partial \bar{\psi}_s}{\partial r} - \bar{\psi}_s \frac{\partial G}{\partial r} \right)_{r=D} D \, d\theta = 0$$

---

[1] $f(r) = o(\log r)$ as $r \to 0$ implies that $f(r)/\log r \to 0$ as $r \to 0$.

It remains to show that

$$\int_0^\alpha \left(G \frac{\partial}{\partial r} e^{ikr\cos(\theta-\alpha)} - e^{ikr\cos(\theta-\alpha)} \frac{\partial G}{\partial r} \right)_{r=D} D\, d\theta = O\!\left(\frac{1}{\sqrt{D}}\right)$$

$$\int_{2\pi-\alpha}^{2\pi} \left(G \frac{\partial}{\partial r} e^{ikr\cos(\theta+\alpha)} - e^{ikr\cos(\theta+\alpha)} \frac{\partial G}{\partial r} \right)_{r=D} D\, d\theta = O\!\left(\frac{1}{\sqrt{D}}\right)$$

as $D \to \infty$.   We consider the first of these integrals only.   The second is very similar.

$$\int_0^\alpha \left(G \frac{\partial}{\partial r} e^{ikr\cos(\theta-\alpha)} - e^{ikr\cos(\theta-\alpha)} \frac{\partial G}{\partial r} \right)_{r=D} D\, d\theta$$

$$= \int_0^\alpha ik\sqrt{D}\, g(\theta)[\cos(\theta-\alpha)-1]e^{ikD[\cos(\theta-\alpha)-1]}\, d\theta + O\!\left(\frac{1}{\sqrt{D}}\right)$$

$$= -\int_0^\alpha 2ik\sqrt{D}\, g(\theta)\sin^2\!\left(\frac{\theta-\alpha}{2}\right)e^{2ikD\cos^2(\theta-\alpha)/2}\, d\theta + O\!\left(\frac{1}{\sqrt{D}}\right)$$

$$= \frac{1}{\sqrt{D}}\int_0^\alpha g(\theta)\tan\left(\frac{\theta-\alpha}{2}\right)e^{2ikD\cos^2(\theta-\alpha)/2}\, d[e^{ikD\cos^2(\theta-\alpha)/2}] + O\!\left(\frac{1}{\sqrt{D}}\right)$$

$$= \left[\frac{g(\theta)}{\sqrt{D}} \tan\left(\frac{\theta-\alpha}{2}\right)e^{2ikD\cos^2(\theta-\alpha)/2} \right]_0^\alpha$$

$$- \frac{1}{\sqrt{D}}\int_0^\alpha e^{2ikD\cos^2(\theta-\alpha)/2}\frac{d}{d\theta}\left[g(\theta)\tan\left(\frac{\theta-\alpha}{2}\right) \right] d\theta + O\!\left(\frac{1}{\sqrt{D}}\right)$$

$$= O\!\left(\frac{1}{\sqrt{D}}\right)$$

The integration by parts is valid since $\dfrac{\theta-\alpha}{2} \neq \dfrac{\pi}{2}$ in the range of integration.

The discussion of the other integral is identical except for the change of the limits of integration and the change from $\theta - \alpha$ to $\theta + \alpha$ in the integrand. This completes the derivation of the Wiener-Hopf integral equation for the half-plane problem.   We shall return to the problem in Sec. 6.4.

Exercise 4.5

Derive the appropriate Wiener-Hopf integral equation for the half-plane diffraction problem with the boundary condition $\psi = 0$ on the sheet.   HINT: Use the Green's function

$$G(x,y;\xi,\eta) = \frac{i}{4}H_0^{(1)}[k\sqrt{(x-\xi)^2 + (y-\eta)^2}] - \frac{i}{4}H_0^{(1)}k[\sqrt{(x-\xi)^2 + (y+\eta)^2}]$$

References

Courant, Richard, and David Hilbert: "Methods of Mathematical Physics," Interscience Publishers, Inc., New York, 1953, vol. I.

Friedman, Bernard: "Principles and Techniques of Applied Mathematics," John Wiley & Sons, Inc., New York, 1956.

Hildebrand, F. B.: "Methods of Applied Mathematics," Prentice-Hall, Inc., Englewood Cliffs, N.J., 1952.

Murnaghan, Francis D.: "Introduction to Applied Mathematics," John Wiley & Sons, Inc., New York, 1948.

Noble, Benjamin: "The Wiener-Hopf Technique," Pergamon Press, Inc., New York, 1958.

Page, Chester H.: "Physical Mathematics," D. Van Nostrand Company, Inc., Princeton, N.J., 1955.

Sneddon, Ian N.: "Elements of Partial Differential Equations," McGraw-Hill Book Company, Inc., New York, 1957.

Sommerfeld, Arnold J.: "Partial Differential Equations in Physics," Academic Press, Inc., New York, 1949.

Chapter 5. Integral Equations

5.1 Integral Equations Formulation of Boundary-value Problems

As we have already indicated in the previous chapter, certain nonhomogeneous boundary-value problems can be formulated in terms of integral equations by use of Green's functions. The procedure is much more general than these earlier remarks would indicate and applies to homogeneous problems as well as to nonhomogeneous problems. Consider, for example, the homogeneous boundary-value problem

$$\nabla^2 \psi + \lambda \psi = 0 \qquad \text{in } V$$

$$\frac{d\psi}{dn} + \alpha \psi = 0 \qquad \text{on } S$$

where V is a finite volume bounded by the surface S. Let G be a Green's function with the following properties:

1. $\nabla^2 G = 0$ except at (ξ, η, ζ) in V

2. $\dfrac{dG}{dn} + \alpha G = 0$ on S

3. $G = \dfrac{1}{4\pi} \dfrac{1}{R} + H(\xi, \eta, \zeta; x, y, z)$

where $R = \sqrt{(x - \xi)^2 + (y - \eta)^2 + (z - \zeta)^2}$, and H is a solution of Laplace's equation everywhere in V. Then

$$\iiint\limits_V \left\{ G \nabla^2 \psi - \psi \nabla^2 G \right\} dV = \iint\limits_S \left\{ G \left(\frac{d\psi}{dn} + \alpha \psi \right) - \psi \left(\frac{dG}{dn} + \alpha G \right) \right\} dS = 0$$

or
$$\psi(\xi, \eta, \zeta) = \lambda \iiint\limits_V \psi G \, dV$$

226

The last equation is a **homogeneous integral equation of the second kind.**[1]
Using the same Green's function we can also formulate the solution of the non-homogeneous boundary-value problem

$$\nabla^2 \psi + \lambda \psi = -f \qquad \text{in } V$$

$$\frac{d\psi}{dn} + \alpha \psi = 0 \qquad \text{on } S$$

In this case, the integral equation is

$$\psi(\xi, \eta, \zeta) = F(\xi, \eta, \zeta) + \lambda \iiint_V \psi G \, dV$$

where $F(\xi, \eta, \zeta) = \iiint_V fG \, dV$. This time we have a **nonhomogeneous integral equation of the second kind.** In this case, λ is a known constant, whereas in the homogeneous integral equation above λ is an eigenvalue to be determined in the course of solving the integral equation.

In the one-dimensional case, we have integral equations corresponding to Sturm-Liouville problems. Here the general homogeneous problem is

$$(py')' - qy + \lambda \rho y = 0 \qquad a \le x \le b$$

subject to one of five homogeneous boundary conditions at a and b:

1. $y = 0$
2. $y' = 0$
3. $y' + \alpha y = 0$
4. y and y' finite when $p = 0$
5. $y(a) = y(b)$ and $p(a)y'(a) = p(b)y'(b)$

Let $L(y) = (py')' - qy$. Then the differential equation can be written $L(y) + \lambda \rho y = 0$. We take the Green's function with the following properties:

1. $L(G) = 0$ except at $x = \xi$
2. G continuous at $x = \xi$
3. $G'(\xi; \xi+) - G'(\xi; \xi-) = -1/p(\xi)$
4 G satisfies the same boundary conditions as y

Then $$\int_a^b \{GL(y) - yL(G)\} \, dx = 0$$

---

[1] An integral equation of the form $f(x) = \int_a^b K(\xi; x)\psi(\xi) \, d\xi$ is known as an **integral equation of the first kind.** Here the unknown ψ appears only under the integral sign and f and K are known functions, whereas in the integral equation of the second kind the unknown appears both under the integral and outside.

and
$$y(\xi) = \lambda \int_a^b G(\xi;x)\rho(x)y(x)\,dx$$

We introduce the new unknown $\psi(x) = \sqrt{\rho(x)}\,y(x)$. Then

$$\sqrt{\rho(\xi)}\,y(\xi) = \lambda \int_a^b \sqrt{\rho(\xi)\rho(x)}\,G(\xi;x)\sqrt{\rho(x)}\,y(x)\,dx$$

or
$$\psi(\xi) = \lambda \int_a^b K(\xi;x)\psi(x)\,dx$$

where $K(\xi;x) = \sqrt{\rho(\xi)\rho(x)}\,G(\xi;x)$. We again have a homogeneous integral equation of the second kind. K is called the **kernel** of the integral equation. The same Green's function leads to the equation

$$y(\xi) = \int_a^b f(x)G(\xi;x)\,dx + \lambda \int_a^b G(\xi;x)\rho(x)y(x)\,dx$$

for the solution of the nonhomogeneous Sturm-Liouville equation

$$(py')' - qy + \lambda\rho y = -f$$

Then we have the nonhomogeneous integral equation of the second kind

$$\psi(\xi) = F(\xi) + \int_a^b K(\xi;x)\psi(x)\,dx$$

where $\psi = \sqrt{\rho}\,y$, $F = \int_a^b \sqrt{\rho}\,fG\,dx$, and $K = \sqrt{\rho(\xi)\rho(x)}\,G(\xi;x)$.

As an example of an integral equation, consider the problem corresponding to the Sturm-Liouville problem $y'' + \lambda y$, $0 \le x \le 1$, with $y(0) = y(1) = 0$. Then $G'' = 0$ except at $x = \xi$. Therefore,

$$G = ax + b \qquad 0 \le x < \xi$$
$$G = cx + d \qquad \xi < x \le 1$$

$G(0) = 0$ implies that $b = 0$. $G(1) = 0$ implies that $d = -c$. G is continuous at $x = \xi$. Hence, $a\xi = c\xi - c$. Finally, $G'(\xi+) - G'(\xi-) = -1$ implies that $c - a = -1$. Therefore

$$G = (1 - \xi)x \qquad 0 \le x < \xi$$
$$G = \xi(1 - x) \qquad \xi < x \le 1$$

The integral equation is then

$$y(\xi) = \lambda \int_0^\xi (1 - \xi)xy(x)\,dx + \lambda \int_\xi^1 \xi(1 - x)y(x)\,dx$$

It may not always be possible to define the Green's function from the four properties listed above. Consider, for example, the same equation

$y'' + \lambda y = 0, 0 \le x \le 1$, but with the boundary condition $y'(0) = y'(1) = 0$. If we proceed as above, we have $G'' = 0$, implying

$$G = ax + b \qquad 0 \le x < \xi$$

$$G = cx + d \qquad \xi < x \le 1$$

But the other conditions give $a = c = 0$ and $b = d$, and hence we have no Green's function. The difficulty here is that $\lambda = 0$ is an eigenvalue of the differential equation. In fact, the properties listed above will never yield a Green's function for the Sturm-Liouville problem in the case where $\lambda = 0$ is an eigenvalue of the differential equation. Let u be the solution of the differential equation when $\lambda = 0$, satisfying a set of homogeneous boundary conditions. Then

$$L(u) = 0$$

Let v be a solution of the differential equation for $\lambda \ne 0$, satisfying the same boundary conditions. Then

$$L(v) + \lambda \rho v = 0$$

Therefore, $\qquad \lambda \int_a^b \rho uv \, dx = \int_a^b \{vL(u) - uL(v)\} \, dx = 0$

and u and v are orthogonal. Because of this orthogonality we can define a Green's function satisfying the differential equation

$$L(G) - A\rho u = 0$$

except at $x = \xi$, leaving the other three properties unchanged.

$$\int_a^b \{GL(v) - v[L(G) - A\rho u]\} \, dx = 0$$

$$v(\xi) = \lambda \int_a^b \rho vG \, dx$$

If u is normalized, i.e.,

$$\int_a^b \rho u^2 \, dx = 1$$

then we can determine A, for

$$0 = \int_a^b \{GL(u) - uL(G)\} \, dx = u(\xi) - A\int_a^b \rho u^2 \, dx$$

Hence, $A = u(\xi)$.

Getting back to our example, we wish to solve $G'' = 1$. Therefore,

$$G = \tfrac{1}{2}x^2 + ax + b \qquad 0 \le x < \xi$$
$$G = \tfrac{1}{2}x^2 + cx + d \qquad \xi < x \le 1$$

$G'(0) = 0$ implies $a = 0$. $G'(1) = 0$ implies $c = -1$. $G(\xi+) = G(\xi-)$ implies $b = d - \xi$.   Then

$$G = \tfrac{1}{2}x^2 + d - \xi \qquad 0 \leq x < \xi$$

$$G = \tfrac{1}{2}x^2 + d - x \qquad \xi < x \leq 1$$

In order to make G symmetric, we pick $d = \tfrac{1}{2}\xi^2$.   The integral equation is then

$$y(\xi) = \lambda \int_0^\xi [\tfrac{1}{2}(x^2 + \xi^2) - \xi] y(x)\, dx + \lambda \int_\xi^1 [\tfrac{1}{2}(x^2 + \xi^2) - x] y(x)\, dx$$

Exercises 5.1

1. Formulate an integral equation for the solution of the Sturm-Liouville problem $(xy')' + \lambda xy = 0$, $1 \leq x \leq e$, $y(1) = y(e) = 0$.

2. Formulate an integral equation for the solution of the Sturm-Liouville problem $[(1 - x^2)y']' + \lambda y = 0$, $-1 \leq x \leq 1$, $y(-1)$ and $y(1)$ finite.

5.2 Hilbert-Schmidt Theory

We saw, in the previous section, that the integral equations associated with the homogeneous and nonhomogeneous Sturm-Liouville problems are the **homogeneous Fredholm equation**

$$\psi(\xi) = \lambda \int_a^b K(\xi;x)\psi(x)\, dx$$

and the **nonhomogeneous Fredholm equation**

$$\psi(\xi) = F(\xi) + \lambda \int_a^b K(\xi;x)\psi(x)\, dx$$

In this case, the kernel K is real, symmetric, and continuous over the rectangle $a \leq x \leq b$, $a \leq \xi \leq b$.   Among other things, this implies that

$$\int_a^b \int_a^b K^2(\xi;x)\, d\xi\, dx$$

exists.   In the homogeneous equation λ is an eigenvalue to be determined in the course of solving the equation.   In the nonhomogeneous equation λ is a known constant, and we shall find that, in general, the equation will have a solution unless perhaps λ is an eigenvalue of the homogeneous equation.   If λ is an eigenvalue of the homogeneous equation, a necessary condition for the existence of a solution of the nonhomogeneous equation is that the function $F(x)$ be orthogonal to the eigenfunctions corresponding to that eigenvalue, i.e., if $\lambda = \lambda_i$, where

$$\psi_i(\xi) = \lambda_i \int_a^b K(\xi;x)\psi_i(x)\, dx$$

then $\int_a^b \psi(\xi)\psi_i(\xi)\,d\xi = \int_a^b F(\xi)\psi_i(\xi)\,d\xi + \lambda_i \int_a^b \int_a^b K(\xi;x)\psi(x)\psi_i(\xi)\,dx\,d\xi$

$$= \int_a^b F(\xi)\psi_i(\xi)\,d\xi + \int_a^b \psi(x)\psi_i(x)\,dx$$

Hence, $\int_a^b F(\xi)\psi_i(\xi)\,d\xi = 0$.   In this case, if a solution ψ of the nonhomo-geneous equation exists, it is not unique, for

$$\lambda_i \int_a^b K(\xi;x)[\psi(x) + c\psi_i(x)]\,dx + F(\xi) = F(\xi) + \lambda_i \int_a^b K(\xi;x)\psi(x)\,dx + c\psi_i(\xi)$$
$$= \psi(\xi) + c\psi_i(\xi)$$

implying that $\psi(\xi) + c\psi_i(\xi)$ is also a solution for arbitrary c.

Let ψ_i and ψ_j be solutions of the homogeneous equation corresponding to different eigenvalues λ_i and λ_j.   Then

$$\psi_i(\xi) = \lambda_i \int_a^b K(\xi;x)\psi_i(x)\,dx$$

$$\psi_j(\xi) = \lambda_j \int_a^b K(\xi;x)\psi_j(x)\,dx$$

and

$$(\lambda_i - \lambda_j)\int_a^b \psi_i(\xi)\psi_j(\xi)\,d\xi = \lambda_i\lambda_j \int_a^b \int_a^b K(\xi;x)\psi_i(x)\psi_j(\xi)\,dx\,d\xi$$

$$-\lambda_i\lambda_j \int_a^b \int_a^b K(\xi;x)\psi_j(x)\psi_i(\xi)\,dx\,d\xi$$

$$= \lambda_i\lambda_j \int_a^b \int_a^b K(\xi;x)\psi_i(x)\psi_j(\xi)\,dx\,d\xi$$

$$-\lambda_i\lambda_j \int_a^b \int_a^b K(x;\xi)\psi_i(x)\psi_j(\xi)\,d\xi\,dx$$

Interchanging the order of integration and making use of the symmetry of K, we have

$$(\lambda_i - \lambda_j)\int_a^b \psi_i(\xi)\psi_j(\xi)\,d\xi = 0$$

But $\lambda_i \neq \lambda_j$; therefore, $\int_a^b \psi_i(\xi)\psi_j(\xi)\,d\xi = 0$.   Hence, solutions corresponding to different eigenvalues are orthogonal.   Also, since the equation is homo-geneous, we can assume that the solutions are normalized, i.e.,

$$\int_a^b |\psi|^2\,d\xi = 1$$

Next we show that the eigenvalues are real. Let ψ be a solution with eigenvalue λ. Then

$$\psi(\xi) = \lambda \int_a^b K(\xi;x)\psi(x)\,dx$$

and

$$\psi^*(\xi) = \lambda^* \int_a^b K(\xi;x)\psi^*(x)\,dx$$

If $\lambda \neq \lambda^*$, then

$$\int_a^b \psi\psi^*\,d\xi = \int_a^b |\psi|^2\,d\xi = 0$$

which implies that $\psi \equiv 0$. Therefore, either λ is real or ψ is the trivial solution.

If there are an infinite number of solutions of the homogeneous equation, then there can be only a finite number of linearly independent solutions corresponding to the same eigenvalue. We shall show this as follows. Let $\psi_1, \psi_2, \ldots$ be an infinite set of linearly independent solutions. Since they are linearly independent, we can assume that they are orthonormal, i.e.,

$$\int_a^b \psi_i \psi_j\,dx = \delta_{ij}$$

Let us consider the problem of approximating in the least-mean-square sense the kernel by a series of a finite number of these functions. In other words, we wish to minimize

$$\int_a^b \left| K(\xi;x) - \sum_{i=1}^n c_i \psi_i(x) \right|^2 dx$$

We know from Chap. 1 that to do this we must choose

$$c_i = \int_a^b K(\xi;x)\psi_i(x)\,dx = \frac{\psi_i(\xi)}{\lambda_i}$$

In this case,

$$\min \int_a^b \left| K(\xi;x) - \sum_{i=1}^n c_i \psi_i(x) \right|^2 dx = \int_a^b K^2(\xi;x)\,dx - \sum_{i=1}^n c_i^2 \geq 0$$

Therefore,

$$\sum_{i=1}^n \frac{\psi_i^2(\xi)}{\lambda_i^2} \leq \int_a^b K^2(\xi;x)\,dx$$

and

$$\sum_{i=1}^n \frac{\int_a^b \psi_i^2(\xi)\,dx}{\lambda_i^2} = \sum_{i=1}^n \frac{1}{\lambda_i^2} \leq \int_a^b \int_a^b K^2(\xi;x)\,dx\,d\xi < \infty$$

But this is true for any n. Therefore,

$$\sum_{i=1}^\infty \frac{1}{\lambda_i^2}$$

converges.　This implies that

$$\lim_{i \to \infty} \frac{1}{\lambda_i^2} = 0$$

and that there can be at most a finite number of linearly independent solutions corresponding to the same eigenvalue.　The problem can be degenerate, i.e., more than one linearly independent solution can correspond to the same eigenvalue, but the degeneracy must be finite.

Let us assume that there are an infinite number of linearly independent solutions ψ_i of the homogeneous equation.　We can assume that these functions are orthonormal.　Consider the nonhomogeneous integral equation

$$\psi(\xi) = F(\xi) + \lambda \int_a^b K(\xi;x)\psi(x)\,dx$$

or

$$g(\xi) = \psi(\xi) - F(\xi) = \lambda \int_a^b K(\xi;x)\psi(x)\,dx$$

We wish to approximate g by a series of solutions of the homogeneous equation. The best approximation in the least-mean-square sense would have coefficients.

$$
\begin{aligned}
c_i &= \int_a^b g(\xi)\psi_i(\xi)\,d\xi \\
&= \lambda \int_a^b \int_a^b K(\xi;x)\psi(x)\psi_i(\xi)\,dx\,d\xi \\
&= \frac{\lambda}{\lambda_i} \int_a^b \psi_i(x)\psi(x)\,dx \\
&= \frac{\lambda}{\lambda_i} \int_a^b \psi_i(x)[g(x) + F(x)]\,dx \\
&= \frac{\lambda}{\lambda_i}(c_i + \gamma_i) \qquad \text{(no summation on } i\text{)}
\end{aligned}
$$

where

$$\gamma_i = \int_a^b F(x)\psi_i(x)\,dx$$

Solving for c_i, we have

$$c_i = \frac{\lambda \gamma_i}{\lambda_i - \lambda}$$

Therefore, the c's can be determined provided $\lambda \neq \lambda_i$ for any i.　We shall be able to show that

$$g(\xi) = \sum_{i=1}^{\infty} c_i \psi_i(\xi)$$

and the series converges uniformly.　Hence, the solution of the nonhomogeneous equation exists and is unique if $\lambda \neq \lambda_i$.　If $\lambda = \lambda_i$ for some i, the solution will still exist if $\gamma_i = 0$. But in this case c_i is arbitrary, and so the solution is not unique. We have thus shown that we can concentrate on the solution of the homogeneous equation.

As a first case, let us consider the homogeneous integral equation with a **degenerate kernel.** The kernel is said to be degenerate if it can be expressed as

$$K(\xi;x) = \sum_{i=1}^{n} \alpha_i(\xi)\beta_i(x)$$

Consider the set of $2n$ functions $\alpha_1(x), \alpha_2(x), \ldots, \alpha_n(x), \beta_1(x), \beta_2(x), \ldots, \beta_n(x)$. From this set we can construct a set of linearly independent functions $\gamma_1(x), \gamma_2(x), \ldots, \gamma_p(x)$, with $p \leq 2n$. We can assume that this set is orthonormal, i.e.,

$$\int_a^b \gamma_i(x)\gamma_j(x)\,dx = \delta_{ij}$$

Then
$$\alpha_i(\xi) = a_{ij}\gamma_j(\xi) \qquad i = 1, 2, 3, \ldots, n$$

$$\beta_i(x) = b_{ij}\gamma_j(x) \qquad j = 1, 2, 3, \ldots, p$$

and
$$K(\xi;x) = a_{ij}b_{ik}\gamma_j(\xi)\gamma_k(x)$$

$$= c_{jk}\gamma_j(\xi)\gamma_k(x)$$

By the symmetry of K, we have

$$K(\xi;x) - K(x;\xi) = c_{jk}\gamma_j(\xi)\gamma_k(x) - c_{jk}\gamma_j(x)\gamma_k(\xi)$$

$$= (c_{jk} - c_{kj})\gamma_j(\xi)\gamma_k(x) = 0$$

Therefore, $c_{jk} = c_{kj}$, so the matrix C is symmetric. The integral equation is then

$$\psi(\xi) = \lambda \int_a^b c_{jk}\gamma_j(\xi)\gamma_k(x)\psi(x)\,dx$$

$$= \lambda c_{jk}\gamma_j(\xi)y_k$$

where
$$y_k = \int_a^b \gamma_k(x)\psi(x)\,dx$$

Multiplying by $\gamma_i(\xi)$ and integrating,

$$y_i = \lambda c_{jk}\delta_{ij}y_k$$

$$= \lambda c_{ik}y_k$$

or $[C - (1/\lambda)I]Y = O$. This is a system of p homogeneous linear equations in p unknowns. The characteristic equation is

$$\left| C - \frac{1}{\lambda}I \right| = 0$$

This equation has p roots, and since C is real and symmetric, there are p real roots, $\mu_i = 1/\lambda_i$. Corresponding to each root μ_i there is an eigenvector Y_i and a solution of the integral equation

$$\psi_i(\xi) = \lambda_i c_{jk}\gamma_j(\xi)y_{ik}$$

(no summation on i). Here y_{ik} is the kth component of the ith eigenvector. One can show directly that the solutions are orthonormal, for

$$\int_a^b \psi_i\psi_j \, d\xi = \lambda_i\lambda_j c_{mn}y_{in}c_{pq}y_{jq}\int_a^b \gamma_m(\xi)\gamma_p(\xi) \, d\xi$$

$$= y_{im}y_{jp}\delta_{mp}$$

$$= (Y_i, Y_j) = \delta_{ij}$$

We can approach the general problem from the point of view of the calculus of variations. We first define the quadratic functional

$$Q[f] = \int_a^b\int_a^b K(\xi;x)f(\xi)f(x) \, d\xi \, dx$$

where f is a piecewise continuous function. $Q[f]$ is bounded if f is normalized, since Schwarz's inequality implies

$$(Q[f])^2 \leq \int_a^b f^2(x) \, dx \int_a^b\left[\int_a^b K(\xi;x)f(\xi) \, d\xi\right]^2 dx$$

$$\leq \int_a^b f^2(x) \, dx \int_a^b f^2(\xi) \, d\xi \int_a^b\int_a^b K^2(\xi;x) \, d\xi \, dx$$

$$\leq \int_a^b\int_a^b K^2(\xi;x) \, d\xi \, dx < \infty$$

Furthermore, $Q[f]$ cannot be zero for all f unless $K \equiv 0$, for then

$$Q[f,g] = \tfrac{1}{2}\{Q[f+g] - Q[f] - Q[g]\}$$

would also be zero for all f and g. Then letting

$$g(x) = \int_a^b K(\xi;x)f(\xi) \, d\xi$$

we have
$$Q[f,g] = \int_a^b\left[\int_a^b K(\xi;x)f(\xi) \, d\xi\right]^2 dx = 0$$

This implies that

$$\int_a^b K(\xi;x)f(\xi) \, d\xi = 0$$

for arbitrary f.   Let $f(\xi) = K(\xi;x)$.   Then

$$\int_a^b K^2(\xi;x)\,d\xi = 0$$

which implies that $K \equiv 0$.

Thus $Q[f]$ is greater than zero or less than zero for some f. We also know that it is bounded. Let us assume that $Q[f] > 0$ for some f, and furthermore that it takes on a maximum value $1/\lambda_1$ for some function ψ_1. Letting $f = \psi_1 + \epsilon\eta$, we have

$$Q[\psi_1 + \epsilon\eta] \le \frac{1}{\lambda_1} N[\psi_1 + \epsilon\eta]$$

for an arbitrary function η and an arbitrary constant ϵ.   Here $N[f] = \int_a^b f^2\,dx$. A necessary condition for this inequality to hold is

$$Q[\psi_1,\eta] - \frac{1}{\lambda_1} N[\psi_1,\eta] = 0$$

or
$$\int_a^b \left[\int_a^b K(\xi;x)\psi_1(\xi)\,d\xi - \frac{1}{\lambda_1}\,\psi_1(x)\right]\eta(x)\,dx = 0$$

But since η is arbitrary,

$$\lambda_1 \int_a^b K(\xi;x)\psi_1(\xi)\,d\xi - \psi_1(x) = 0$$

and this is the integral equation. Therefore, a necessary condition for the maximizing function is that it satisfy the integral equation.

To get the next eigenvalue and eigenfunction we maximize $Q[f]$ subject to $N[f] = 1$ and $N[f,\psi_1] = 0$. This can be accomplished by introducing a new symmetric kernel

$$K_1(\xi;x) = K(\xi;x) - \frac{\psi_1(\xi)\psi_1(x)}{\lambda_1}$$

and a new functional

$$Q_1[f] = \int_a^b \int_a^b K_1(\xi;x)f(\xi)f(x)\,d\xi\,dx$$

We maximize $Q_1[f]$ subject to $N[f] = 1$. If the maximum is $1/\lambda_2$ and the maximizing function is ψ_2, then

$$\psi_2(x) = \lambda_2 \int_a^b K_1(\xi;x)\psi_2(\xi)\,d\xi$$

$$= \lambda_2 \int_a^b K(\xi;x)\psi_2(\xi)\,d\xi$$

$$- \frac{\lambda_2}{\lambda_1}\int_a^b \psi_1(x)\psi_1(\xi)\psi_2(\xi)\,d\xi$$

and
$$\int_a^b \psi_1(x)\psi_2(x)\,dx = \lambda_2\int_a^b \psi_2(\xi)\left[\int_a^b K(\xi;x)\psi_1(x)\,dx\right]d\xi$$

$$-\frac{\lambda_2}{\lambda_1}\int_a^b \psi_1(\xi)\psi_2(\xi)\,d\xi\int_a^b \psi_1^2(x)\,dx$$

$$=\frac{\lambda_2}{\lambda_1}\int_a^b \psi_1(\xi)\psi_2(\xi)\,d\xi - \frac{\lambda_2}{\lambda_1}\int_a^b \psi_1(\xi)\psi_2(\xi)\,d\xi$$

$$= 0$$

Therefore, the integral equation is in reality

$$\psi_2(x) = \lambda_2\int_a^b K(\xi;x)\psi_2(\xi)\,d\xi$$

Also

$$\frac{1}{\lambda_2} = Q_1[\psi_2] = \int_a^b\int_a^b K(\xi;x)\psi_2(\xi)\psi_2(x)\,d\xi\,dx - \frac{1}{\lambda_1}\left[\int_a^b \psi_1(x)\psi_2(x)\,dx\right]^2$$

$$=\int_a^b\int_a^b K(\xi;x)\psi_2(\xi)\psi_2(x)\,d\xi\,dx = Q[\psi_2] \le Q[\psi_1] = \frac{1}{\lambda_1}$$

Therefore, $\lambda_1 \le \lambda_2$. We continue in this way generating a sequence of eigen-functions and eigenvalues

$$\lambda_1 \le \lambda_2 \le \lambda_3 \le \cdots$$

keeping in mind that we can get only a finite number of solutions corresponding to the same eigenvalue. This process will continue indefinitely, unless at some stage

$$Q_n[f] = \int_a^b\int_a^b\left[K(\xi;x) - \sum_{i=1}^n \frac{\psi_i(\xi)\psi_i(x)}{\lambda_i}\right]f(\xi)f(x)\,d\xi\,dx$$

is zero for all f. But this would imply that

$$K(\xi;x) = \sum_{i=1}^n \frac{\psi_i(\xi)\psi_i(x)}{\lambda_i}$$

and the kernel would be degenerate.

It may happen that $Q[f]$ is negative for some f. We then would minimize $Q[f]$ subject to $N[f] = 1$. If the minimum is $1/\lambda_{-1}$, and the minimizing function is ψ_{-1}, then

$$Q[\psi_{-1} + \epsilon\eta] \ge \frac{1}{\lambda_{-1}}N[\psi_{-1} + \epsilon\eta]$$

for arbitrary ϵ and η. A necessary condition for ψ_{-1} is

$$Q[\psi_{-1},\eta] - \frac{1}{\lambda_{-1}}N[\psi_{-1},\eta] = 0$$

and we have the integral equation

$$\psi_{-1}(x) = \lambda_{-1} \int_a^b K(\xi;x)\psi_{-1}(\xi)\, d\xi$$

ψ_{-1} is orthogonal to every solution with a positive eigenvalue, since λ_{-1} is negative. We next minimize

$$Q_{-1}[f] = \int_a^b \int_a^b \left[K(\xi;x) - \frac{\psi_{-1}(\xi)\psi_{-1}(x)}{\lambda_{-1}} \right] f(\xi)f(x)\, d\xi\, dx$$

subject to $N[f] = 1$. If the minimum is $1/\lambda_{-2}$ and the minimizing function is ψ_{-2}, then we arrive at the integral equation

$$\psi_{-2}(x) = \lambda_{-2} \int_a^b K(\xi;x)\psi_{-2}(\xi)\, d\xi$$

with $\int_a^b \psi_{-1}(x)\psi_{-2}(x)\, dx = 0$ and $\lambda_{-2} \le \lambda_{-1}$. Continuing, we generate a sequence of eigenvalues

$$\lambda_{-1} \ge \lambda_{-2} \ge \lambda_{-3} \ge \cdots$$

Let us renumber the eigenvalues and eigenfunctions according to increasing absolute value of the eigenvalue, i.e.,

$$|\lambda_1| \le |\lambda_2| \le |\lambda_3| \le \cdots$$

We then have the following expansion theorem. Every continuous function $g(x)$ which is an integral transform of $K(\xi;x)$, i.e.,

$$g(x) = \int_a^b K(\xi;x)h(\xi)\, d\xi$$

where h is piecewise continuous, can be expanded in a uniformly convergent series in the eigenfunctions of the integral equation

$$\psi(x) = \lambda \int_a^b K(\xi;x)\psi(\xi)\, d\xi$$

i.e.,

$$g(x) = \sum_{i=1}^{\infty} c_i \psi_i(x)$$

where

$$c_i = \int_a^b g(x)\psi_i(x)\, dx$$

We prove this as follows.

$$c_i = \int_a^b g(x)\psi_i(x)\, dx = \int_a^b \int_a^b K(\xi;x)h(\xi)\psi_i(x)\, d\xi\, dx$$

$$= \frac{b_i}{\lambda_i} \qquad \text{(no summation on } i\text{)}$$

where $b_i = \int_a^b h(x)\psi_i(x)\,dx$. By Bessel's inequality, we have

$$\sum_{i=1}^{\infty} b_i^2 \leq \int_a^b h^2(x)\,dx$$

$$\sum_{i=1}^{\infty} \frac{\psi_i^2(x)}{\lambda_i^2} \leq \int_a^b K^2(\xi;x)\,d\xi \leq M^2(b-a)$$

where M is the maximum of $|K(\xi;x)|$ in the square $a \leq \xi \leq b$, $a \leq x \leq b$. Now consider the series

$$\sum_{i=1}^{\infty} c_i\psi_i(x) = \sum_{i=1}^{\infty} b_i \frac{\psi_i(x)}{\lambda_i}$$

The remainder after n terms in this series is

$$R_n = \frac{b_{n+1}\psi_{n+1}(x)}{\lambda_{n+1}} + \frac{b_{n+2}\psi_{n+1}(x)}{\lambda_{n+2}} + \cdots$$

By Schwarz's inequality we have

$$R_n^2 \leq [b_{n+1}^2 + b_{n+2}^2 + \cdots]\left[\frac{\psi_{n+1}^2(x)}{\lambda_{n+1}^2} + \frac{\psi_{n+2}^2(x)}{\lambda_{n+2}^2} + \cdots\right]$$

Since $\sum_{i=1}^{\infty} b_i^2$ converges, $\sum_{i=n+1}^{\infty} b_i^2$ can be made arbitrarily small by making n sufficiently large. Also $\sum_{i=n+1}^{\infty} \frac{\psi_i^2(x)}{\lambda_i^2}$ is bounded uniformly in x. Therefore, $R_n \to 0$ as $n \to \infty$, and the convergence is uniform in x. Therefore, the series converges to a continuous function $\gamma(x)$. It remains to show that $\gamma(x)$ and $g(x)$ are the same. Let

$$K_n(\xi;x) = K(\xi;x) - \sum_{i=1}^{n} \frac{\psi_i(\xi)\psi_i(x)}{\lambda_i}$$

Then

$$\int_a^b K_n(\xi;x)h(\xi)\,d\xi = g(x) - \gamma_n(x)$$

where

$$\gamma_n(x) = \sum_{i=1}^{n} \frac{b_i\psi_i(x)}{\lambda_i}$$

and we know that

$$\lim_{n\to\infty} \gamma_n(x) = \gamma(x)$$

Next we have

$$\int_a^b [g(x) - \gamma_n(x)]\eta(x)\,dx = \int_a^b\int_a^b K_n(\xi;x)h(\xi)\eta(x)\,dx$$

$$= Q_n[h,\eta]$$

where $\eta(x)$ is an arbitrary continuous function. From the variational problem we have

$$|Q_n[h]| \leq \frac{1}{|\lambda_{n+1}|} N[h] \to 0 \qquad \text{as } n \to \infty$$

$$|Q_n[\eta]| \leq \frac{1}{|\lambda_{n+1}|} N[\eta] \to 0 \qquad \text{as } n \to \infty$$

$$|Q_n[h + \eta]| \leq \frac{1}{|\lambda_{n+1}|} N[h + \eta] \to 0 \qquad \text{as } n \to \infty$$

Therefore, $|Q_n[h,\eta]| \leq \frac{1}{2}\{|Q_n[h + \eta]| + |Q_n[h]| + |Q_n[\eta]|\}$

and $Q_n[h,\eta] = \int_a^b [g(x) - \gamma_n(x)] \eta(x) \, dx \to 0 \qquad \text{as } n \to \infty$

Then, by the uniform convergence,

$$\lim_{n \to \infty} \int_a^b [g(x) - \gamma_n(x)]\eta(x) \, dx$$

$$= \int_a^b [g(x) - \lim_{n \to \infty} \gamma_n(x)]\eta(x) \, dx$$

$$= \int_a^b [g(x) - \gamma(x)]\eta(x) \, dx = 0$$

But $\eta(x)$ is arbitrary, implying that $g(x) \equiv \gamma(x)$. This completes the proof of the expansion theorem.

Next we let $h(\xi) = K(\xi;y)$. Then

$$\bar{K}(x;y) = \int_a^b K(\xi;x)K(\xi;y) \, d\xi$$

is an integral transform. Therefore, $\bar{K}$ has an expansion

$$\bar{K}(x;y) = \sum_{i=1}^{\infty} \frac{\psi_i(x)}{\lambda_i} \int_a^b K(\xi;y)\psi_i(\xi) \, d\xi$$

$$= \sum_{i=1}^{\infty} \frac{\psi_i(x)\psi_i(y)}{\lambda_i^2}$$

which is uniformly convergent in x. Also

$$\bar{K}(x;x) = \sum_{i=1}^{\infty} \frac{\psi_i^2(x)}{\lambda_i^2} = \int_a^b K^2(\xi;x) \, d\xi$$

Then $\quad \displaystyle\int_a^b \left[K(\xi;x) - \sum_{i=1}^n \frac{\psi_i(\xi)\psi_i(x)}{\lambda_i} \right]^2 d\xi$

$$= \bar{K}(x;x) + \sum_{i=1}^n \frac{\psi_i^2(x)}{\lambda_i^2} - 2\sum_{i=1}^n \frac{\psi_i(x)}{\lambda_i} \int_a^b K(\xi;x)\psi_i(\xi)\, d\xi$$

$$= \bar{K}(x;x) - \sum_{i=1}^n \frac{\psi_i^2(x)}{\lambda_i^2}$$

Therefore, $\quad \displaystyle\lim_{n\to\infty} \int_a^b \left[K(\xi;x) - \sum_{i=1}^n \frac{\psi_i(\xi)\psi_i(x)}{\lambda_i} \right]^2 d\xi = 0$

and $$\sum_{i=1}^\infty \frac{\psi_i(\xi)\psi_i(x)}{\lambda_i}$$

converges in mean to the kernel $K(\xi;x)$.

If the nonhomogeneous Fredholm equation has a solution, then

$$g(\xi) = \psi(\xi) - F(\xi) = \lambda \int_a^b K(\xi;x)\psi(x)\, dx$$

is an integral transform, and hence

$$g(x) = \sum_{i=1}^\infty c_i \psi_i(x)$$

where $$c_i = \int_a^b g(x)\psi_i(x)\, dx$$

$$= \frac{\lambda}{\lambda_i - \lambda} \int_a^b F(x)\psi_i(x)\, dx$$

converges uniformly. Hence,

$$\psi(x) = F(x) + \sum_{i=1}^\infty \frac{\lambda\psi_i(x)}{\lambda_i - \lambda} \int_a^b F(x)\psi_i(x)\, dx$$

Alternatively, consider the series $\displaystyle\sum_{i=1}^\infty \frac{\lambda\gamma_i}{\lambda_i - \lambda} \psi_i(x)$, where $\gamma_i = \displaystyle\int_a^b F(x)\psi_i(x)\, dx$.
Let R_n be the remainder after n terms of the series. Then by Schwarz's inequality

$$R_n^2 \leq \sum_{i=n+1}^\infty \left[\frac{\lambda\lambda_i\gamma_i}{\lambda_i - \lambda} \right]^2 \sum_{i=n+1}^\infty \frac{[\psi_i(x)]^2}{\lambda_i^2}$$

For n sufficiently large $\left(\dfrac{\lambda\lambda_i}{\lambda_i - \lambda} \right)^2 < 4\lambda^2$ for all $i \geq n+1$. Thus,

$$\sum_{i=n+1}^\infty \left[\frac{\lambda\lambda_i\gamma_i}{\lambda_i - \lambda} \right]^2 < 4\lambda^2 \sum_{i=n+1}^\infty \gamma_i^2 \to 0$$

as $n \to \infty$. $\displaystyle\sum_{i=n+1}^{\infty} \frac{[\psi_i(x)]^2}{\lambda_i^2}$ is uniformly bounded. Therefore, $R_n \to 0$ as $n \to \infty$ uniformly in x, and hence

$$\sum_{i=1}^{\infty} \frac{\lambda \gamma_i}{\lambda_i - \lambda} \, \psi_i(x)$$

converges uniformly. Substituting in the integral equation, we have

$$\sum_{i=1}^{\infty} \frac{\lambda \gamma_i}{\lambda_i - \lambda} \, \psi_i(x) = \lambda \int_a^b K(\xi;x)F(\xi)\,d\xi + \lambda^2 \sum_{i=1}^{\infty} \frac{\gamma_i}{\lambda_i - \lambda} \int_a^b K(\xi;x)\psi_i(\xi)\,d\xi$$

$$= \lambda \int_a^b K(\xi;x)F(\xi)\,d\xi + \sum_{i=1}^{\infty} \frac{\lambda \gamma_i}{\lambda_i - \lambda} \, \psi_i(x) - \lambda \sum_{i=1}^{\infty} \frac{\gamma_i}{\lambda_i} \, \psi_i(x)$$

Now if $F(x)$ is a piecewise continuous function, then

$$\int_a^b K(\xi;x)F(\xi)\,d\xi = \sum_{i=1}^{\infty} \frac{\gamma_i}{\lambda_i} \, \psi_i(x)$$

where the convergence is uniform. Thus we see that the integral equation is satisfied by

$$\psi(x) = F(x) + \sum_{i=1}^{\infty} \frac{\lambda \gamma_i}{\lambda_i - \lambda} \, \psi_i(x)$$

We have thus established both existence and uniqueness of the solution of the nonhomogeneous integral equation in the case where λ is not an eigenvalue of the homogeneous equation. We have already seen that no solution can exist if $\lambda = \lambda_i$ for some i and $\int_a^b F(x)\psi_i(x)\,dx \neq 0$. However, if

$$\gamma_i = \int_a^b F(x)\psi_i(x)\,dx = 0$$

then the troublesome term in the series does not appear, and the above argument still holds, showing the existence of a solution. In this case, as we have seen, the solution is not unique, for any multiple of $\psi_i(x)$ can be added to the solution.

Recall that in solving boundary-value problems in Chap. 3, we had to obtain series expansions for the initial value of the solution in terms of eigenfunctions of the appropriate linear differential operator. For example, if we were to solve

$$\frac{\partial}{\partial x}\left(p \frac{\partial \phi}{\partial x}\right) - q\phi = \rho(x) \frac{\partial^2 \phi}{\partial t^2} \qquad a \leq x \leq b \qquad 0 \leq t$$

$$\phi(a,t) = \phi(b,t) = 0$$

$$\phi(x,0) = g(x)$$

$$\phi_t(x,0) = h(x)$$

we would attempt to find a solution in the form

$$\phi(x,t) = \sum_{i=1}^{\infty} (A_i \cos \sqrt{\lambda_i} t + B_i \sin \sqrt{\lambda_i} t) y_i(x)$$

where
$$(py_i')' - qy_i + \lambda_i \rho y_i = 0 \qquad a \leq x \leq b$$

$$y_i(a) = y_i(b) = 0$$

For the method to be valid it must be possible to obtain series expansions for the initial values, i.e.,

$$g(x) = \sum_{i=1}^{\infty} A_i y_i(x)$$

$$h(x) = \sum_{i=1}^{\infty} \sqrt{\lambda_i} B_i y_i(x)$$

Using the results of the present section, we can find conditions on $g(x)$ and $h(x)$ which will guarantee that such expansions can be found.

Let $g(x)$ be an arbitrary continuous function with a continuous first derivative and a piecewise continuous second derivative, which satisfies the same homogeneous boundary conditions as $y(x)$ in the Sturm-Liouville problem

$$(py')' - qy + \lambda \rho y = 0$$

Then
$$(pg')' - qg = -f(x)$$

where $f(x)$ is a piecewise continuous function. Let $G(\xi;x)$ be the Green's function satisfying

$$(pG')' - qG = -\delta(x - \xi)$$

Then
$$g(x) = -\int_a^b gL[G]\, d\xi = -\int_a^b GL[g]\, d\xi = \int_a^b G(\xi;x) f(\xi)\, d\xi$$

$$\sqrt{\rho(x)}g(x) = \int_a^b \sqrt{\rho(x)\rho(\xi)}\, G(\xi;x)\, \frac{f(\xi)}{\sqrt{\rho(\xi)}}\, d\xi$$

$$= \int_a^b K(\xi;x)\, \frac{f(\xi)}{\sqrt{\rho(\xi)}}\, d\xi$$

Therefore, $\sqrt{\rho(x)}g(x)$ is an integral transform of a piecewise continuous function,[1] and as such has a uniformly convergent series expansion

$$\sqrt{\rho(x)}g(x) = \sum_{i=1}^{\infty} c_i \psi_i$$

in terms of the normalized eigenfunctions of the integral equation

$$\psi(x) = \lambda \int_a^b K(x;\xi)\, \psi(\xi)\, d\xi$$

---

[1] Here we are assuming that $\rho(x) > 0$.

with
$$c_i = \int_a^b \sqrt{\rho(x)}\,g(x)\,\psi_i(x)\,dx$$
$$= \int_a^b \rho(x)g(x)y_i(x)\,dx$$

since $\psi_i(x) = \sqrt{\rho(x)}\,y_i(x)$.

Finally, we shall generalize the entire discussion to the corresponding problems in two and three dimensions. The corresponding nonhomogeneous integral equations associated with Helmholtz's equation are, in two dimensions,

$$\psi(\xi,\eta) = F(\xi,\eta) + \lambda \iint\limits_R K(\xi,\eta;x,y)\psi(x,y)\,dx\,dy$$

where
$$K(\xi,\eta;x,y) = -\frac{1}{2\pi}\log\sqrt{(x-\xi)^2 + (y-\eta)^2} + H(\xi,\eta;x,y)$$

where H is a harmonic function with appropriate boundary values so that $\dfrac{dK}{dn} + \alpha K = 0$ on the boundary of R; and, in three dimensions,

$$\psi(\xi,\eta,\zeta) = F(\xi,\eta,\zeta) + \lambda \iiint\limits_V K(\xi,\eta,\zeta;x,y,z)\psi(x,y,z)\,dx\,dy\,dz$$

where
$$K(\xi,\eta,\zeta;x,y,z) = \frac{1}{4\pi\sqrt{(x-\xi)^2 + (y-\eta)^2 + (z-\zeta)^2}} + H(\xi,\eta,\zeta;x,y,z)$$

and H is a harmonic function with appropriate boundary values so that $\dfrac{dK}{dn} + \alpha K = 0$ on the boundary of V.

In these cases, the kernel is not continuous, but the integrals

$$\iint\limits_R [K(\xi,\eta;x,y)]^2\,dx\,dy$$

$$\iiint\limits_V [K(\xi,\eta,\zeta;x,y,z)]^2\,dx\,dy\,dz$$

exist and are continuous functions of the parameters in each case. The demonstration of this will be left for the exercises. The reader should reread the above development, making appropriate changes where necessary to obtain the same results in these more general cases.

In these cases, we again have expansion theorems for the initial conditions in the initial value problem. For example, in the two-dimensional case, let $g(x,y)$ be a function defined in R and on C, the boundary of R, where it is continuous, with continuous first partial derivatives and piecewise continuous

second partial derivatives, and satisfying the boundary condition $\dfrac{dg}{dn} + \alpha g$
$= 0$ on C.   Then $\nabla^2 g = -f(x,y)$ in R, where f is piecewise continuous and

$$g(x,y) = \iint_R K(x,y;\xi,\eta)f(\xi,\eta)\, d\xi\, d\eta$$

is the integral transform of a piecewise continuous function.   Hence,

$$g(x,y) = \sum_{i=1}^{\infty} c_i \psi_i(x,y)$$

where
$$c_i = \iint_R g(x,y)\psi_i(x,y)\, dx\, dy$$

and the convergence is uniform.   A similar theorem holds in the three-dimensional case.

Exercises 5.2

1. Let $K(\xi;x)$ be a continuous complex-valued "hermitian kernel" defined on the square $a \le \xi \le b$, $a \le x \le b$ such that $K(\xi;x) = K^*(x;\xi)$.   Prove that the eigenvalues of the homogeneous integral equation

$$\psi(\xi) = \lambda \int_a^b K(\xi;x)\psi(x)\, dx$$

are real.   Also show that eigenfunctions corresponding to different eigenvalues are orthogonal in the sense

$$\int_a^b \psi_i(x)\psi_j^*(x)\, dx = 0$$

if $\lambda_i \ne \lambda_j$.   Note that the theory of Fredholm integral equations with hermitian kernels runs parallel to the theory for real symmetric kernels, just as the theory of hermitian forms parallels that for quadratic forms.[1]   How then would one expect to solve the nonhomogeneous equation

$$\psi(\xi) = F(\xi) + \lambda \int_a^b K(\xi;x)\psi(x)\, dx$$

2. Describe a Rayleigh-Ritz procedure for obtaining sequences of upper bounds for the eigenvalues of the homogeneous Fredholm equation with real, symmetric, continuous kernel.

3. Solve the integral equation $\psi(\xi) = \xi + \displaystyle\int_0^1 (1 + \xi x)\psi(x)\, dx$.

4. Solve the integral equation

$$\psi(\xi) = \xi + \int_0^\xi \left(\frac{x}{\xi} - x\xi\right)\psi(x)\, dx + \int_\xi^1 \left(\frac{\xi}{x} - x\xi\right)\psi(x)\, dx$$

Hint: Find the boundary-value problem equivalent to the integral equation.

[1] See Sec. 1.10.

5. Find a series representation of the kernel

$$K(\xi;x) = x \qquad 0 \le x \le \xi$$
$$K(\xi;x) = \xi \qquad \xi \le x \le 1$$

Show that the series converges uniformly to the kernel.

6. Show that $\int_0^\rho (\log r)^2 r \, dr$, $\int_0^\rho r \log r \, dr$ exist. Use these results to show that

$$\iint_R [K(\xi,\eta;x,y)]^2 \, dx \, dy$$

exists and is a continuous function of ξ and η in R.

*7. Show that the homogeneous Fredholm equation can have no nontrivial continuous solution for $|\lambda| < [M(b - a)]^{-1}$, where $|K(\xi;x)| \le M$.

5.3 Fredholm Theory

In the last section we obtained solutions of the nonhomogeneous Fredholm equation

$$\psi(\xi) = F(\xi) + \lambda \int_a^b K(\xi;x)\psi(x) \, dx$$

under the assumption that the kernel $K(\xi;x)$ was symmetric. In this section, we shall obtain series solutions of the equation, assuming only that the kernel is continuous in the square $a \le \xi \le b, a \le x \le b$. The kernel need not be symmetric.

To begin with, let $\psi_0(x)$ be any piecewise continuous function. Then

$$\lambda \int_a^b K(\xi;x)\psi_0(x) \, dx$$

is a continuous function of ξ, and if $F(\xi)$ is piecewise continuous,

$$\psi_1(\xi) = F(\xi) + \lambda \int_a^b K(\xi;t_1)\psi_0(t_1) \, dt_1$$

is a piecewise continuous first approximation to the solution of the integral equation. A second approximation is given by

$$\psi_2(\xi) = F(\xi) + \lambda \int_a^b K(\xi;t_1)\psi_1(t_1) \, dt_1$$

$$= F(\xi) + \lambda \int_a^b K(\xi;t_1)F(t_1) \, dt_1 + \lambda^2 \int_a^b \int_a^b K(\xi;t_1)K(t_1;t_2)\psi_0(t_2) \, dt_1 \, dt_2$$

Continuing by successive substitution we obtain an nth approximation as follows:

$$\psi_n(\xi) = F(\xi) + \lambda \int_a^b K(\xi;t_1)F(t_1)\,dt_1 + \lambda^2 \int_a^b \int_a^b K(\xi;t_1)K(t_1;t_2)F(t_2)\,dt_1\,dt_2$$

$$+ \cdots + \lambda^n \int_a^b \cdots \int_a^b K(\xi;t_1)K(t_1;t_2)\cdots K(t_{n-1};t_n)\psi_0(t_n)\,dt_1 \cdots dt_n$$

Without loss of generality, we can assume that $|\psi_0(x)| \leq 1$; hence

$$\left| \lambda^n \int_a^b \cdots \int_a^b K(\xi;t_1)K(t_1;t_2)\cdots K(t_{n-1};t_n)\psi_0(t_n)\,dt_1 \cdots dt_n \right|$$

$$\leq |\lambda|^n M^n (b-a)^n$$

where $|K(\xi;x)| \leq M$. Therefore, if $|\lambda| < [M(b-a)]^{-1}$,

$$\lim_{n \to \infty} \psi_n(\xi) = F(\xi) + \lambda \int_a^b K(\xi;t_1)F(t_1)\,dt_1$$

$$+ \lambda^2 \int_a^b \int_a^b K(\xi;t_1)K(t_1;t_2)F(t_2)\,dt_1\,dt_2$$

$$+ \cdots + \lambda^n \int_a^b \cdots \int_a^b K(\xi;t_1)K(t_1;t_2)\cdots K(t_{n-1};t_n)F(t_n)\,dt_1 \cdots dt_n + \cdots$$

exists, and the convergence of the series is uniform in ξ. It remains to show that this is actually a solution of the integral equation. Multiplying the right-hand side of the last equation by $\lambda K(x;\xi)$ and integrating term by term, using the uniform convergence, we obtain the original series back again except for the term $F(x)$. Hence, by adding $F(x)$, we obtain again

$$\psi(x) = \lim_{n \to \infty} \psi_n(x)$$

which we have now shown is a solution of the integral equation provided $|\lambda| < [M(b-a)]^{-1}$.

Notice that the result is independent of the choice of ψ_0. This fact allows us to prove the uniqueness of the solution in the present case. If a second solution $\bar{\psi}$ exists, let $\psi_0 = \bar{\psi}$. But then $\psi_n = \bar{\psi}$ for all n, and $\psi \equiv \bar{\psi}$. This of course implies that there can be no nontrivial solution of the homogeneous integral equation for $|\lambda| < [M(b-a)]^{-1}$.

We notice that we can write the solution of the integral equation as follows:

$$\psi(\xi) = F(\xi) + \lambda \int_a^b k(\xi,x,\lambda)F(x)\,dx$$

where $k(\xi,x,\lambda) = K(\xi;x) + \lambda \int_a^b K(\xi;t_1)K(t_1;x)\,dt_1 + \cdots$

$$+ \lambda^n \int_a^b \cdots \int_a^b K(\xi;t_1)K(t_1;t_2) \cdots K(t_n;x)\,dt_1 \cdots dt_n + \cdots$$

and the series converges uniformly if $|\lambda| < [M(b-a)]^{-1}$. $k(\xi,x,\lambda)$ is called the **reciprocal kernel.** We see from the definition of the reciprocal kernel that

$$k(\xi,x,\lambda) = K(\xi;x) + \lambda \int_a^b K(\xi;t)k(t,x,\lambda)\,dt$$

$$k(\xi,x,\lambda) = K(\xi;x) + \lambda \int_a^b k(\xi,t,\lambda)K(t;x)\,dt$$

Conversely, if we find a reciprocal kernel which satisfies this integral equation, we can construct a solution of the nonhomogeneous Fredholm equation as

$$\psi(\xi) = F(\xi) + \lambda \int_a^b k(\xi,x,\lambda)F(x)\,dx$$

for then $\lambda \int_a^b K(\xi;x)\psi(x)\,dx = \lambda \int_a^b F(x)K(\xi;x)\,dx$

$$+ \lambda^2 \int_a^b \int_a^b k(x,t,\lambda)F(t)K(\xi;x)\,dt\,dx$$

$$= \lambda \int_a^b K(\xi;x)F(x)\,dx$$

$$+ \lambda \int_a^b [k(\xi,t,\lambda) - K(\xi;t)]F(t)\,dt$$

$$= \lambda \int_a^b k(\xi,t,\lambda)F(t)\,dt$$

$$= \psi(\xi) - F(\xi)$$

The restriction $|\lambda| < [M(b-a)]^{-1}$ on the above series solution of the integral equation is much too severe. Fredholm showed that it is possible to obtain series solutions for almost all values of λ. To illustrate his approach let us consider a special case where we can get an explicit solution. We shall consider the degenerate kernel.

$$K(\xi;x) = \alpha_1(\xi)\beta_1(x) + \alpha_2(\xi)\beta_2(x) + \alpha_3(\xi)\beta_3(x)$$

then $\psi(\xi) = F(\xi) + \lambda \int_a^b \alpha_i(\xi)\beta_i(x)\psi(x)\,dx$

$$= F(\xi) + \lambda\alpha_i y_i \qquad i = 1,2,3$$

where $\qquad y_i = \int_a^b \beta_i(x)\psi(x)\,dx$

Therefore, $y_j = \int_a^b \beta_j(\xi)\psi(\xi)\,d\xi = c_j + \lambda a_{ji}y_i$

where $\qquad c_j = \int_a^b \beta_j(\xi)F(\xi)\,d\xi \qquad \text{and} \qquad a_{ji} = \int_a^b \beta_j(\xi)\alpha_i(\xi)\,d\xi$

We thus have a system of nonhomogeneous linear equations which can be written in matrix notation,

$$Y = C + \lambda A Y$$

$$(I - \lambda A)Y = C$$

If $|I - \lambda A| \neq 0$, then by Cramer's rule we have

$$y_i = \frac{D_i}{|I - \lambda A|}$$

where D_i is the determinant of the matrix formed from $I - \lambda A$ by replacing the ith column by the vector C. Then

$$\psi(\xi) = F(\xi) + \frac{\lambda \alpha_i D_i}{|I - \lambda A|}$$

The denominator of the last expression can be expanded as follows:

$$|I - \lambda A| = \begin{vmatrix} 1 - \lambda a_{11} & -\lambda a_{12} & -\lambda a_{13} \\ -\lambda a_{21} & 1 - \lambda a_{22} & -\lambda a_{23} \\ -\lambda a_{31} & -\lambda a_{32} & 1 - \lambda a_{33} \end{vmatrix}$$

$$= 1 - \lambda(a_{11} + a_{22} + a_{33})$$

$$+ \lambda^2(a_{11}a_{22} + a_{11}a_{33} + a_{22}a_{33} - a_{12}a_{21} - a_{13}a_{31} - a_{23}a_{31})$$

$$- \lambda^3(a_{11}a_{22}a_{33} + a_{12}a_{23}a_{31} + a_{13}a_{21}a_{32}$$

$$- a_{11}a_{23}a_{32} - a_{13}a_{22}a_{31} - a_{12}a_{21}a_{33})$$

$$= 1 - \lambda \int_a^b K(t;t)\,dt + \frac{\lambda^2}{2!} \int_a^b \int_a^b \begin{vmatrix} K(t_1;t_1) & K(t_1;t_2) \\ K(t_2;t_1) & K(t_2;t_2) \end{vmatrix} dt_1\,dt_2$$

$$- \frac{\lambda^3}{3!} \int_a^b \int_a^b \int_a^b \begin{vmatrix} K(t_1;t_1) & K(t_1;t_2) & K(t_1;t_3) \\ K(t_2;t_1) & K(t_2;t_2) & K(t_2;t_3) \\ K(t_3;t_1) & K(t_3;t_2) & K(t_3;t_3) \end{vmatrix} dt_1\,dt_2\,dt_3$$

We see that these are the first four terms of a series

$$D(\lambda) = \sum_{k=0}^{\infty} \frac{(-1)^k \lambda^k}{k!} \gamma_k$$

where
$$\gamma_k = \int_a^b \cdots \int_a^b \begin{vmatrix} K(t_1;t_1) & K(t_1;t_2) & \cdots & K(t_1;t_k) \\ K(t_2;t_1) & K(t_2;t_2) & \cdots & K(t_2;t_k) \\ \cdots\cdots\cdots\cdots\cdots\cdots\cdots\cdots\cdots\cdots\cdots \\ K(t_k;t_1) & K(t_k;t_2) & \cdots & K(t_k;t_k) \end{vmatrix} dt_1 \cdots dt_k$$

We shall show that this series converges for all values of λ for any continuous kernel. However, before returning to the general case, let us consider the numerator in our above explicit solution. Expanding the determinants, we have

$$\lambda\alpha_i(\xi)D_i = \lambda\alpha_1(\xi) \begin{vmatrix} c_1 & -\lambda a_{12} & -\lambda a_{13} \\ c_2 & 1-\lambda a_{22} & -\lambda a_{23} \\ c_3 & -\lambda a_{32} & 1-\lambda a_{33} \end{vmatrix}$$

$$+\lambda\alpha_2(\xi) \begin{vmatrix} 1-\lambda a_{11} & c_1 & -\lambda a_{13} \\ -\lambda a_{21} & c_2 & -\lambda a_{23} \\ -\lambda a_{31} & c_3 & 1-\lambda a_{33} \end{vmatrix}$$

$$+\lambda\alpha_3(\xi) \begin{vmatrix} 1-\lambda a_{11} & -\lambda a_{12} & c_1 \\ -\lambda a_{21} & 1-\lambda a_{22} & c_2 \\ -\lambda a_{31} & -\lambda a_{32} & c_3 \end{vmatrix}$$

$$= \lambda\int_a^b K(\xi;x)F(x)\,dx - \lambda^2\int_a^b\int_a^b \begin{vmatrix} K(\xi;x) & K(\xi;t_1) \\ K(t_1;x) & K(t_1;t_1) \end{vmatrix} F(x)\,dt_1\,dx$$

$$+ \frac{\lambda^3}{2!}\int_a^b\int_a^b\int_a^b \begin{vmatrix} K(\xi;x) & K(\xi;t_1) & K(\xi;t_2) \\ K(t_1;x) & K(t_1;t_1) & K(t_1;t_2) \\ K(t_2;x) & K(t_2;t_1) & K(t_2;t_2) \end{vmatrix} F(x)\,dt_1\,dt_2\,dx$$

We see that we can write our solution in terms of the reciprocal kernel

$$k(\xi,x,\lambda) = \frac{1}{D(\lambda)}\left[K(\xi;x) - \lambda\int_a^b \begin{vmatrix} K(\xi;x) & K(\xi;t_1) \\ K(t_1;x) & K(t_1,t_1) \end{vmatrix} dt_1 \right.$$

$$\left. + \frac{\lambda^2}{2!}\int_a^b\int_a^b \begin{vmatrix} K(\xi;x) & K(\xi;t_1) & K(\xi;t_2) \\ K(t_1;x) & K(t_1;t_1) & K(t_1;t_2) \\ K(t_2;x) & K(t_2;t_1) & K(t_2;t_2) \end{vmatrix} dt_1\,dt_2 \right]$$

if λ is not a zero of $D(\lambda)$.   Then

$$\psi(\xi) = F(\xi) + \lambda \int_a^b k(\xi,x,\lambda)F(x)\,dx$$

Taking our cue from this special case, we attempt to find a solution of the nonhomogeneous Fredholm equation in the general case along the same lines. We begin by defining two infinite series which we shall show converge for all values of λ.   The first is **Fredholm's determinant**

$$D(\lambda) = \sum_{k=0}^{\infty} \frac{(-1)^k \lambda^k}{k!}\, \gamma_k$$

where
$$\gamma_k = \int_a^b \cdots \int_a^b
\begin{vmatrix}
K(t_1;t_1) & K(t_1;t_2) & \cdots & K(t_1;t_k) \\
K(t_2;t_1) & K(t_2;t_2) & \cdots & K(t_2;t_k) \\
\cdots\cdots\cdots\cdots\cdots\cdots\cdots\cdots\cdots\cdots \\
K(t_k;t_1) & K(t_k;t_2) & \cdots & K(t_k;t_k)
\end{vmatrix}
dt_1 \cdots dt_k$$

$$\gamma_0 = 1$$

The second is **Fredholm's first minor**

$$D_1(\xi,x,\lambda) = \sum_{k=0}^{\infty} \frac{(-1)^k \lambda^k}{k!}\, \delta_k$$

where
$$\delta_k = \int_a^b \cdots \int_a^b
\begin{vmatrix}
K(\xi;x) & K(\xi;t_1) & \cdots & K(\xi;t_k) \\
K(t_1;x) & K(t_1;t_1) & \cdots & K(t_1;t_k) \\
\cdots\cdots\cdots\cdots\cdots\cdots\cdots\cdots\cdots\cdots \\
K(t_k;x) & K(t_k;t_1) & \cdots & K(t_k;t_k)
\end{vmatrix}
dt_1 \cdots dt_k$$

$$\delta_0 = K(\xi;x)$$

To show the convergence of these two series we need **Hadamard's inequality** for determinants: If A is an nth-order determinant with elements a_{ij} satisfying the inequality $|a_{ij}| \le M$ for all i and j, then

$$|A| \le M^n n^{n/2}$$

We prove this as follows.   If any row contains all zeros, $A = 0$, and the inequality follows immediately.   Otherwise we can write

$$A = a_1 a_2 \cdots a_n B$$

where
$$a_i = \left(\sum_{j=1}^{n} |a_{ij}|^2 \right)^{\frac{1}{2}}$$

and B is a determinant with normalized rows.   Obviously

$$a_i \le M n^{\frac{1}{2}}$$

Hence, it remains to show that $|B| \leq 1$.   Now

$$B = b_{\alpha j} B_{\alpha j} \qquad j = 1,2,3, \ldots, n$$

where $B_{\alpha j}$ is the cofactor of $b_{\alpha j}$.   By Schwarz's inequality,

$$|B|^2 \leq \sum_{j=1}^{n} |b_{\alpha j}|^2 \sum_{j=1}^{n} |B_{\alpha j}|^2$$

Equality holds if and only if $b_{\alpha j} = \mu_\alpha B_{\alpha j}^*$.[1]   Now $|B|^2$ is equal to the determinant of the product of the matrix with elements b_{ij} with its own conjugate transposed matrix.   But when b_{ij} is proportional to the conjugate of its cofactor, this product is the identity matrix, and hence the maximum value of $|B|$ is 1.   Therefore,

$$|A| \leq a_1 a_2 \cdots a_n \leq M^n n^{n/2}$$

Now consider $|\gamma_k|$ and $|\delta_k|$.   By Hadamard's inequality,

$$|\gamma_k| \leq (b - a)^k M^k k^{k/2}$$

$$|\delta_k| \leq (b - a)^k M^{k+1} (k + 1)^{(k+1)/2}$$

Then

$$\lim_{k \to \infty} \frac{|\lambda| \, (b - a) M (k + 1)^{(k+1)/2}}{(k + 1) \, k^{k/2}} = |\lambda| \, (b - a) M \lim_{k \to \infty} \left(1 + \frac{1}{k}\right)^{k/2} \frac{1}{(k + 1)^{\frac{1}{2}}} = 0$$

$$\lim_{k \to \infty} \frac{|\lambda| \, (b - a) M (k + 2)^{(k+2)/2}}{(k + 1)(k + 1)^{(k+1)/2}}$$

$$= |\lambda| \, (b - a) M \lim_{k \to \infty} \left(1 + \frac{1}{k + 1}\right)^{(k+1)/2} \left[\frac{k + 2}{(k + 1)^2}\right]^{\frac{1}{2}} = 0$$

Therefore, both series converge absolutely for all values of λ, and the series for $D_1(\xi,x,\lambda)$ converges uniformly in ξ and x.

Finally, we define

$$k(\xi,x,\lambda) = \frac{D_1(\xi,x,\lambda)}{D(\lambda)}$$

provided $D(\lambda) \neq 0$, and show that this is a reciprocal kernel and hence that

$$\psi(\xi) = F(\xi) + \lambda \int_a^b \frac{D_1(\xi,x,\lambda)}{D(\lambda)} \, F(x) \, dx$$

is the solution of the integral equation.   To this end we expand δ_k, using the

[1] See exercise 3, Sec. 1.6.

elements of the first column:

$$\delta_k(\xi,x) = \int_a^b \cdots \int_a^b K(\xi;x) \begin{vmatrix} K(t_1;t_1) & K(t_1;t_2) & \cdots & K(t_1;t_k) \\ K(t_2;t_1) & K(t_2;t_2) & \cdots & K(t_2;t_k) \\ \cdots\cdots\cdots\cdots\cdots\cdots\cdots\cdots\cdots \\ K(t_k;t_1) & K(t_k;t_2) & \cdots & K(t_k;t_k) \end{vmatrix} dt_1 \cdots dt_k$$

$$+ \sum_{i=1}^{k} (-1)^i \int_a^b \cdots \int_a^b K(t_i;x) \begin{vmatrix} K(\xi;t_1) & K(\xi;t_2) & \cdots & K(\xi;t_k) \\ \cdots\cdots\cdots\cdots\cdots\cdots\cdots\cdots\cdots \\ K(t_{i-1};t_1) & K(t_{i-1};t_2) & \cdots & K(t_{i-1};t_k) \\ K(t_{i+1};t_1) & K(t_{i+1};t_2) & \cdots & K(t_{i+1};t_k) \\ \cdots\cdots\cdots\cdots\cdots\cdots\cdots\cdots\cdots \\ K(t_k;t_1) & K(t_k;t_2) & \cdots & K(t_k;t_k) \end{vmatrix} dt_1 \cdots dt_k$$

By replacing t_i by t, t_{i+1} by t_i, t_{i+2} by t_{i+1}, etc., and moving the ith column to the first position, we can write

$$\delta_k(\xi,x) = K(\xi;x)\gamma_k + \sum_{i=1}^{k} (-1)^{2i-1} \int_a^b \cdots \int_a^b K(t;x)$$

$$\times \begin{vmatrix} K(\xi;t) & K(\xi;t_1) & \cdots & K(\xi;t_{k-1}) \\ K(t_1;t) & K(t_1;t_1) & \cdots & K(t_1;t_{k-1}) \\ \cdots\cdots\cdots\cdots\cdots\cdots\cdots\cdots\cdots \\ K(t_{k-1};t) & K(t_{k-1};t_1) & \cdots & K(t_{k-1};t_{k-1}) \end{vmatrix} dt_1 \cdots dt_{k-1}\, dt$$

$$= K(\xi;x)\gamma_k - k \int_a^b K(t;x)\, \delta_{k-1}(\xi,t)\, dt$$

Then

$$D_1(\xi,x,\lambda) = \sum_{k=0}^{\infty} \frac{(-1)^k \lambda^k \, \delta_k}{k!}$$

$$= K(\xi;x) \sum_{k=0}^{\infty} \frac{(-1)^k \lambda^k \gamma_k}{k!} + \lambda \int_a^b \sum_{k=1}^{\infty} \frac{(-1)^{k-1}\lambda^{k-1}\, \delta_{k-1}(\xi,t)}{(k-1)!} K(t;x)\, dt$$

$$= K(\xi;x) D(\lambda) + \lambda \int_a^b D_1(\xi,t,\lambda) K(t;x)\, dt$$

where we have used the uniform convergence to interchange the summation and the integration. If $D(\lambda) \neq 0$, we have

$$k(\xi,x,\lambda) = \frac{D_1(\xi,x,\lambda)}{D(\lambda)} = K(\xi;x) + \lambda \int_a^b \frac{D_1(\xi,t,\lambda)}{D(\lambda)} K(t;x)\, dt$$

$$= K(\xi;x) + \lambda \int_a^b k(\xi,t,\lambda) K(t;x)\, dt$$

Similarly, if we expand δ_k by the first row rather than the first column, we find

$$\delta_k(\xi,x) = K(\xi;x)\gamma_k - k\int_a^b K(\xi;t)\,\delta_{k-1}(t,x)\,dt$$

and it follows that

$$D_1(\xi,x,\lambda) = K(\xi;x)D(\lambda) + \lambda\int_a^b K(\xi;t)D_1(t,x,\lambda)\,dt$$

and

$$k(\xi,x,\lambda) = K(\xi;x) + \lambda\int_a^b K(\xi;t)k(t,x,\lambda)\,dt$$

Hence, we have a unique solution if $D(\lambda) \neq 0$, given by

$$\psi(\xi) = F(\xi) + \lambda\int_a^b k(\xi,x,\lambda)F(x)\,dx$$

Suppose $D(\lambda_1) = 0$ for some λ_1. We know that $\lambda_1 \neq 0$, since $D(0) = 1$. Then we have

$$D_1(\xi,x_1,\lambda_1) = \lambda_1\int_a^b K(\xi;t)D_1(t,x_1,\lambda_1)\,dt$$

Thus we see that $D_1(\xi,x_1,\lambda_1)$ is a nontrivial solution of the homogeneous Fredholm equation for some x_1, unless of course it is identically zero for all values of x. We shall show, however, that this cannot be the case if $D'(\lambda_1) \neq 0$. Differentiating $D(\lambda)$, we have

$$-D'(\lambda) = \sum_{k=0}^{\infty} \frac{(-1)^k\lambda^k}{k!}\gamma_{k+1}$$

Now

$$\gamma_{k+1} = \int_a^b\cdots\int_a^b \begin{vmatrix} K(t_1;t_1) & K(t_1;t_2) & \cdots & K(t_1;t_{k+1}) \\ K(t_2;t_1) & K(t_2;t_2) & \cdots & K(t_2;t_{k+1}) \\ \cdots\cdots\cdots\cdots\cdots\cdots\cdots\cdots\cdots\cdots\cdots \\ K(t_{k+1};t_1) & K(t_{k+1};t_2) & \cdots & K(t_{k+1};t_{k+1}) \end{vmatrix} dt_1\cdots dt_{k+1}$$

$$= \int_a^b\left\{\int_a^b\cdots\int_a^b \begin{vmatrix} K(\xi;\xi) & K(\xi;t_1) & \cdots & K(\xi;t_k) \\ K(t_1;\xi) & K(t_1;t_1) & \cdots & K(t_1;t_k) \\ \cdots\cdots\cdots\cdots\cdots\cdots\cdots\cdots\cdots\cdots\cdots \\ K(t_k;\xi) & K(t_k;t_1) & \cdots & K(t_k;t_k) \end{vmatrix} dt_1\cdots dt_k\right\}d\xi$$

$$= \int_a^b \delta_k(\xi;\xi)\,d\xi$$

Hence,

$$-D'(\lambda) = \sum_{k=0}^{\infty} \frac{(-1)^k \lambda^k}{k!} \int_a^b \delta_k(\xi,\xi) \, d\xi$$

$$= \int_a^b \left[\sum_{k=0}^{\infty} \frac{(-1)^k \lambda^k}{k!} \delta_k(\xi,\xi) \right] d\xi$$

$$= \int_a^b D_1(\xi,\xi,\lambda) \, d\xi$$

This shows that if $D'(\lambda_1) \neq 0$, then $D_1(\xi,\xi,\lambda_1) \not\equiv 0$, and an x_1 exists such that $D_1(\xi,x_1,\lambda_1) \not\equiv 0$. We now have a solution of the homogeneous Fredholm equation corresponding to the eigenvalue λ_1. We shall show that in this case, i.e., $D(\lambda_1) = 0$, $D'(\lambda_1) \neq 0$, any other solution of the homogeneous equation is a multiple of this solution, and hence there is a one-parameter family of non-trivial solutions, and therefore λ_1 is not a degenerate eigenvalue.

To show this we introduce **Fredholm's second minor,**

$$D_2(\xi,\eta,x,\lambda) = \sum_{k=0}^{\infty} \frac{(-1)^k \lambda^k}{k!} \Gamma_k(\xi,\eta,x,y)$$

where

$$\Gamma_k(\xi,\eta,x,y) = \int_a^b \cdots \int_a^b \begin{vmatrix} K(\xi;\eta) & K(\xi;y) & K(\xi;t_1) & \cdots & K(\xi;t_k) \\ K(x;\eta) & K(x;y) & K(x;t_1) & \cdots & K(x;t_k) \\ K(t_1;\eta) & K(t_1;y) & K(t_1;t_1) & \cdots & K(t_1;t_k) \\ \cdots\cdots\cdots\cdots\cdots\cdots\cdots\cdots\cdots\cdots\cdots\cdots \\ K(t_k;\eta) & K(t_k;y) & K(t_k;t_1) & \cdots & K(t_k;t_k) \end{vmatrix} dt_1 \cdots dt_k$$

$$\Gamma_0(\xi,\eta,x,y) = \begin{vmatrix} K(\xi;\eta) & K(\xi;y) \\ K(x;\eta) & K(x;y) \end{vmatrix}$$

By use of Hadamard's inequality it can be shown that the series converges absolutely for all λ and uniformly in ξ, η, x, and y. Expanding $\Gamma_k(\xi,\eta,x,y)$ using the elements in the first column, we have

$$\Gamma_k(\xi,\eta,x,y) = K(\xi;\eta)\delta_k(x,y) - K(x;\eta)\delta_k(\xi,y)$$

$$- k\int_a^b K(t;\eta)\Gamma_{k-1}(\xi,t,x,y) \, dt$$

$$\Gamma_0(\xi,\eta,x,y) = K(\xi;\eta)\delta_0(x,y) - K(x;\eta)\delta_0(\xi,y)$$

Hence,

$$D_2(\xi,\eta,x,y,\lambda) = K(\xi;\eta)D_1(x,y,\lambda) - K(x;\eta)D_1(\xi,y,\lambda)$$

$$+ \lambda\int_a^b K(t;\eta)D_2(\xi,t,x,y,\lambda) \, dt$$

Let $\psi(\xi)$ be a solution of the homogeneous Fredholm equation corresponding to the eigenvalue λ_1, i.e.,

$$\psi(\xi) = \lambda_1 \int_a^b K(\xi;\eta)\psi(\eta)\,d\eta$$

Then

$$\psi(\xi) = \lambda_1 \int_a^b K(\xi;\eta)\psi(\eta)\,d\eta$$

$$= \lambda_1 \int_a^b \frac{D_2(\xi,\eta,x_0,x_1,\lambda_1)}{D_1(x_0,x_1,\lambda_1)}\,\psi(\eta)\,d\eta$$

$$+ \lambda_1 \int_a^b K(x_0;\eta)\frac{D_1(\xi,x_1,\lambda_1)}{D_1(x_0,x_1,\lambda_1)}\,\psi(\eta)\,d\eta$$

$$- \lambda_1^2 \int_a^b \int_a^b K(t;\eta)\frac{D_2(\xi,t,x_0,x_1,\lambda_1)}{D_1(x_0,x_1,\lambda_1)}\,\psi(\eta)\,dt\,d\eta$$

$$= \left\{\frac{\lambda_1}{D_1(x_0,x_1,\lambda_1)} \int_a^b K(x_0;\eta)\psi(\eta)\,d\eta\right\}D_1(\xi,x_1,\lambda_1)$$

Here we have used the fact that $D'(\lambda_1) \neq 0$ to ensure us that there exist numbers x_0 and x_1 such that $D_1(x_0,x_1,\lambda_1) \neq 0$.

This discussion can be generalized to the case where

$$D(\lambda_1) = D'(\lambda_1) = \cdots = D^{(p-1)}(\lambda_1) = 0 \qquad D^{(p)}(\lambda_1) \neq 0$$

In this case[1] there are p linearly independent solutions of the homogeneous Fredholm equation corresponding to the eigenvalue λ_1, and hence there is a p-fold infinity of solutions. Each eigenvalue must have a finite degeneracy, however, or $D(\lambda)$ would vanish identically.

Finally, let us consider the solution of the nonhomogeneous Fredholm equation in the case where λ is an eigenvalue of the homogeneous equation. To do this we must consider the **associated integral equation**

$$\bar{\psi}(\xi) = F(\xi) + \lambda \int_a^b K(x;\xi)\bar{\psi}(x)\,dx$$

We see immediately that $\bar{D}(\lambda) = D(\lambda)$, since interchanging the rows and columns will not change the values of the determinants involved. On the other hand, $\bar{D}_1(\xi,x,\lambda) = D_1(x,\xi,\lambda)$. Therefore, the solution of the associated equation is

$$\bar{\psi}(\xi) = F(\xi) + \lambda \int_a^b k(x,\xi,\lambda)F(x)\,dx$$

[1] See William V. Lovitt, "Linear Integral Equations," Dover Publications, New York, 1950, pp. 46ff.

provided that $D(\lambda) \neq 0$. We also see that the eigenvalues of the associated homogeneous equation are the same as for the original equation, and the degeneracy, if there is any, is the same.

Let $D(\lambda_1) = D'(\lambda_1) = \cdots = D^{(p-1)}(\lambda_1) = 0$ and $D^{(p)}(\lambda_1) \neq 0$. Then there are p linearly independent solutions of the associated homogeneous equation, $\bar{\psi}_1, \bar{\psi}_2, \ldots, \bar{\psi}_p$. A necessary condition for the existence of a solution of the nonhomogeneous equation

$$\psi(\xi) = F(\xi) + \lambda_1 \int_a^b K(\xi;x)\psi(x)\,dx$$

is that $F(\xi)$ be orthogonal to $\bar{\psi}_1, \bar{\psi}_2, \ldots, \bar{\psi}_p$. We show this as follows:

$$\int_a^b F(\xi)\bar{\psi}_j(\xi)\,d\xi = \int_a^b \psi(\xi)\bar{\psi}_j(\xi)\,d\xi - \lambda_1 \int_a^b \int_a^b K(\xi;x)\psi(x)\bar{\psi}_j(\xi)\,dx\,d\xi$$

$$= \int_a^b \psi(\xi)\bar{\psi}_j(\xi)\,d\xi - \int_a^b \psi(x)\bar{\psi}_j(x)\,dx$$

$$= 0 \qquad j = 1, 2, \ldots, p$$

This condition is also sufficient. We shall show this in the case where λ_1 is a nondegenerate eigenvalue. The proof involves Fredholm's second minor. The extension of the proof to degenerate eigenvalues is straightforward, but it involves the definition of Fredholm's third minor, fourth minor, etc., and we shall not carry it out here.[1]

If λ_1 is nondegenerate, there exists just one nontrivial solution $\bar{\psi}(x)$ of the associated homogeneous integral equation satisfying

$$\bar{\psi}(\xi) = \lambda_1 \int_a^b K(x;\xi)\bar{\psi}(x)\,dx$$

We are assuming that $F(\xi)$ is orthogonal to $\bar{\psi}(\xi)$, i.e.,

$$\int_a^b F(\xi)\bar{\psi}(\xi)\,d\xi = 0$$

By previous considerations we can take

$$\bar{\psi}(\xi) = D_1(x_1,\xi,\lambda_1)$$

and we know by the condition $D'(\lambda_1) \neq 0$ that there exists an x_1 such that $D_1(x_1,\xi,\lambda_1) \neq 0$. From the definition of Fredholm's second minor, if we expand $\Gamma_k(\xi,\eta,x,y)$ using the elements in the first row, we obtain the relation

$$D_2(\xi,\eta,x,y,\lambda) = K(\xi;\eta)D_1(x,y,\lambda) - K(\xi;y)D_1(x,\eta,\lambda)$$

$$+ \lambda \int_a^b K(\xi;t)D_2(t,\eta,x,y,\lambda)\,dt$$

---

[1] *Ibid.*, pp. 64ff.

Now $\quad 0 = \lambda_1 \int_a^b K(\xi;\eta) D_1(x_1,y,\lambda_1) F(y) \, dy$

$$= \lambda_1 \int_a^b D_2(\xi,\eta,x_1,y,\lambda_1) F(y) \, dy + \lambda_1 \int_a^b K(\xi;y) D_1(x_1,\eta,\lambda_1) F(y) \, dy$$

$$- \lambda_1^2 \int_a^b \int_a^b K(\xi;t) D_2(t,\eta,x_1,y,\lambda_1) F(y) \, dt \, dy$$

There exists an η_0 such that $D_1(x_1,\eta_0,\lambda_1) \neq 0$.   Therefore,

$$0 = \lambda_1 \int_a^b \frac{D_2(\xi,\eta_0,x_1,y,\lambda_1)}{D_1(x_1,\eta_0,\lambda_1)} F(y) \, dy + \lambda_1 \int_a^b K(\xi;y) F(y) \, dy$$

$$- \lambda_1^2 \int_a^b \int_a^b K(\xi;y) \frac{D_2(y,\eta_0,x_1,t,\lambda_1)}{D_1(x_1,\eta_0,\lambda_1)} F(t) \, dt \, dy$$

Hence, $\quad F(\xi) - \lambda_1 \int_a^b \frac{D_2(\xi,\eta_0,x_1,y,\lambda_1)}{D_1(x_1,\eta_0,\lambda_1)} F(y) \, dy$

$$= F(\xi) + \lambda_1 \int_a^b K(\xi;y) \left[F(y) - \lambda_1 \int_a^b \frac{D_2(y,\eta_0,x_1,t,\lambda_1)}{D_1(x_1,\eta_0,\lambda_1)} F(t) \, dt \right] dy$$

Therefore, $\quad \psi(\xi) = F(\xi) - \lambda_1 \int_a^b \frac{D_2(\xi,\eta_0,x_1,y,\lambda_1)}{D_1(x_1,\eta_0,\lambda_1)} F(y) \, dy$

is a solution of the nonhomogeneous integral equation.

If λ_1 is a degenerate eigenvalue of the homogeneous integral equation corresponding to p linearly independent solutions $\psi_1, \psi_2, \ldots, \psi_p$, then there exist solutions of the nonhomogeneous equation, provided $F(\xi)$ is orthogonal to each of the solutions of the homogeneous associated equation.   However, the solution is not unique, for if

$$u(\xi) = F(\xi) + \lambda_1 \int_a^b K(\xi;x) u(x) \, dx$$

$$v(\xi) = F(\xi) + \lambda_1 \int_a^b K(\xi;x) v(x) \, dx$$

then $\qquad u(\xi) - v(\xi) = \lambda_1 \int_a^b K(\xi;x)[u(x) - v(x)] \, dx$

and $\qquad u(\xi) - v(\xi) = c_i \psi_i(\xi) \qquad i = 1, 2, \ldots, p$

Exercises 5.3

1. If the kernel in the homogeneous Fredholm integral equation is nonsymmetric, the equation may have no eigenfunctions.   Show that there are no nontrivial solutions of $\psi(\xi) = \lambda \int_0^\pi \sin \xi \cos x \, \psi(x) \, dx$.

2. If $K(\xi;x)$ is symmetric, prove that the reciprocal kernel takes the form

$$k(\xi,x,\lambda) = K(\xi;x) + \lambda \sum_{i=1}^{\infty} \frac{\psi_i(\xi)\psi_i(x)}{\lambda_i(\lambda_i - \lambda)}$$

where $\psi_i(\xi) = \lambda_i \int_a^b K(\xi;x)\psi_i(x)\,dx$. Show that the series converges for all values of $\lambda \neq \lambda_i$.

3. Show the following: If $\psi(\xi)$ is a nontrivial solution of

$$\psi(\xi) = \lambda_1 \int_a^b K(\xi;x)\psi(x)\,dx$$

and $\bar{\psi}(\xi)$ is a nontrivial solution of the associated equation

$$\bar{\psi}(\xi) = \lambda_2 \int K(x;\xi)\bar{\psi}(x)\,dx$$

with $\lambda_1 \neq \lambda_2$, then $\int_a^b \psi(x)\bar{\psi}(x)\,dx = 0$.

4. Solve the following Fredholm equations:

a. $\psi(\xi) = 3 \int_0^1 \xi x \psi(x)\,dx$

b. $\psi(\xi) = \sin \xi + \int_0^\pi \cos \xi \sin x\, \psi(x)\,dx$

c. $\psi(\xi) = 2\xi - 1 + 2 \int_0^1 \xi \psi(x)\,dx$

5. The integral equation

$$\psi(\xi) = F(\xi) + \lambda \int_a^\xi K(\xi;x)\psi(x)\,dx$$

where $K(\xi;x)$ is continuous for $a \leq x \leq b$, $a \leq \xi \leq b$, is known as the **Volterra integral equation.** Construct a series solution by successive approximations and show that it converges for all values of λ.

HINT: $$\left| \int_a^\xi K(\xi;x)\psi_0(x)\,dx \right| \leq M \int_a^\xi dx = M(\xi - a)$$

6. Show that the solution of the Volterra equation $\psi(\xi) = 1 + \int_0^\xi (x - \xi)\psi(x)\,dx$ satisfies the differential equation $\psi'' + \psi = 0$ and the boundary conditions

$$\psi(0) = 1 \qquad \psi'(0) = 0$$

The solution is evidently $\psi(\xi) = \cos \xi$, but find the series representation by the method of exercise 5, for illustrative purposes.

7. Let $AX + \lambda X = C$ be a system of n linear equations in n unknowns. The matrix A is nonsymmetric. Prove the following:

a. The system has a unique solution if λ is not an eigenvalue of A.

b. If λ is an eigenvalue of A, the system has a solution if and only if the vector C is orthogonal to all the eigenvectors of the associated equation $A'Z + \lambda Z = 0$.

Relate this algebraic problem to the Fredholm integral equation with degenerate kernel.

5.4   Integral Equations of the First Kind

We shall conclude this chapter with a brief discussion of integral equations of the first kind.   The general linear integral equation of the first kind can be written in the one-dimensional case as

$$f(x) = \int_a^b K(x;\xi)\psi(\xi)\,d\xi$$

where $f(x)$ is a known function, $K(x;\xi)$ is a given kernel, and $\psi(\xi)$ is the unknown to be determined.   We have already seen an example of this type in the **Wiener–Hopf equation**

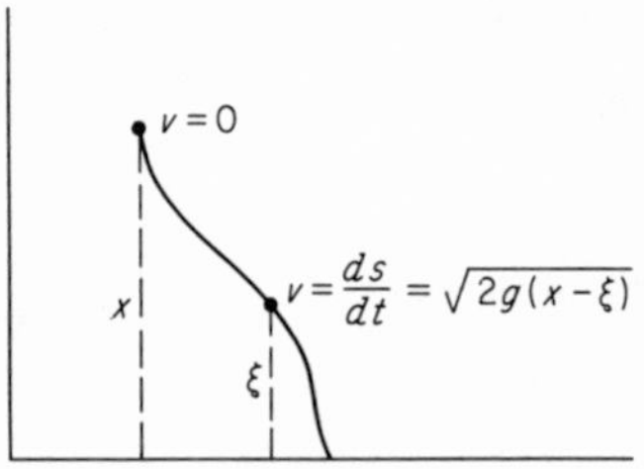

$$f(x) = \int_{-\infty}^{\infty} K(|x - \xi|)\psi(\xi)\,d\xi$$

which appeared in Sec. 4.5.   This equation comes up quite frequently in diffraction theory and also in the theory of smoothing and prediction.[1]

FIGURE 10

Historically, one of the first integral equations to be studied was **Abel's equation**

$$f(x) = \int_0^x \frac{\psi(\xi)}{\sqrt{x - \xi}}\,d\xi$$

This equation arises in the following physical problem (see Fig. 10).   A particle slides down a smooth curve under the influence of gravity, starting from rest.   The total time of descent is

$$T = -\int_0^x \frac{ds}{\sqrt{2g(x - \xi)}} = \int_0^x \frac{\dfrac{1}{\sqrt{2g}}\dfrac{ds}{d\xi}}{\sqrt{x - \xi}}\,d\xi$$

$$= \int_0^x \frac{\psi(\xi)\,d\xi}{\sqrt{x - \xi}}$$

where $\psi(\xi) = \dfrac{1}{\sqrt{2g}}\dfrac{ds}{d\xi}$.   If the path is known, the time of descent can be computed.   The problem of finding the path which leads to a given time as a function of the initial height x leads to Abel's integral equation.[2]

[1] See Norbert Wiener, "Extrapolation, Interpolation, and Smoothing of Stationary Time Series," Technology Press, M.I.T., Cambridge, Mass., and John Wiley & Sons, Inc., New York, 1949.

[2] In Sec. 2.2 we considered the problem of finding the curve which minimizes the time of descent between two points.   This is a problem in the calculus of variations.

In Chap. 6 we shall discuss integral transform methods. Let $\psi(\xi)$ be a function for which the integral transform

$$f(x) = T[\psi] = \int_a^b K(x;\xi)\psi(\xi)\, d\xi$$

exists. Then the problem of finding the inverse transform, i.e.,

$$\psi(\xi) = T^{-1}[f]$$

reduces to solving an integral equation of the first kind. Some examples of these are

$$f(x) = \frac{1}{\sqrt{2\pi}} \int_{-\infty}^{\infty} \psi(\xi)e^{-ix\xi}\, d\xi$$

$$f(x) = \sqrt{\frac{2}{\pi}} \int_0^{\infty} \psi(\xi) \cos(x\xi)\, d\xi$$

$$f(x) = \sqrt{\frac{2}{\pi}} \int_0^{\infty} \psi(\xi) \sin(x\xi)\, d\xi$$

$$f(x) = \int_0^{\infty} \psi(\xi)e^{-x\xi}\, d\xi$$

$$f(x) = \int_0^{\infty} \xi J_\nu(\xi x)\psi(\xi)\, d\xi$$

$$f(x) = \int_0^{\infty} \xi^{x-1}\psi(\xi)\, d\xi$$

These are respectively the **Fourier, Fourier cosine, Fourier sine, Laplace, Hankel,** and **Mellin transforms.** In each of these cases the inverse transformation problem has been solved for large classes of functions. Hence, in each case the corresponding integral equations have been solved.

As a further example of an integral equation of the first kind, consider the diffraction of a plane acoustic wave by a slit with perpendicular incidence (see Fig. 11). The xz plane is a plane rigid barrier except where it is slit between $x = \pm 1$. The plane wave is incident perpendicular to the slit so that there is no z variation, making the problem essentially two-dimensional. The problem is to find an acoustic field $\phi(x,y,t)$ satisfying the two-dimensional wave equation

$$\nabla^2 \phi = \frac{1}{a^2} \frac{\partial^2 \phi}{\partial t^2}$$

throughout the xy plane except on the x axis for $x \le -1$ and $1 \le x$. On the rigid boundary ($x \le -1$, $1 \le x$) the boundary condition is $\dfrac{\partial \phi}{\partial y} = 0$. We expect a reflected wave in the lower half plane, so we write

$$\phi = \phi_i + \phi_r + \phi_s$$

where ϕ_i is the incident plane wave, ϕ_r is a reflected plane wave, and ϕ_s is the diffracted wave. The diffraction effects are contained in ϕ_s, and it is on this part of the solution that we shall concentrate our attention. Now

$$\phi_i = e^{i(ku-\omega t)}$$
$$= e^{i(xk_x+yk_y)}e^{-i\omega t}$$
$$= e^{i(r\cos\theta\cos\alpha+r\sin\theta\sin\alpha)}e^{-i\omega t}$$
$$= e^{ikr\cos(\theta-\alpha)}e^{-i\omega t}$$

where $k_x^2 + k_y^2 = k^2 = \omega^2/a^2$. Then ϕ_i satisfies the wave equation. We take

$$\phi_r = e^{ikr\cos(\theta+\alpha)}e^{-i\omega t}$$

If the slit were closed, then we would have simply the incident plane wave plus

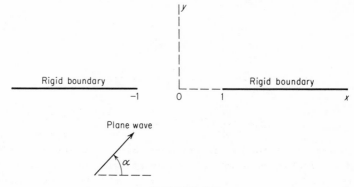

FIGURE 11

the reflected wave in the lower half plane as an unperturbed solution which we designate as ϕ_0, i.e.,

$$\phi_0 = [e^{ikr\cos(\theta-\alpha)} + e^{ikr\cos(\theta+\alpha)}]e^{-i\omega t}$$
$$= 2e^{ikx\cos\alpha}\cos(k_y y)e^{-i\omega t}$$

ϕ_0 obviously satisfies the wave equation and the boundary condition $\dfrac{\partial\phi_0}{\partial y} = 0$ at $y = 0$, which is the boundary condition for the unperturbed solution. We, of course, take $\phi_0 \equiv 0$ in the upper half plane. Next we break down the solution as follows:

$$\phi = \phi_0 + \phi_1 \qquad y < 0$$
$$\phi = \phi_2 \qquad y > 0$$

Now ϕ_0, ϕ_1, ϕ_2 must all satisfy the wave equation. In addition the boundary conditions are $\dfrac{\partial \phi_1}{\partial y} = \dfrac{\partial \phi_2}{\partial y} = 0$ on the rigid boundary. In the slit we must have continuity of ϕ and its first partial derivatives. Hence,

$$\left(\frac{\partial \phi_0}{\partial y}\right)_{y=0} + \left(\frac{\partial \phi_1}{\partial y}\right)_{y=0} = \left(\frac{\partial \phi_2}{\partial y}\right)_{y=0}$$

$$\left(\frac{\partial \phi_1}{\partial y}\right)_{y=0} = \left(\frac{\partial \phi_2}{\partial y}\right)_{y=0}$$

since $\left(\dfrac{\partial \phi_0}{\partial y}\right)_{y=0} = 0$. Also

$$\phi_0(x,0) + \phi_1(x,0) = \phi_2(x,0)$$

for $-1 < x < 1$. We note that trivially $\left(\dfrac{\partial \phi_1}{\partial y}\right)_{y=0} = \left(\dfrac{\partial \phi_2}{\partial y}\right)_{y=0}$ outside the slit and therefore this boundary condition holds everywhere on the x axis. This suggests that the scattered field is skew-symmetric in y,[1] i.e.,

$$\phi_2(x,y) = -\phi_1(x,-y)$$

It follows that $\phi_2 - \phi_1 = 2\phi_2 = \phi_0$ in the slit, i.e.,

$$\phi_2(x,0) = \tfrac{1}{2} e^{ikx \cos \alpha} \qquad -1 < x < 1$$

As a Green's function we pick

$$G(x,y;\xi,\eta) = \frac{i}{4} H_0^{(1)}\left(k\sqrt{(x - \xi)^2 + (y - \eta)^2}\right)$$

which satisfies $\qquad \nabla^2 G + k^2 G = -\delta(x - \xi)\delta(y - \eta)$

Let $\phi_1 = \psi_1(x,y)e^{-i\omega t}$ and $\phi_2 = \psi_2(x,y)e^{-i\omega t}$. Then

$$\nabla^2 \psi_1 + k^2 \psi_1 = 0 \qquad \nabla^2 \psi_2 + k^2 \psi_2 = 0$$

away from the rigid boundary. From the usual theory of Green's functions we have

$$\psi_2(\xi,\eta) = -\int_{-\infty}^{\infty} \psi_2 \frac{\partial G}{\partial y}\, dx + \int_{-1}^{1} G \frac{\partial \psi_2}{\partial y}\, dx$$

$$-\psi_1(\xi,\eta) = -\int_{-\infty}^{\infty} \psi_1 \frac{\partial G}{\partial y}\, dx + \int_{-1}^{1} G \frac{\partial \psi_1}{\partial y}\, dx$$

---

[1] Another attack on the problem is to break up ϕ into symmetric and skew-symmetric parts, i.e., $\phi(x,y) = \tfrac{1}{2}[\phi(x,y) + \phi(x,-y)] + \tfrac{1}{2}[\phi(x,y) - \phi(x,-y)] = \phi_+ + \phi_-$. Then by continuity $\dfrac{\partial \phi_+}{\partial y} = 0$ on the x axis. Therefore, $\phi_+ = \phi_0$ for $y < 0$ and $\phi_+ = 0$ for $y > 0$ is the solution with the slit closed. It follows that $\phi_- = \phi_1, y < 0$, $\phi_- = \phi_2, y > 0$.

We obtain the first equation by integrating along the x axis and then along a large semicircle in the upper half plane. The second equation is obtained by integrating along the x axis and along a large semicircle in the lower half plane. The contributions of the semicircular arcs can be shown to go to zero as their radii go to infinity using the radiation condition on ψ_1 and ψ_2. Adding and letting $\eta \to 0$, we have for $-1 < \xi < 1$

$$e^{ik\xi \cos \alpha} = \psi_2(\xi,0) - \psi_1(\xi,0) = \int_{-1}^{1} G\left(\frac{\partial \psi_1}{\partial y} + \frac{\partial \psi_2}{\partial y}\right) dx - \int_{-\infty}^{\infty} (\psi_1 + \psi_2)\frac{\partial G}{\partial y} dx$$

But by the skew-symmetry, $\psi_1(x,0-) + \psi_2(x,0+) = 0$ and

$$\left(\frac{\partial \psi_1}{\partial y}\right)_{y=0} = \left(\frac{\partial \psi_2}{\partial y}\right)_{y=0}.$$

Therefore $$\tfrac{1}{2}e^{ik\xi \cos \alpha} = \frac{i}{4}\int_{-1}^{1} H_0^{(1)}(k\,|x - \xi|)\left(\frac{\partial \psi_1}{\partial y}\right)_{y=0} dx$$

which is again an integral equation of the first kind.[1] Having solved this equation for $\left(\dfrac{\partial \psi_1}{\partial y}\right)_{y=0} = \left(\dfrac{\partial \psi_2}{\partial y}\right)_{y=0}$ for $-1 < x < 1$, we obtain

$$2\psi_2(\xi,\eta) = \psi_2(\xi,\eta) - \psi_1(\xi, -\eta)$$

$$= \frac{i}{4}\int_{-1}^{1} H_0^{(1)}(k\,\sqrt{(x - \xi)^2 + \eta^2})\left[\left(\frac{\partial \psi_1}{\partial y}\right)_{y=0} + \left(\frac{\partial \psi_2}{\partial y}\right)_{y=0}\right] dx$$

giving us the solution throughout the plane.

There is one case where the integral equation of the first kind has a particularly easy solution. That is the case where $K(x;\xi)$ is a continuous symmetric kernel and $f(x)$ has a series representation $\sum_{i=1}^{\infty} c_i \psi_i(x)$ in terms of the eigenfunctions of the kernel, such that $\sum_{i=1}^{\infty} \lambda_i c_i \psi_i(x)$ converges uniformly. If this is the case, this gives us a solution, since the uniform convergence allows us to integrate term by term giving

$$\int_{a}^{b}\left[K(\xi;x)\sum_{i=1}^{\infty} \lambda_i c_i \psi_i(x)\right] dx = \sum_{i=1}^{\infty} c_i \lambda_i \int_{a}^{b} K(\xi;x)\psi_i(x)\, dx$$

$$= \sum_{i=1}^{\infty} c_i \psi_i(\xi)$$

$$= f(\xi)$$

[1] Integral equations of this type have been studied by G. Latta, The Solution of a Class of Integral Equations, *Journal of Rational Mechanics and Analysis*, vol. 5, pp. 821–834, 1956.

If a piecewise continuous solution to the integral equation exists, $\sum\limits_{i=1}^{\infty} c_i \psi_i(x)$ with $c_i = \int_a^b f(x)\psi_i(x)\,dx$ is uniformly convergent.   This follows from the work of Sec. 5.2, since in this case $f(x)$ is an integral transform.   However, here the restriction on $f(x)$ is more severe, since $\sum\limits_{i=1}^{\infty} \lambda_i c_i \psi_i(x)$ must converge uniformly and the λ_i are increasing as $i \to \infty$.

We shall see in the next chapter that integral transform methods are also sometimes quite effective in solving integral equations of the first kind.

Exercises 5.4

1. Solve Abel's equation by the following device.   Multiply both sides of the equation by $(t - x)^{-\frac{1}{2}}$ and integrate from 0 to t.

HINT:
$$\int_\xi^t \frac{dx}{\sqrt{(x - \xi)(t - x)}} = \int_0^1 \frac{du}{\sqrt{u(1 - u)}} = \pi$$

2. Discuss the diffraction of a plane acoustic wave by a circular hole in an infinite plane rigid barrier.   Set up the integral equation whose solution leads to the scattered field.   What is the appropriate Green's function?

3. Solve the integral equation

$$x(1 - x) = \int_0^1 K(x;\xi)\psi(\xi)\,d\xi$$

where
$$K(x;\xi) = \xi(1 - x) \qquad 0 \le \xi \le x$$
$$K(x;\xi) = x(1 - \xi) \qquad x \le \xi \le 1$$

References

Courant, Richard, and David Hilbert: "Methods of Mathematical Physics," Interscience Publishers, Inc., New York, 1953, vol. I.

Friedman, Bernard: "Principles and Techniques of Applied Mathematics," John Wiley & Sons, Inc., New York, 1956.

Hildebrand, F. B.: "Methods of Applied Mathematics," Prentice-Hall, Inc., Englewood Cliffs, N.J., 1952.

Lovitt, Willian V.: "Linear Integral Equations," Dover Publications, New York, 1950.

Mikhlin, Solomon G.: "Integral Equations," Pergamon Press, Inc., New York, 1957.

Murnaghan, Francis D.: "Introduction to Applied Mathematics," John Wiley & Sons, Inc., New York, 1948.

Petrovskii, Ivan G.: "Integral Equations," Graylock Press, Rochester, N.Y., 1957.

Tricomi: "Integral Equations," Interscience Publishers, Inc., New York, 1957.

Chapter 6. Integral Transform Methods

6.1 Fourier Transforms

In Sec. 4.1, we considered the solution of certain nonhomogeneous boundary-value problems in which the unknown satisfies a nonhomogeneous partial differential equation of the type

$$\nabla^2 \phi = c \frac{\partial^2 \phi}{\partial t^2} - u(x,y,z)h(t)$$

and a homogeneous boundary condition $(d\phi/dn) + \alpha\phi = 0$. In the case where $h(t)$ is periodic, we expanded it in a Fourier series and effected a separation of variables, reducing the problem to solving a sequence of nonhomogeneous boundary-value problems of the type

$$\nabla^2 \psi + \lambda\psi = -u \quad \text{in } V$$

$$\frac{d\psi}{dn} + \alpha\psi = 0 \quad \text{on } S$$

where S is the surface of the bounded volume V. If $h(t)$ is not periodic, the separation-of-variables technique is not available. However, the problem may still be solvable by integral transform methods.

The representation of a function in a Fourier series for all values of the independent variable depends on the function's being periodic with a finite period. If the function is not periodic, it may still be possible to get a **Fourier integral representation** of the function. Roughly speaking, this can be thought of as the limiting form of the Fourier series when the period approaches infinity.[1] We shall approach the problem in a manner similar to that used in Sec. 1.8, where we attempted to obtain approximations to functions over a finite interval in terms of orthonormal sets of functions.

---

[1] See E. C. Titchmarsh, "The Theory of Functions," 2d ed., Oxford University Press, New York, 1937, pp. 432 and 433.

Let $f(x)$ be a complex-valued function of the real variable x defined for $-\infty < x < \infty$, be piecewise continuous and have a piecewise continuous derivative in any finite interval, and be absolutely integrable, i.e., $\int_{-\infty}^{\infty} |f(x)|\, dx < \infty$, and square integrable, i.e., $\int_{-\infty}^{\infty} |f(x)|^2\, dx < \infty$. We attempt to find a function $g(t)$ which will minimize

$$\int_{-\infty}^{\infty} \left| f(x) - \frac{1}{\sqrt{2\pi}} \int_{-T}^{T} g(t)e^{ixt}\, dt \right|^2 dx$$

This is completely analogous to our approach to the generalized Fourier series of Sec. 1.8, where $g(t)$ plays the role of the Fourier coefficient, and instead of a summation from $-n$ to n we now have an integral from $-T$ to T.

To proceed further with the development of this section we shall need the results of the following lemmas, which we shall take time out to prove so that the following discussion can continue uninterrupted.

Lemma 1. If $f(x)$ is piecewise continuous for $a \leq x \leq b$, then

$$\lim_{R \to \infty} \int_a^b f(x) \sin Rx\, dx = 0$$

To prove this, we can assume without loss of generality that $f(x)$ is continuous, for the interval can always be broken up into a finite number of subintervals and proved for each of the subintervals where the function is continuous. We first make the change of variables $x = t + \pi/R$. Then

$$\int_a^b f(x) \sin Rx\, dx = -\int_{a-\frac{\pi}{R}}^{b-\frac{\pi}{R}} f\left(t + \frac{\pi}{R}\right) \sin Rt\, dt$$

$$2\int_a^b f(x) \sin Rx\, dx = \int_a^b f(t) \sin Rt\, dt - \int_{a-\frac{\pi}{R}}^{b-\frac{\pi}{R}} f\left(t + \frac{\pi}{R}\right) \sin Rt\, dt$$

$$= -\int_a^{b-\frac{\pi}{R}} \left[f\left(t + \frac{\pi}{R}\right) - f(t) \right] \sin Rt\, dt$$

$$+ \int_{b-\frac{\pi}{R}}^b f(t) \sin Rt\, dt - \int_{a-\frac{\pi}{R}}^a f\left(t + \frac{\pi}{R}\right) \sin Rt\, dt$$

Now if $f(x)$ is continuous for $a \leq x \leq b$, it is uniformly continuous, so we can pick R sufficiently large that $\left| f\left(t + \frac{\pi}{R}\right) - f(t) \right| < \epsilon/(b - a)$ for all t in the interval. Also we can pick R large enough that $\frac{\pi}{R} < \frac{\epsilon}{2M}$, where $|f(t)| < M$ in the interval. Hence,

$$2 \left| \int_a^b f(x) \sin Rx\, dx \right| < \frac{\epsilon}{(b - a)} (b - a) + \frac{M\epsilon}{2M} + \frac{M\epsilon}{2M} = 2\epsilon$$

Since ϵ is arbitrary, this completes the proof.

Lemma 2.   If $f(x)$ is piecewise continuous and has a piecewise continuous derivative in any finite interval and $\int_{-\infty}^{\infty} |f(x)|\, dx < \infty$, then

$$\lim_{R \to \infty} \int_{-T}^{T} f(x + t) \frac{\sin Rt}{t}\, dt = \frac{\pi}{2} [f(x+) + f(x-)]$$

where T may be finite or infinite.

We first prove it for T finite.   Breaking up the integral into four parts, we have

$$\int_{-T}^{T} f(x + t) \frac{\sin Rt}{t}\, dt = \int_{-T}^{-\delta} \frac{f(x + t)}{t} \sin Rt\, dt + \int_{-\delta}^{0} \frac{f(x + t)}{t} \sin Rt\, dt$$

$$+ \int_{0}^{\delta} \frac{f(x + t)}{t} \sin Rt\, dt + \int_{\delta}^{T} \frac{f(x + t)}{t} \sin Rt\, dt$$

The first and the last of these integrals approach zero as $R \to \infty$ by lemma 1. Now

$$\lim_{R \to \infty} \int_{0}^{\delta} \frac{\sin Rt}{t}\, dt = \lim_{R \to \infty} \int_{0}^{R\delta} \frac{\sin \tau}{\tau}\, d\tau = \int_{0}^{\infty} \frac{\sin \tau}{\tau}\, d\tau = \frac{\pi}{2}$$

Therefore, our first result follows if we can show that

$$\lim_{R \to \infty} \int_{0}^{\delta} \frac{f(x + t) - f(x+)}{t} \sin Rt\, dt = 0$$

$$\lim_{R \to \infty} \int_{0}^{\delta} \frac{f(x - t) - f(x-)}{t} \sin Rt\, dt = 0$$

But this follows from lemma 1, since

$$[f(x + t) - f(x+)]/t \qquad \text{and} \qquad [f(x - t) - f(x-)]/t$$

are piecewise continuous by the hypothesis that $f(x)$ has a piecewise continuous derivative.   That the integration can be extended to infinity follows from the fact that

$$\int_{A}^{\infty} \frac{|f(t)|}{t}\, dt < \infty \qquad \text{and} \qquad \int_{-\infty}^{-B} \left| \frac{f(t)}{t} \right| dt < \infty$$

for $A > 0, B > 0$.   Therefore for arbitrary $\epsilon > 0, T$ can be chosen sufficiently large that

$$\int_{-\infty}^{-T} \left| \frac{f(t)}{t} \right| dt + \int_{T}^{\infty} \left| \frac{f(t)}{t} \right| dt < \epsilon$$

Getting back to the original problem, we have

$$\lim_{R \to \infty} \int_{-R}^{R} \left| f(x) - \frac{1}{\sqrt{2\pi}} \int_{-T}^{T} g(t)e^{ixt} \, dt \right|^2 dx$$

$$= \lim_{R \to \infty} \left[\int_{-R}^{R} |f|^2 \, dx - \frac{1}{\sqrt{2\pi}} \int_{-R}^{R} \int_{-T}^{T} f(x)g^*(t)e^{-ixt} \, dt \, dx \right.$$

$$- \frac{1}{\sqrt{2\pi}} \int_{-R}^{R} \int_{-T}^{T} f^*(x)g(t)e^{ixt} \, dt \, dx$$

$$\left. + \frac{1}{2\pi} \int_{-R}^{R} \int_{-T}^{T} \int_{-T}^{T} g(t)g^*(\tau)e^{ix(t-\tau)} \, dt \, d\tau \, dx \right]$$

In the last integral we integrate first with respect to x.

$$\int_{-R}^{R} e^{ix(t-\tau)} \, dx = \int_{-R}^{R} \cos x(t - \tau) \, dx + i \int_{-R}^{R} \sin x(t - \tau) \, dx$$

$$= 2 \frac{\sin R(t - \tau)}{t - \tau}$$

Next we integrate with respect to t.

$$\lim_{R \to \infty} 2 \int_{-T}^{T} g(t) \frac{\sin R(t - \tau)}{(t - \tau)} \, dt = \lim_{R \to \infty} 2 \int_{-T-\tau}^{T-\tau} g(\xi + \tau) \frac{\sin R\xi}{\xi} \, d\xi$$

$$= 2\pi g(\tau)$$

This follows from lemma 2, where of course we must assume that $g(t)$ satisfies the hypotheses of the lemma.   Hence

$$\int_{-\infty}^{\infty} \left| f(x) - \frac{1}{\sqrt{2\pi}} \int_{-T}^{T} g(t)e^{ixt} \, dt \right|^2 dx$$

$$= \int_{-\infty}^{\infty} |f|^2 \, dx + \int_{-T}^{T} |g|^2 \, dt - \int_{-T}^{T} g(t)h^*(t) \, dt - \int_{-T}^{T} g^*(t)h(t) \, dt$$

$$= \int_{-\infty}^{\infty} |f|^2 \, dx - \int_{-T}^{T} |h|^2 \, dt + \int_{-T}^{T} |g(t) - h(t)|^2 \, dt$$

where

$$h(t) = \frac{1}{\sqrt{2\pi}} \int_{-\infty}^{\infty} f(x)e^{-ixt} \, dx$$

The function $h(t)$ exists and is continuous because the integral is uniformly convergent in t.   It is now obvious that to minimize the above expression we must chose $g(t) = h(t)$, and

$$\min \int_{-\infty}^{\infty} \left| f(x) - \frac{1}{\sqrt{2\pi}} \int_{-T}^{T} g(t)e^{ixt} \, dt \right|^2 dx$$

$$= \int_{-\infty}^{\infty} |f(x)|^2 \, dx - \int_{-T}^{T} |g(t)|^2 \, dt \geq 0$$

This is true for all T.   Hence we have Bessel's inequality

$$\int_{-\infty}^{\infty} |g|^2\, dt \leq \int_{-\infty}^{\infty} |f|^2\, dx < \infty$$

from which it follows that g is square integrable.

The function

$$g(t) = \frac{1}{\sqrt{2\pi}} \int_{-\infty}^{\infty} f(x) e^{-ixt}\, dx$$

is known as the **Fourier transform** of $f(x)$.   It exists if $f(x)$ is absolutely integrable, and it is square integrable if $f(x)$ is square integrable by Bessel's inequality.   The function

$$f_T(x) = \frac{1}{\sqrt{2\pi}} \int_{-T}^{T} g(t) e^{ixt}\, dt$$

is the best approximation in the least-mean-square sense to $f(x)$.   If we could show that

$$\int_{-\infty}^{\infty} |g(t)|^2\, dt = \int_{-\infty}^{\infty} |f(x)|^2\, dx$$

then

$$\lim_{T \to \infty} \int_{-\infty}^{\infty} |f(x) - f_T(x)|^2\, dx = 0$$

or, in other words, $f_T(x)$ converges in mean to $f(x)$.   This is the analogue of completeness for sets of orthonormal functions.   In this case we again have convergence in mean.   This result is known as **Plancherel's Theorem,**[1] although we shall not attempt to prove it here.

Actually, under our present hypotheses, we can show directly that

$$\frac{1}{\sqrt{2\pi}} \int_{-\infty}^{\infty} g(t) e^{ixt}\, dt = \tfrac{1}{2}[f(x+) + f(x-)]$$

without using the theory of mean convergence or, for that matter, the square integrability of $f(x)$.   We have

$$\lim_{T \to \infty} \frac{1}{2\pi} \int_{-T}^{T} \int_{-\infty}^{\infty} f(\tau) e^{it(x-\tau)}\, d\tau\, dt$$

$$= \lim_{T \to \infty} \frac{1}{2\pi} \int_{-\infty}^{\infty} f(\tau) \frac{\sin T(x - \tau)}{(x - \tau)}\, d\tau$$

$$= \lim_{T \to \infty} \frac{1}{2\pi} \int_{-\infty}^{\infty} f(x + u) \frac{\sin Tu}{u}\, du$$

$$= \tfrac{1}{2}[f(x+) + f(x-)]$$

by lemma 2.

[1] *Ibid.*, pp. 436 and 437.

As an example, let us consider the transform of the function $f(x) = e^{-|x|}$.
Then

$$g(t) = \frac{1}{\sqrt{2\pi}} \int_{-\infty}^{\infty} e^{-|x|} e^{-ixt}\, dx$$

$$= \frac{1}{\sqrt{2\pi}} \int_{-\infty}^{0} e^{x(1-it)}\, dx + \frac{1}{\sqrt{2\pi}} \int_{0}^{\infty} e^{-x(1+it)}\, dx$$

$$= \frac{1}{\sqrt{2\pi}} \left[\frac{1}{1-it} + \frac{1}{1+it} \right]$$

$$= \frac{1}{\sqrt{2\pi}} \frac{2}{1+t^2}$$

We can invert the transform in this case by complex contour integration.
First consider $x > 0$.   Then

$$\frac{1}{2\pi} \int_{-\infty}^{\infty} \frac{2}{1+t^2} e^{ixt}\, dt = \lim_{T \to \infty} \frac{1}{\pi} \int_{C} \frac{1}{1+z^2} e^{ixz}\, dz$$

where C is the contour shown in Fig. 12.
There is a simple pole at $z = i$ and
by the residue theorem

$$\frac{1}{2\pi} \int_{-\infty}^{\infty} \frac{2}{1+t^2} e^{ixt}\, dt$$

$$= 2\pi i \ (\text{residue at } i)$$

$$= e^{-x}$$

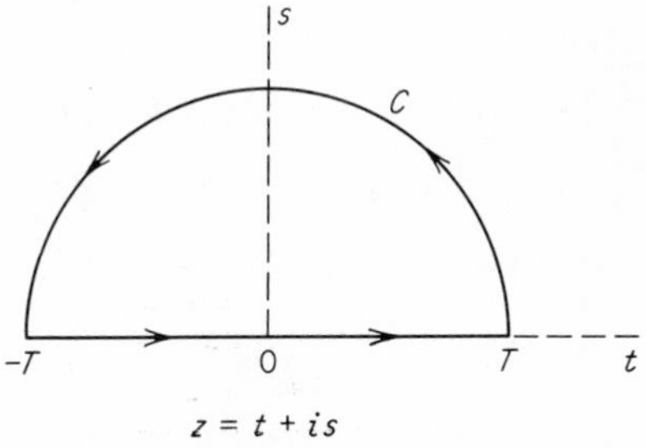

provided we can show that the con-
tribution to the contour integral on

$z = t + is$

FIGURE 12

the semicircular arc goes to zero as $T \to \infty$.   Letting $z = Te^{i\theta}$, we have

$$\left| \frac{1}{\pi} \int_{0}^{\pi} \frac{1}{1+T^2 e^{2i\theta}} e^{ixT(\cos\theta + i\sin\theta)} iTe^{i\theta}\, d\theta \right| \leq \frac{T}{|T^2 - 1|} \to 0 \qquad \text{as } T \to \infty$$

For $x < 0$, we must close the contour with a semicircular arc below the real
axis.   Then the simple pole at $z = -i$ contributes e^x.   Of course if $x = 0$,
the integration can be performed directly, i.e.,

$$\frac{1}{2\pi} \int_{-\infty}^{\infty} \frac{2}{1+t^2}\, dt = \frac{1}{\pi} \tan^{-1} t \Big]_{-\infty}^{\infty} = 1$$

The Fourier transform is obviously a linear transformation, for letting

$$T[f] = \frac{1}{\sqrt{2\pi}} \int_{-\infty}^{\infty} f(x) e^{-ixt}\, dx$$

we have $T[af + bg] = \dfrac{1}{\sqrt{2\pi}} \displaystyle\int_{-\infty}^{\infty} [af(x) + bg(x)]e^{-ixt}\, dx$

$$= \frac{a}{\sqrt{2\pi}} \int_{-\infty}^{\infty} f(x)e^{-ixt}\, dx + \frac{b}{\sqrt{2\pi}} \int_{-\infty}^{\infty} g(x)e^{-ixt}\, dx$$

$$= aT[f] + bT[g]$$

For square integrable functions we have already seen that the transform preserves norms, i.e.,

$$\|f\| = \left[\int_{-\infty}^{\infty} |f(x)|^2\, dx\right]^{\frac{1}{2}} = \left[\int_{-\infty}^{\infty} |T[f]|^2\, dt\right]^{\frac{1}{2}}$$

$$= \|T[f]\|$$

We also have Parseval's relation, i.e.,

$$\int_{-\infty}^{\infty} f^*(x)g(x)\, dx = \int_{-\infty}^{\infty} T^*[f]T[g]\, dt$$

This is proved as follows.[1]

$$\|f + g\|^2 = \|T[f] + T[g]\|^2$$

$$\|f\|^2 + \|g\|^2 + (f,g) + (g,f) = \|T[f]\|^2 + \|T[g]\|^2 + (T[f],T[g]) + (T[g],T[f])$$

$$(f,g) + (f,g)^* = (T[f],T[g]) + (T[f],T[g])^*$$

$$\|f + ig\|^2 = \|T[f] + iT[g]\|^2$$

$$\|f\|^2 + \|g\|^2 + (f,ig) + (ig,f) = \|T[f]\|^2 + \|T[g]\|^2 + (T[f],iT[g])$$
$$+ (iT[g],T[f])$$

$$(f,g) - (f,g)^* = (T[f],T[g]) - (T[f],T[g])^*$$

Adding, we have $\qquad (f,g) = (T[f],T[g])$

Let us now turn to some of the other properties of the Fourier transform. First consider the effect of a translation of the independent variable, i.e.,

$$T[f(x - a)] = \frac{1}{\sqrt{2\pi}} \int_{-\infty}^{\infty} f(x - a)e^{-ixt}\, dx$$

$$= \frac{1}{\sqrt{2\pi}} \int_{-\infty}^{\infty} f(\xi)e^{-i(\xi+a)t}\, d\xi$$

$$= e^{-iat} \frac{1}{\sqrt{2\pi}} \int_{-\infty}^{\infty} f(\xi)e^{-i\xi t}\, d\xi$$

$$= e^{-iat}T[f(x)]$$

---

[1] Compare with Sec. 1.8.

A change of scale has the following effect.

$$T[f(ax)] = \frac{1}{\sqrt{2\pi}} \int_{-\infty}^{\infty} f(ax)e^{-ixt}\,dx$$

$$= \frac{1}{|a|}\frac{1}{\sqrt{2\pi}} \int_{-\infty}^{\infty} f(\xi)e^{-i\xi(t/a)}\,d\xi$$

$$= \frac{1}{|a|}\, T[f(x)]_{t \to \frac{t}{a}}$$

Since we are going to be using the Fourier transform to solve differential equations, we must know how it transforms the derivative of a function. Let $f(x)$ be a function which is continuous in any finite interval and is absolutely integrable. Assume that its first derivative is piecewise continuous and absolutely integrable. Then

$$T[f'(x)] = \frac{1}{\sqrt{2\pi}} \int_{-\infty}^{\infty} f'(x)e^{-ixt}\,dx$$

$$= \frac{1}{\sqrt{2\pi}} [f(x)e^{-ixt}]_{-\infty}^{\infty} + \frac{it}{\sqrt{2\pi}} \int_{-\infty}^{\infty} f(x)e^{-ixt}\,dx$$

$$= itT[f]$$

since $f(x) \to 0$ as $x \to \pm\infty$. Generalizing, we can say that if $f(x)$ and its first $k-1$ derivatives are all continuous and absolutely integrable and its kth derivative is piecewise continuous and absolutely integrable, then

$$T[f^{(k)}(x)] = (it)^k T[f]$$

For the purpose of solving certain integral equations we must determine how the integral of a function is transformed. Let $f(x)$ be a function which is piecewise continuous and absolutely integrable. Then

$$h(x) = \int_{a}^{x} f(\xi)\,d\xi$$

is continuous. Assume that $h(x)$ is absolutely integrable. Then

$$T[h(x)] = \frac{1}{\sqrt{2\pi}} \int_{-\infty}^{\infty} h(x)e^{-ixt}\,dx$$

$$= \frac{1}{\sqrt{2\pi}} \left[\frac{h(x)e^{-ixt}}{-it}\right]_{-\infty}^{\infty} + \frac{1}{it}\frac{1}{\sqrt{2\pi}} \int_{-\infty}^{\infty} f(x)e^{-ixt}\,dx$$

$$= \frac{1}{it} T[f]$$

We see then that integration has the effect of dividing the transform by it, whereas differentiation has the effect of multiplying the transform by it.

For the applications it is very important that we should know the transform of a certain integral, namely,

$$h(x) = \frac{1}{\sqrt{2\pi}} \int_{-\infty}^{\infty} f(x - \xi)g(\xi) \, d\xi$$

$$= \frac{1}{\sqrt{2\pi}} \int_{-\infty}^{\infty} g(x - \xi)f(\xi) \, d\xi$$

This is called the **convolution integral.** Taking the transform of $h(x)$, we have

$$T[h] = \frac{1}{2\pi} \int_{-\infty}^{\infty} g(\xi) \int_{-\infty}^{\infty} f(x - \xi)e^{-ixt} \, dx \, d\xi$$

$$= \frac{1}{2\pi} \int_{-\infty}^{\infty} g(\xi) \int_{-\infty}^{\infty} f(\eta)e^{-i(\xi + n)t} \, d\eta \, d\xi$$

$$= \left(\frac{1}{\sqrt{2\pi}} \int_{-\infty}^{\infty} g(\xi)e^{-i\xi t} \, d\xi \right) \left(\frac{1}{\sqrt{2\pi}} \int_{-\infty}^{\infty} f(\eta)e^{-int} \, d\eta \right)$$

$$= T[f]T[g]$$

Finally, before turning to the applications of Fourier transforms, let us consider the transform as a function of the complex variable $\zeta = t + is$. Suppose $f(x) = O(e^{\alpha x})$ as $x \to \infty$. If $\alpha \geq 0$, then $f(x)$ will not have a Fourier transform in the usual sense. Let $g(x) = e^{sx}f(x)$ with s real. Now $g(x) = O[e^{(\alpha + s)x}]$ as $x \to \infty$, and it will have a Fourier transform if $s < -\alpha$, provided it behaves properly as $x \to -\infty$. The Fourier integral theorem states that

$$g(x) = \frac{1}{2\pi} \int_{-\infty}^{\infty} e^{ixt} \int_{-\infty}^{\infty} g(\xi)e^{-i\xi t} \, d\xi \, dt$$

$$e^{sx}f(x) = \frac{1}{2\pi} \int_{-\infty}^{\infty} e^{ixt} \int_{-\infty}^{\infty} f(\xi)e^{-i\xi(t + is)} \, d\xi \, dt$$

$$f(x) = \frac{1}{2\pi} \int_{-\infty}^{\infty} e^{ix(t + is)} \int_{-\infty}^{\infty} f(\xi)e^{-i\xi(t + is)} \, d\xi \, dt$$

$$f(x) = \frac{1}{2\pi} \int_{-\infty + is}^{\infty + is} e^{ix\zeta} \int_{-\infty}^{\infty} f(\xi)e^{-i\xi\zeta} \, d\xi \, d\zeta$$

where the integral in the complex ζ plane is taken along the line $\zeta = t + is$, $-\infty < t < \infty$. The **complex Fourier transform** of $f(x)$ is defined as follows:

$$\phi(\zeta) = \frac{1}{\sqrt{2\pi}} \int_{-\infty}^{\infty} f(x)e^{-ix\zeta} \, dx$$

and the inverse transform is

$$f(x) = \frac{1}{\sqrt{2\pi}} \int_{-\infty + is}^{\infty + is} \phi(\zeta)e^{ix\zeta} \, d\zeta$$

Let us investigate more carefully the conditions under which the complex Fourier transform exists. Suppose $f(x)$ is continuous and has a piecewise continuous first derivative in any finite interval. Let $f(x) = O(e^{\alpha x})$ as $x \to \infty$ and $f(x) = O(e^{\beta x})$ as $x \to -\infty$, i.e., there exists numbers M, N, and R such that $|f(x)| \le Me^{\alpha x}$ for $x \ge R$ and $|f(x)| \le Ne^{\beta x}$ for $x \le -R$. Then

$$\phi(\zeta) = \frac{1}{\sqrt{2\pi}} \int_{-\infty}^{-R} f(x)e^{-i\zeta x}\,dx + \frac{1}{\sqrt{2\pi}} \int_{-R}^{R} f(x)e^{-i\zeta x}\,dx + \frac{1}{\sqrt{2\pi}} \int_{R}^{\infty} f(x)e^{-i\zeta x}\,dx$$

and

$$\left| \int_{-\infty}^{-R} f(x)e^{-i\zeta x}\,dx \right| \le N \int_{-\infty}^{-R} e^{x(\beta+s)}\,dx = \frac{Ne^{-(\beta+s)R}}{\beta+s}$$

provided $s > -\beta$. Similarly,

$$\left| \int_{R}^{\infty} f(x)e^{-i\zeta x}\,dx \right| \le M \int_{R}^{\infty} e^{x(\alpha+s)}\,dx = \frac{Me^{(\alpha+s)R}}{s+\alpha}$$

provided $s < -\alpha$. Therefore, the integral exists for $-\beta < \mathrm{Im}\,(\zeta) < -\alpha$. In fact, the integrals converge uniformly in the strip

$$-\beta < \rho_1 \le \mathrm{Im}\,(\zeta) \le \rho_2 < -\alpha$$

where ρ_1 and ρ_2 are arbitrary numbers satisfying the inequality. Therefore, $\phi(\zeta)$ is an analytic function of ζ in the strip $-\beta < \mathrm{Im}\,(\zeta) < -\alpha$. If the strip $-\beta < \mathrm{Im}\,(\zeta) < -\alpha$ contains the t axis of the ζ plane, then the Fourier transform will exist in the ordinary sense. Furthermore, by the theory of analytic continuation,

$$\phi(\zeta) = \frac{1}{\sqrt{2\pi}} \int_{-\infty}^{\infty} f(x)e^{-ix\zeta}\,dx$$

is the only function analytic in the strip which takes on the values

$$\phi(t) = \frac{1}{\sqrt{2\pi}} \int_{-\infty}^{\infty} f(x)e^{-ixt}\,dx$$

when ζ is real.

Under rather general conditions the inverse transform can be computed by integrating along any line parallel to the real axis lying in the strip of analyticity of the complex Fourier transform, i.e.,

$$\frac{1}{\sqrt{2\pi}} \int_{-\infty+i\gamma_1}^{\infty+i\gamma_1} \phi(\zeta)e^{ix\zeta}\,d\zeta = \frac{1}{\sqrt{2\pi}} \int_{-\infty+i\gamma_2}^{\infty+i\gamma_2} \phi(\zeta)e^{ix\zeta}\,d\zeta$$

where γ_1 and γ_2 are any real numbers between $-\beta$ and $-\alpha$. This can be shown by applying Cauchy's theorem to the rectangular contour shown and then letting $T \to \infty$, provided

$$|\phi(T + is)| \le M(T) \to 0 \qquad \text{and} \qquad |\phi(-T + is)| \le N(T) \to 0$$

as $T \to \infty$ uniformly in s.   The integrals on the vertical sides approach zero at $T \to \infty$ since

$$\left| \frac{1}{\sqrt{2\pi}} \int_{T+i\gamma_1}^{T+i\gamma_2} \phi(\zeta)e^{ix\zeta} \right| \leq \frac{M}{\sqrt{2\pi}} \int_{\gamma_1}^{\gamma_2} e^{-xs}ds \to 0 \qquad \text{as } T \to \infty$$

$$\left| \frac{1}{\sqrt{2\pi}} \int_{-T+i\gamma_1}^{-T+i\gamma_2} \phi(\zeta)e^{ix\zeta} \right| \leq \frac{N}{\sqrt{2\pi}} \int_{\gamma_1}^{\gamma_2} e^{-xs}ds \to 0 \qquad \text{as } T \to \infty$$

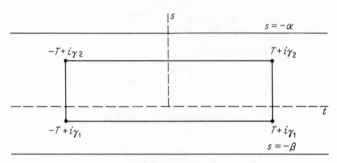

FIGURE 13

Therefore, since the closed contour lies entirely in the strip of analyticity, the result follows by Cauchy's theorem.

Exercises 6.1

1. Find the Fourier transform of $f(x) = e^{-ax}$, $x \geq 0$, $f(x) = 0$, $x < 0$, with $a > 0$.   Verify the inverse transformation by direct integration.   Note that the transform is not absolutely integrable, although it is square integrable.

*2. Show that $f(x) = e^{-x^2/2}$ is its own Fourier transform.

*3. If $f(x)$ is real and satisfies the conditions of Fourier's integral theorem, show that

$$\tfrac{1}{2}[f(x+) + f(x-)] = \frac{1}{\pi} \int_0^\infty \int_{-\infty}^\infty f(\xi) \cos t(x - \xi) \, d\xi \, dt$$

Furthermore, if $f(x)$ is even, show that

$$\tfrac{1}{2}[f(x+) + f(x-)] = \frac{2}{\pi} \int_0^\infty \cos xt \int_0^\infty f(\xi) \cos \xi t \, d\xi \, dt$$

and if $f(x)$ is odd,

$$\tfrac{1}{2}[f(x+) + f(x-)] = \frac{2}{\pi} \int_0^\infty \sin xt \int_0^\infty f(\xi) \sin \xi t \, d\xi \, dt$$

NOTE:

$$\sqrt{\frac{2}{\pi}} \int_0^\infty f(x) \cos xt \, dx$$

is called the **Fourier cosine transform,** and

$$\sqrt{\frac{2}{\pi}} \int_0^\infty f(x) \sin xt\, dx$$

is called the **Fourier sine transform.**

4. Compute the complex Fourier transform of $f(x) = e^{-|x|}$ and show that it is analytic in the strip $-1 < \text{Im}(\zeta) < 1$.

*5. Let $f(x)$ be continuous and absolutely integrable for $-\infty < x < \infty$. Let $f'(x)$ be piecewise continuous and absolutely integrable. Show that if both $f(x)$ and $f'(x)$ are $O(e^{\alpha x})$ as $x \to \infty$ and $O(e^{\beta x})$ as $x \to -\infty$, $\phi(\zeta) = O\left(\dfrac{1}{\zeta}\right)$ in the strip $-\beta < \rho_1 \le \text{Im}(\zeta) \le \rho_2 < -\alpha$. Note that this is then a sufficient condition for the inversion integral to be independent of γ.

*6. Let $f(x)$ and $g(x)$ be absolutely integrable, $O(e^{\alpha x})$ as $x \to \infty$, and $O(e^{\beta x})$ as $x \to -\infty$. Show that the convolution

$$h(x) = \frac{1}{\sqrt{2\pi}} \int_{-\infty}^\infty f(x - \xi) g(\xi)\, d\xi$$

is $O(e^{\alpha_1 x})$ as $x \to \infty$ and $O(e^{\beta_1 x})$ as $x \to -\infty$, where $-\beta < -\beta_1 < -\alpha_1 < -\alpha$. Also show that

$$T[h] = T[f]T[g]$$

where these are the complex Fourier transforms and equality holds in the strip $-\beta < \text{Im}(\zeta) < -\alpha$, where all three transforms are analytic.

7. Let $f(x) = \sin \omega x$ for $x \ge 0$ and $f(x) = 0$ for $x < 0$. Find the complex Fourier transform of $f(x)$ and show that it is analytic for $\text{Im}(\zeta) < 0$. Verify the inversion integral directly, where $\gamma < 0$.

6.2 Applications of Fourier Transforms. Ordinary Differential Equations

We shall first apply the Fourier transform method to the solution of certain ordinary differential equations. To start with, consider the linear nth-order equation with constant coefficients

$$a_n \frac{d^n y}{dx^n} + a_{n-1} \frac{d^{n-1} y}{dx^{n-1}} + \cdots + a_1 \frac{dy}{dx} + a_0 y = f(x)$$

Denote the operator on the left by

$$L = a_n D^n + a_{n-1} D^{n-1} + \cdots + a_1 D + a_0$$

Then the equation can be written as

$$L(y) = f(x)$$

Assuming that we are interested in a solution for $-\infty < x < \infty$ where $f(x)$ is defined and has a Fourier transform, we can proceed as follows:

$$T[L(y)] = [a_n(it)^n + a_{n-1}(it)^{n-1} + \cdots + a_1(it) + a_0]T[y]$$

$$= P(it)T[y] = T[f] = F(t)$$

Then
$$T[y] = \frac{F(t)}{P(it)} = F(t)G(t)$$

where $G(t) = 1/P(it)$. Then, using the convolution theorem, we have

$$y(x) = T^{-1}[F(t)G(t)] = \frac{1}{\sqrt{2\pi}} \int_{-\infty}^{\infty} f(\xi)g(x - \xi)\, d\xi$$

where
$$g(x) = T^{-1}[G(t)] = T^{-1}\left[\frac{1}{P(it)}\right]$$

Proceeding formally we have the following interesting interpretation of the result. The Fourier transform of the Dirac delta function is[1]

$$T[\delta(x)] = \frac{1}{\sqrt{2\pi}} \int_{-\infty}^{\infty} \delta(x)e^{-ixt}\, dx = \frac{1}{\sqrt{2\pi}}$$

Then consider the following differential equation:

$$L(\gamma) = \delta(x)$$

Then
$$T[L(\gamma)] = P(it)T[\gamma] = \frac{1}{\sqrt{2\pi}}$$

$$\gamma(x) = T^{-1}\left[\frac{1}{\sqrt{2\pi}\,P(it)}\right] = \frac{1}{\sqrt{2\pi}}T^{-1}[G(t)] = \frac{1}{\sqrt{2\pi}}g(x)$$

so that
$$y(x) = \int_{-\infty}^{\infty} f(\xi)\gamma(x - \xi)\, d\xi$$

Therefore, γ behaves like a Green's function, i.e., it is the response of the system to a delta function (unit impulse), and we have a superposition principle with $y(x)$, the response to $f(x)$, given by the above integral. The electrical engineer describes this phenomenon as follows. The function $f(x)$ is the **input**, while $y(x)$ is the **output**. The function $\gamma(x)$ is the **response to a unit impulse**. The transform of $\sqrt{2\pi}\gamma$ is the **admittance** $Y = 1/P(it)$. To get

[1] This can be made rigorous by treating the delta function as a generalized function or distribution.

the response to a given input you find the transform of the input, multiply by the admittance, and then take the inverse transform of the product.

Let us illustrate these ideas by an elementary electrical circuit problem (see Fig. 14).

Here we have $E_0 = RI$ $L\dfrac{dI}{dt} + RI = E_i$

Let $E_i = Ee^{-|t|}$. Then[1]

$$(is)LT[I] + RT[I] = \frac{2E}{\sqrt{2\pi}}\frac{1}{1+s^2}$$

$$T[I] = \frac{2E}{\sqrt{2\pi}}\frac{1}{1+s^2}\frac{1}{isL+R}$$

$$I(t) = \frac{E}{\pi}\int_{-\infty}^{\infty}\frac{e^{ist}\,ds}{(1+s^2)(isL+R)}$$

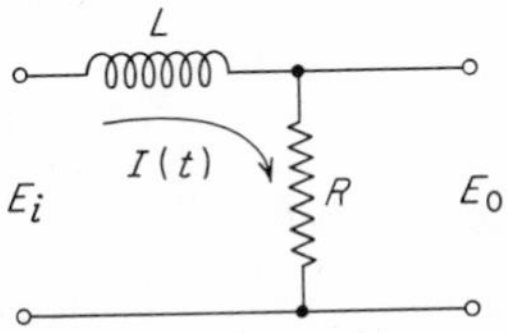

FIGURE 14

The last integral can be evaluated by complex contour integration. For $t > 0$

$$I(t) = \frac{E}{\pi}\,2\pi i\left(\text{residue at } s = i + \text{residue at } s = \frac{iR}{L}\right)$$

$$= 2Ei\left[\frac{e^{-t}}{2i(R-L)} + \frac{e^{-Rt/L}}{iL(1-R^2/L^2)}\right]$$

$$= E\left[\frac{e^{-t}}{R-L} + \frac{2Le^{-Rt/L}}{L^2-R^2}\right]$$

For $t < 0$

$$I(t) = \frac{-E}{\pi}\,2\pi i\,(\text{residue at } s = -i) = \frac{Ee^{t}}{L+R}$$

At $t = 0$ the current is continuous, i.e.,

$$I(0) = \lim_{t\to 0} I(t) = \frac{E}{R+L}$$

If we are interested in a phenomenon which begins at a specific time, say $t = 0$, we can still use the Fourier transform technique if we exercise a bit of care in computing the transform. Suppose in the above example

$$E_i = Ee^{-at}\sin \omega t \qquad t \geq 0$$

$$E_i = 0 \qquad t < 0$$

---

[1] Here we change to the variable s in the transform to avoid the time variable t in the differential equation.

and we specify that $I = \dfrac{dI}{dt} = 0$ for $t < 0$, while $I(0+) = I_0$.   Then

$$T[I'] = \frac{1}{\sqrt{2\pi}} \int_0^\infty \frac{dI}{dt} e^{-ist} dt$$

$$= \frac{-I_0}{\sqrt{2\pi}} + \frac{is}{\sqrt{2\pi}} \int_0^\infty I e^{-ist} dt$$

$$= \frac{-I_0}{\sqrt{2\pi}} + isT[I]$$

Then we have

$$\frac{-I_0 L}{\sqrt{2\pi}} + [isL + R]T[I] = \frac{1}{\sqrt{2\pi}} \int_0^\infty E e^{-at} \sin \omega t\, e^{-ist} dt$$

$$= \frac{E}{2i\sqrt{2\pi}} \left[\frac{1}{a + is - i\omega} - \frac{1}{a + is + i\omega} \right]$$

Therefore,

$$T[I] = \frac{E}{2i\sqrt{2\pi}(isL + R)} \left[\frac{1}{a + is - i\omega} - \frac{1}{a + is + i\omega} \right] + \frac{I_0 L}{\sqrt{2\pi}(isL + R)}$$

Inverting the transform by complex contour integration, we see that for $t < 0$, $I = 0$, since in this case we close the contour below the real axis and there are no poles in the lower half plane.   For $t > 0$ we close the contour above the real axis and evaluate the required residues.   Then

$$I(t) = \frac{\omega E e^{-Rt/L}}{L[(a - R/L)^2 + \omega^2]} + I_0 e^{-Rt/L}$$

$$+ \frac{(R/L - a)E/L\, e^{-at} \sin \omega t}{(a - R/L)^2 + \omega^2} - \frac{\omega E/L\, e^{-at} \cos \omega t}{(a - R/L)^2 + \omega^2}$$

Notice that I is discontinuous at $t = 0$ but that $\lim_{t \to 0+} I(t) = I_0$ as specified.

If there is a capacitor in the circuit (see Fig. 15), then the basic equation is the integrodifferential equation

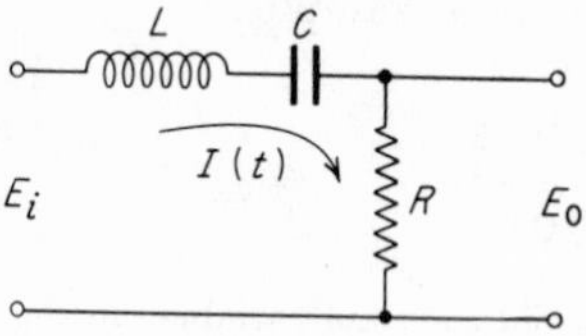

$$L \frac{dI}{dt} + RI + \frac{1}{C} \left[q_0 + \int_0^t I\, dt \right] = E_i(t)$$

where q_0 is the initial charge on the capacitor.

FIGURE 15

$$q = q_0 + \int_0^t I\, dt$$

is the change, and obviously $\dfrac{dq}{dt} = I$. Let us assume that I, q, and E_i are all zero for $t < 0$, but that $I(0+) = I_0$ and $q(0+) = q_0$. Then

$$T[q] = \frac{1}{\sqrt{2\pi}} \int_0^\infty q(t)e^{-ist}\, dt$$

$$= \left[\frac{q(t)e^{-ist}}{-is\,\sqrt{2\pi}}\right]_0^\infty + \frac{1}{is\,\sqrt{2\pi}} \int_0^\infty I(t)e^{-ist}\, dt$$

$$= \frac{q_0}{\sqrt{2\pi}\,is} + \frac{T[I]}{is}$$

and we have

$$\frac{-I_0 L}{\sqrt{2\pi}} + \frac{q_0}{C\sqrt{2\pi}\,is} + \left[isL + R + \frac{1}{isC}\right]T[I] = T[E_i]$$

Then
$$T[I] = \frac{T[E_i] + I_0 L/\sqrt{2\pi} - q_0/(C\sqrt{2\pi}\,is)}{[isL + R + 1/(isC)]}$$

and the transform may be inverted using complex contour integration or by referring to a set of tables.[1]

Before leaving the discussion of ordinary differential equations, let us consider how the use of the complex Fourier transform facilitates the solution of some problems where the input does not have a Fourier transform in the usual sense. Consider the following input to the circuit of the last example:

$$E_i = 1 \qquad t \geq 0$$
$$E_i = 0 \qquad t < 0$$

This is the so-called **unit step function.** This input does not have a Fourier transform in the ordinary sense, but it does have a complex transform, i.e.,

$$T[E_i] = \frac{1}{\sqrt{2\pi}} \int_0^\infty e^{-i\zeta t}\, dt$$

$$= \frac{1}{\sqrt{2\pi}\,i\zeta}$$

provided $\text{Im}\,(\zeta) < 0$. The inversion integral yields E_i by complex contour integration. If $t > 0$

$$\frac{1}{2\pi} \int_{-\infty - i\gamma}^{\infty - i\gamma} \frac{e^{i\zeta t}}{i\zeta}\, d\zeta = 2\pi i \left(\text{residue of } \frac{e^{i\zeta t}}{2\pi i \zeta} \text{ at } \zeta = 0\right)$$

$$= 1$$

[1] See George A. Campbell and Ronald M. Foster, "Fourier Integrals for Practical Applications," D. Van Nostrand Company, Inc., Princeton, N.J., 1948.

because here the contour is closed by a semicircular arc in an upper half plane and the pole at $\zeta = 0$ is inside the contour. If $t < 0$, the contour is closed below the real axis, there are no singularities inside the contour, and by Cauchy's theorem the integral is zero. If $t = 0$, the integral is evaluated as a Cauchy principal value which is easily shown to be $\frac{1}{2}$.

Let $I_0 = q_0 = 0$. Then we have, taking complex Fourier transforms,

$$\left[(i\zeta)L + R + \frac{1}{(i\zeta)C} \right] T[I] = \frac{1}{\sqrt{2\pi i\zeta}}$$

$$T[I] = \frac{1}{\sqrt{2\pi}[(i\zeta)^2 L + (i\zeta)R + 1/C]}$$

Notice that the transform of the response to a unit step function is the same as the transform of the solution of the differential equation

$$L\frac{d^2\gamma}{dt^2} + R\frac{d\gamma}{dt} + \frac{1}{C}\gamma = \delta(t)$$

with the unit impulse as input. This leads to the observation that *the unit impulse is the derivative of the unit step function.*[1] Also, since

$$L\frac{d^2I}{dt^2} + R\frac{dI}{dt} + \frac{1}{C}I = \frac{d}{dt}E_i$$

for an arbitrary input E_i, we have the following result:

$$T[I] = \frac{1}{\sqrt{2\pi}[(i\zeta)^2 L + (i\zeta)R + 1/C]} T[E_i']$$

$$I = \int_{-\infty}^{\infty} E_i'(\tau) A(t - \tau)\, d\tau$$

where $A(t)$ is the **indicial admittance**, i.e., the response to a unit step input.

$$A(t) = T^{-1}\left\{ \frac{1}{\sqrt{2\pi}[(i\zeta)^2 L + (i\zeta)R + 1/C]} \right\}$$

This is a very important result from the practical point of view, because it is much easier to simulate a unit step function than it is to simulate a unit impulse. Hence the response to a unit step can be determined experimentally much more easily than the response to a unit impulse.

Exercises 6.2

1. Solve the differential equation $y'' + 3y' + 2y = e^{-t}$, $0 < t$, subject to $y(0+) = y_0$ and $y'(0+) = y_0'$, using the Fourier transform.

---

[1] This statement is made rigorous in the theory of distributions.

2. Solve the differential equation $y'' + \omega_0^2 y = \sin \omega t$, $0 < t$, $\omega \neq \omega_0$, subject to $y(0+) = 0$ and $y'(0+) = 0$, using the complex Fourier transform. Also consider the case $\omega = \omega_0$.

3. Solve the integrodifferential equation $y' + \int_0^t y(\tau)\,d\tau = e^{-t}$, $0 < t$, subject to $y(0+) = y_0$, using the Fourier transform.

4. Solve the following pair of simultaneous differential equations for $t > 0$, using the Fourier transform.

$$x' + y' - x + 3y = e^{-t}$$
$$x' + y' + 2x + y = e^{-2t}$$

subject to $x(0+) = x_0$, $y(0+) = y_0$.

6.3 Applications of Fourier Transforms. Partial Differential Equations

Next we consider the Fourier transform technique for solving certain partial differential equations. As a general class of problem consider the solution of the partial differential equation

$$\nabla^2 \phi = a\phi + b\frac{\partial \phi}{\partial t} + c\frac{\partial^2 \phi}{\partial t^2} - f(x,y,z,t)$$

to hold in a bounded volume V, bounded by the closed surface S. On S we prescribe the boundary condition $\dfrac{d\phi}{dn} + \alpha\phi = 0$. We also specify initially that $\phi(x,y,z,0) = u(x,y,z)$ and $\left(\dfrac{\partial \phi}{\partial t}\right)_{t=0} = v(x,y,z)$. This problem was considered in Sec. 4.1, where the method of separation of variables was employed under certain special conditions on $f(x,y,z,t)$. Let us assume that $\phi \equiv 0$ and that $f \equiv 0$ for $t < 0$. We proceed by taking the Fourier transform of every term in the equation with respect to the variable t. Let

$$T(x,y,z,s) = \frac{1}{\sqrt{2\pi}}\int_0^\infty \phi(x,y,z,t)e^{-ist}\,dt$$

$$F(x,y,z,s) = \frac{1}{\sqrt{2\pi}}\int_0^\infty f(x,y,z,t)e^{-ist}\,dt$$

Then we have

$$\nabla^2 T = aT - \frac{b}{\sqrt{2\pi}}u + isb\,T - \frac{c}{\sqrt{2\pi}}v - \frac{isc}{\sqrt{2\pi}}u - s^2T - F(x,y,z,s)$$

or

$$\nabla^2 T + \lambda(s)T = -g(x,y,z,s)$$

where

$$\lambda(s) = -a + isb - s^2$$

$$g(x,y,z,s) = \frac{b}{\sqrt{2\pi}}u + \frac{cv}{\sqrt{2\pi}} + \frac{isc}{\sqrt{2\pi}}u + F(x,y,z,s)$$

Let us further assume that

$$\frac{dT}{dn} + \alpha T = \frac{1}{\sqrt{2\pi}} \int_0^\infty \left(\frac{d\phi}{dn} + \alpha\phi\right) e^{-ist}\, dt = 0$$

on S. The transform technique has thus led us to the solution of a non-homogeneous boundary-value problem based on the Helmholtz equation of the type considered in Chap. 4. Here s plays the role of a parameter, not a variable. If the problem has a unique solution (which of course depends on the values that λ may attain), then we obtain T and attempt to find its inverse transform.

Of course we have made many gross assumptions, the most basic of which is that the solution of our problem has a Fourier transform. Even if it has, our procedure may not obtain it. To justify rigorously the technique at every step of the way would be impractical if not impossible. In this method one must take great liberties, but of course any possible solution so obtained must be checked against the stated conditions of the original problem. Surprisingly enough, sometimes a solution is obtained even though the intervening steps cannot be justified rigorously. The use of the complex Fourier transform will often help when some of the functions involved do not have transforms in the ordinary sense.

Let us illustrate the method in a few simple examples. Consider an elastic string of density ρ stretched between two fixed points ($x = 0$, $x = 1$) with a tension σ. Until time $t = 0$ the string is at rest. Then a force of linear density $F_0 \sin \pi x$ is applied to the string. What is the resulting motion? Let $\phi(x,t)$ be the displacement. The differential equation is

$$\frac{\partial^2 \phi}{\partial x^2} = \frac{\rho}{\sigma}\frac{\partial^2 \phi}{\partial t^2} - \frac{F_0}{\sigma}\sin \pi x \qquad 0 < x < 1 \qquad 0 < t$$

The boundary conditions are $\phi(0,t) = \phi(1,t) = 0$. The initial conditions are $\phi(x,0) = \left(\dfrac{\partial \phi}{\partial t}\right)_{t=0} = 0$. Taking the complex Fourier transform, we have

$$\frac{d^2 T}{dx^2} = -\zeta^2 \frac{\rho}{\sigma} T - \frac{F_0 \sin \pi x}{i\zeta\sigma\sqrt{2\pi}}$$

The solution of this equation is

$$T(x,\zeta) = A \sin \zeta \sqrt{\frac{\rho}{\sigma}}\, x + B \cos \zeta \sqrt{\frac{\rho}{\sigma}}\, x - \frac{F_0 \sin \pi x}{\sqrt{2\pi}\, i\zeta\sigma[\zeta^2(\rho/\sigma) - \pi^2]}$$

Using the derived conditions $T(0,\zeta) = T(1,\zeta) = 0$, we find $A = B = 0$. Hence,

$$T(x,\zeta) = -\frac{F_0 \sin \pi x}{\sqrt{2\pi}\, i\zeta\sigma[\zeta^2(\rho/\sigma) - \pi^2]}$$

By use of the complex inversion integral,

$$\phi(x,t) = \frac{-F_0 \sin \pi x}{2\pi i \sigma} \int_{-\infty+i\gamma}^{\infty+i\gamma} \frac{e^{i\zeta t}\, d\zeta}{\zeta[\zeta^2(\rho/\sigma) - \pi^2]}$$

where $\gamma < 0$. This can be evaluated by use of complex contour integration closing the contour with a semicircle in an upper half plane when $t > 0$ and in a lower half plane when $t < 0$. The result is

$$\phi(x,t) = \frac{F_0}{\pi^2 \sigma} \sin \pi x \left(1 - \cos \pi \sqrt{\frac{\sigma}{\rho}} t\right) \qquad t > 0$$

$$\phi(x,t) = 0 \qquad\qquad\qquad\qquad\qquad t < 0$$

We see that $\lim_{t \to 0+} \phi(x,t) = 0$ and $\lim_{t \to 0+} \partial\phi/\partial t = 0$, the prescribed initial conditions. $\phi(0,t) = \phi(1,t) = 0$, the prescribed boundary conditions. It is easily checked that $\phi(x,t)$ satisfies the differential equation and hence is the solution of the problem. We see that the result is a vibration about some deflected position produced by the constant distributed force.

The choice of force $F_0 \sin \pi x$, which vanishes at the ends of the string, made it easy to evaluate the constants A and B in the above example. This is not essential. For example, if the force were uniform, i.e., $F = F_0$, $t > 0$, then we would have had

$$\frac{d^2 T}{dx^2} = -\zeta^2 \frac{\rho}{\sigma} T - \frac{F_0}{\sqrt{2\pi} i \zeta \sigma}$$

and
$$T = A \sin \zeta \sqrt{\frac{\rho}{\sigma}} x + B \cos \zeta \sqrt{\frac{\rho}{\sigma}} x - \frac{\rho F_0}{\sqrt{2\pi} i \zeta^3 \sigma^2}$$

By use of the boundary conditions,

$$T(0,\zeta) = B - \frac{\rho F_0}{\sqrt{2\pi} i \zeta^3 \sigma^2} = 0$$

$$T(1,\zeta) = A \sin \zeta \sqrt{\frac{\rho}{\sigma}} + B \cos \zeta \sqrt{\frac{\rho}{\sigma}} - \frac{\rho F_0}{\sqrt{2\pi} i \zeta^3 \sigma^2} = 0$$

from which we get

$$B = \frac{\rho F_0}{\sqrt{2\pi} i \zeta^3 \sigma^2}$$

$$A = \frac{\rho F_0}{\sqrt{2\pi} i \zeta^3 \sigma^2} \frac{(1 - \cos \zeta \sqrt{\rho/\sigma})}{\sin \zeta \sqrt{\rho/\sigma}}$$

Then

$$
T(x,\zeta) = \frac{\rho F_0}{\sqrt{2\pi}i\zeta^3\sigma^2}\left[\frac{\sin\zeta\sqrt{\rho/\sigma}\,x + \sin\zeta\sqrt{\rho/\sigma}(1-x)}{\sin\zeta\sqrt{\rho/\sigma}} - 1\right]
$$

$$
= \frac{\rho F_0}{\sqrt{2\pi}i\zeta^3\sigma^2}\left[\frac{e^{i\zeta\sqrt{\rho/\sigma}x} - e^{-i\zeta\sqrt{\rho/\sigma}x} + e^{i\zeta\sqrt{\rho/\sigma}(1-x)} - e^{-i\zeta\sqrt{\rho/\sigma}(1-x)}}{e^{i\zeta\sqrt{\rho/\sigma}} - e^{-i\zeta\sqrt{\rho/\sigma}}} - 1\right]
$$

$$
= \frac{\rho F_0}{\sqrt{2\pi}i\zeta^3\sigma^2}\left[\sum_{n=0}^{\infty}\left(e^{i\zeta\sqrt{\rho/\sigma}(x-1-2n)} - e^{-i\zeta\sqrt{\rho/\sigma}(x+1+2n)}\right)\right.
$$

$$
\left. + \sum_{n=0}^{\infty}\left(e^{-i\zeta\sqrt{\rho/\sigma}(x+2n)} - e^{-i\zeta\sqrt{\rho/\sigma}(-x+2+2n)}\right) - 1\right]
$$

provided $|e^{-i2\zeta\sqrt{\rho/\sigma}}| = e^{2\eta\sqrt{\rho/\sigma}} < 1$, i.e., $\eta = \operatorname{Im}(\zeta) < 0$.

We shall assume that we can invert T term by term. To recognize the inverse transform consider the complex Fourier transform of the function

$$
f(t) = (t - \tau)^2 \qquad t \geq \tau
$$

$$
f(t) = 0 \qquad t < \tau
$$

Then
$$
T[f] = \frac{1}{\sqrt{2\pi}}\int_\tau^\infty (t - \tau)^2 e^{-i\zeta t}\,dt
$$

$$
= \frac{e^{-i\zeta\tau}}{\sqrt{2\pi}}\int_0^\infty y^2 e^{-i\zeta y}\,dy
$$

$$
= \frac{2e^{-i\zeta\tau}}{\sqrt{2\pi}(i\zeta)^3}
$$

provided $\operatorname{Im}(\zeta) < 0$. Comparing this result with $T(x,\zeta)$, we have for $t > 0$

$$
\begin{aligned}
\phi(x,t) = \frac{\rho F_0}{2\sigma^2}\Bigg\{ & t^2 - \sum_{n=0}^{\infty}{}^{*}\left[t - \sqrt{\frac{\rho}{\sigma}}(2n+1-x)\right]^2 + \sum_{n=0}^{\infty}{}^{*}\left[t - \sqrt{\frac{\rho}{\sigma}}(2n+1+x)\right]^2 \\
& - \sum_{n=0}^{\infty}{}^{*}\left[t - \sqrt{\frac{\rho}{\sigma}}(2n+x)\right]^2 + \sum_{n=0}^{\infty}{}^{*}\left[t - \sqrt{\frac{\rho}{\sigma}}(2n+2-x)\right]^2\Bigg\}
\end{aligned}
$$

Here the asterisk denotes a convention that the summation shall contain the given term only when the quantity in the square bracket is positive. The convergence is assured by the fact that for any finite t and $0 \leq x \leq 1$ there are only a finite number of terms to be summed, since for n sufficiently large the quantities in all the square brackets can be made negative. It can be verified directly that this is a solution to the problem.

If the space variable ranges over an infinite interval, it may be convenient to transform the partial differential equation with respect to the space variable.

For example, consider the infinite string as an approximation to a very long string.   Suppose over an interval $a \leq x \leq b$, small compared with the length of the string, the string is given an initial displacement $\phi(x,0) = f(x)$ and an initial velocity $\left(\dfrac{\partial \phi}{\partial t}\right)_{t=0} = g(x)$.   Then the boundary-value problem to be solved is the following:

$$\frac{\partial^2 \phi}{\partial x^2} = \frac{\rho}{\sigma} \frac{\partial^2 \phi}{\partial t^2} \qquad -\infty < x < \infty \qquad t > 0$$

$\phi \to 0$ as $x \to \pm\infty$.   Assuming

$$T(\zeta,t) = \frac{1}{\sqrt{2\pi}} \int_{-\infty}^{\infty} \phi(x,t) e^{-i\zeta x}\, dx$$

we have

$$-\zeta^2 T(\zeta,t) = \frac{\rho}{\sigma} \ddot{T}$$

Solving the transformed equation, we have

$$T(\zeta,t) = A \sin \zeta \sqrt{\frac{\sigma}{\rho}} t + B \cos \zeta \sqrt{\frac{\sigma}{\rho}} t$$

Now

$$T(\zeta,0) = \frac{1}{\sqrt{2\pi}} \int_{-\infty}^{\infty} \phi(x,0) e^{-i\zeta x}\, dx$$

$$= \frac{1}{\sqrt{2\pi}} \int_{-\infty}^{\infty} f(x) e^{-i\zeta x}\, dx = F(\zeta)$$

$$\left(\frac{\partial T}{\partial t}\right)_{t=0} = \frac{1}{\sqrt{2\pi}} \int_{-\infty}^{\infty} \left(\frac{\partial \phi}{\partial t}\right)_{t=0} e^{-i\zeta x}\, dx$$

$$= \frac{1}{\sqrt{2\pi}} \int_{-\infty}^{\infty} g(x) e^{-i\zeta x}\, dx = G(\zeta)$$

Using these derived conditions, we have

$$T(\zeta,0) = F(\zeta) = B$$

$$\dot{T}(\zeta,0) = G(\zeta) = \zeta \sqrt{\frac{\sigma}{\rho}} A$$

Hence, $$T(\zeta,t) = \frac{G(\zeta)}{\zeta} \sqrt{\frac{\rho}{\sigma}} \sin \zeta \sqrt{\frac{\sigma}{\rho}} t + F(\zeta) \cos \zeta \sqrt{\frac{\sigma}{\rho}} t$$

$$= \tfrac{1}{2}[F(\zeta) e^{i\zeta \sqrt{\sigma/\rho}\, t} + F(\zeta) e^{-i\zeta \sqrt{\sigma/\rho}\, t}]$$

$$+ \frac{\sqrt{\rho/\sigma}}{2} \left[\frac{G(\zeta)}{i\zeta} e^{i\zeta \sqrt{\sigma/\rho}\, t} - \frac{G(\zeta)}{i\zeta} e^{-i\zeta \sqrt{\sigma/\rho}\, t} \right]$$

Using the inversion integral, we have

$$\phi(x,t) = \frac{1}{2\sqrt{2\pi}} \int_{-\infty}^{\infty} \left[F(\zeta)e^{i\zeta(x+\sqrt{\sigma/\rho}\, t)} + F(\zeta)e^{i\zeta(x-\sqrt{\sigma/\rho}\, t)} \right] d\zeta$$

$$+ \frac{\sqrt{\rho/\sigma}}{2\sqrt{2\pi}} \int_{-\infty}^{\infty} \left[\frac{G(\zeta)}{i\zeta} e^{i\zeta(x+\sqrt{\sigma/\rho}\, t)} - \frac{G(\zeta)}{i\zeta} e^{i\zeta(x-\sqrt{\sigma/\rho}\, t)} \right] d\zeta$$

$$= \frac{1}{2}\left[f\left(x + \sqrt{\frac{\sigma}{\rho}}\, t\right) + f\left(x - \sqrt{\frac{\sigma}{\rho}}\, t\right) \right]$$

$$+ \frac{\sqrt{\rho/\sigma}}{2} \left[\int_{a}^{x+\sqrt{\sigma/\rho}\, t} g(\xi)\, d\xi - \int_{a}^{x-\sqrt{\sigma/\rho}\, t} g(\xi)\, d\xi \right]$$

The choice of a as the lower limit in both integrals is dictated by the condition that $\phi(x,0) = f(x)$. We may therefore write

$$\phi(x,t) = \frac{1}{2}\left[f\left(x + \sqrt{\frac{\sigma}{\rho}}\, t\right) + f\left(x - \sqrt{\frac{\sigma}{\rho}}\, t\right) \right] + \frac{\sqrt{\rho/\sigma}}{2} \left[\int_{x-\sqrt{\sigma/\rho}\, t}^{x+\sqrt{\sigma/\rho}\, t} g(\xi)\, d\xi \right]$$

It may be verified directly that this is a solution of the problem. Compare this result with Sec. 2.5.

Next let us consider some problems in the study of the heat equation. Consider an infinite heat-conducting rod as an approximation to a very long rod. We assume that the lateral surface is insulated against the flow of heat so that heat flows along the axis of the rod and the problem is essentially one-dimensional. The rod has some initial temperature distribution $\phi(x,0) = f(x)$, $-\infty < x < \infty$. We also assume that the ends are maintained at zero temperature and that $f(x)$ falls off to zero rapidly enough at $\pm\infty$ that it has a Fourier transform. The problem then is to solve the one-dimensional heat equation

$$\frac{\partial^2 \phi}{\partial x^2} = \frac{1}{a^2} \frac{\partial \phi}{\partial t} \qquad -\infty < x < \infty \qquad 0 < t$$

subject to $\phi(x,0) = f(x)$ and $\phi(x,t) \to 0$ as $x \to \pm\infty$. Let

$$T(\zeta,t) = \frac{1}{\sqrt{2\pi}} \int_{-\infty}^{\infty} \phi(x,t)e^{-ix\zeta}\, dx$$

Then

$$\frac{dT}{dt} + a^2 \zeta^2 T = 0$$

$$T(\zeta,t) = T_0 e^{-\zeta^2 a^2 t}$$

$$T_0 = T(\zeta,0) = F(\zeta)$$

where
$$F(\zeta) = \frac{1}{\sqrt{2\pi}} \int_{-\infty}^{\infty} f(x)e^{-ix\zeta}\, dx$$

The transform of $\phi(x,t)$ can be inverted by use of the convolution theorem, but first we must determine $T^{-1}[e^{-\zeta^2 a^2 t}]$. Recall that

$$\frac{1}{\sqrt{2\pi}} \int_{-\infty}^{\infty} e^{-x^2/2} e^{-iux}\, dx = e^{-u^2/2}$$

We let $u^2/2 = \zeta^2 a^2 t$. Then

$$T^{-1}[e^{-\zeta^2 a^2 t}] = \frac{1}{\sqrt{2\pi}} \int_{-\infty}^{\infty} e^{-\zeta^2 a^2 t} e^{i\zeta x}\, d\zeta$$

$$= \frac{1}{2a\sqrt{\pi t}} \int_{-\infty}^{\infty} e^{-u^2/2} e^{iu(x/a\sqrt{2t})}\, du$$

$$= \frac{1}{a\sqrt{2t}} e^{-x^2/4a^2 t}$$

Therefore, $$T^{-1}[F(\zeta)e^{-\zeta^2 a^2 t}] = \frac{1}{2a\sqrt{\pi t}} \int_{-\infty}^{\infty} f(\xi) e^{-(x-\xi)^2/4a^2 t}\, d\xi$$

A slight modification of this technique will allow us to handle the case of the semi-infinite heat-conducting rod. In this case we will solve

$$\frac{\partial^2 \phi}{\partial x^2} = \frac{1}{a^2} \frac{\partial \phi}{\partial t} \qquad 0 < x < \infty \qquad 0 < t < \infty$$

subject to $\phi(x,0) = f(x)$, $0 < x$, $\phi(x,t) \to 0$ as $x \to \infty$. To solve our problem we must specify a missing boundary condition at $x = 0$. We note from the above solution for the infinite rod that if $f(x)$ is an odd function, $\phi(0,t) = 0$. Furthermore, $\phi(x,t)$ is then odd. Therefore, if we specify the boundary condition $\phi(0,t) = 0$, we will obtain a solution of our problem from the infinite-rod case if we merely continue $f(x)$ as an odd function. This is admittedly a special case but we shall now generalize it.

Alternatively, let us seek a solution for the semi-infinite rod with $\phi(x,0) = 0$ but $\phi(0,t) = g(t)$. In other words, we have a constant initial temperature distribution, but we are heating the end so that the temperature there is determined. The function $\phi(x,0) = 0$ is trivially an odd function, so we can again seek an odd solution of the differential equation. We know that the inverse transform of an odd function will give us zero at $x = 0$. However, we shall specify the boundary condition in the sense of a right-hand limit, i.e.,

$$\lim_{x \to 0+} \phi(x,t) = g(t)$$

This will mean that $\lim\limits_{x \to 0-} \phi(x,t) = -g(t)$, but we are not concerned with what happens to the left of the origin. Assuming that $\phi(x,t) = -\phi(-x,t)$, we have

$$T[\phi] = T(\zeta,t) = \frac{1}{\sqrt{2\pi}} \int_{-\infty}^{\infty} \phi(x,t) e^{-ix\zeta} \, dx$$

$$= -\sqrt{\frac{2}{\pi}} \, i \int_{-\infty}^{\infty} \phi(x,t) \sin x\zeta \, dx$$

$$T\left[\frac{\partial^2 \phi}{\partial x^2}\right] = -\sqrt{\frac{2}{\pi}} \, i \int_{0}^{\infty} \frac{\partial^2 \phi}{\partial x^2} \sin x\zeta \, dx$$

$$= -\sqrt{\frac{2}{\pi}} \, i \left[\frac{\partial \phi}{\partial x} \sin x\zeta\right]_{0}^{\infty} + \sqrt{\frac{2}{\pi}} \, i\zeta \int_{0}^{\infty} \frac{\partial \phi}{\partial x} \cos x\zeta \, dx$$

$$= \sqrt{\frac{2}{\pi}} \, i\zeta[\phi \cos x\zeta]_{0}^{\infty} + \sqrt{\frac{2}{\pi}} \, i\zeta^2 \int_{0}^{\infty} \phi \sin x\zeta \, dx$$

$$= -\sqrt{\frac{2}{\pi}} \, i\zeta g(t) - \zeta^2 T(\zeta,t)$$

The differential equation then transforms to

$$\frac{dT}{dt} + a^2\zeta^2 T = -\sqrt{\frac{2}{\pi}} \, i\zeta a^2 g(t)$$

subject to $T(\zeta,0) = \sqrt{2/\pi} \, i \int_{0}^{\infty} \phi(x,0) \sin x\zeta \, dx = 0$. Solving this differential equation, we have

$$T(\zeta,t) = -\sqrt{\frac{2}{\pi}} \, i\zeta a^2 \int_{0}^{t} g(\xi) e^{-a^2\zeta^2(t-\xi)} \, d\xi$$

We already know that

$$T^{-1}[e^{-a^2\zeta^2(t-\xi)}] = \frac{1}{a\sqrt{2(t-\xi)}} \, e^{-x^2/[4a^2(t-\xi)]}$$

Therefore, $$T^{-1}[i\zeta e^{-a^2\zeta^2(t-\xi)}] = \frac{\partial}{\partial x} \frac{1}{a\sqrt{2(t-\xi)}} \, e^{-x^2/[4a^2(t-\xi)]}$$

$$= \frac{-x}{2\sqrt{2a^3(t-\xi)^{\frac{3}{2}}}} \, e^{-x^2/[4a^2(t-\xi)]}$$

Hence, $$\phi(x,t) = \frac{x}{2\sqrt{\pi}a} \int_{0}^{t} \frac{g(\xi)}{(t-\xi)^{\frac{3}{2}}} \, e^{-x^2/[4a^2(t-\xi)]} \, d\xi$$

In inverting the transform we have assumed that integration and inversion are interchangeable. This of course does not have to be justified if the final result can be shown to satisfy the conditions of the original problem. This can be done, although we shall not do it here.

Finally, the general problem for the semi-infinite rod, i.e.,

$$\frac{\partial^2 \phi}{\partial x^2} = \frac{1}{a^2} \frac{\partial \phi}{\partial t} \qquad 0 < x < \infty \qquad 0 < t < \infty$$

with $\phi(x,0) = f(x)$ and $\phi(0,t) = g(t)$, can be solved by adding the solutions of the last two problems.

Exercises 6.3

1. Solve the following boundary-value problem using the Fourier transform method:

$$\frac{\partial^2 \phi}{\partial x^2} = \frac{\rho}{\sigma} \frac{\partial^2 \phi}{\partial t^2} - \frac{F_0}{\sigma} x(1-x) \qquad 0 < x < 1 \qquad 0 < t$$

subject to $\phi(0,t) = \phi(1,t) = 0$, $\phi(x,0+) = 0$, $\phi_t(x,0+) = 0$. Check the solution.

2. Solve the following boundary-value problem for the semi-infinite string:

$$\frac{\partial^2 \phi}{\partial x^2} = \frac{\rho}{\sigma} \frac{\partial^2 \phi}{\partial t^2} \qquad 0 < x \qquad 0 < t$$

subject to $\phi(0,t) = f(t)$, $\phi \to 0$ as $x \to \infty$, $\phi(x,0+) = 0$, $\phi_t(x,0+) = 0$. Check and interpret the result.

3. Using Fourier transform methods solve for the steady-state temperature distribution in a semi-infinite heat-conducting slab, $0 < x < \infty, 0 \le y \le 1$, if the edges at $y = 0$ and $y = 1$ are maintained at temperature zero while the end $x = 0$ is heated to maintain a temperature distribution $\phi(0,y) = f(y)$. HINT: Continue the solution as an odd function of x, i.e., $\phi(-x,y) = -\phi(x,y)$, and use the Fourier sine transform.

6.4 Applications of Fourier Transforms. Integral Equations

The right-hand side of the Wiener-Hopf integral equation

$$f(x) = \int_{-\infty}^{\infty} k(x - \xi)\phi(\xi) \, d\xi$$

is in the form of a convolution integral, and this fact allows us to solve it using the Fourier transform. Let $F(\zeta)$ be the Fourier transform of $1/\sqrt{2\pi}\, f(x)$, and let $K(\zeta)$ and $T(\zeta)$ be the transforms of $k(x)$ and $\phi(x)$, respectively. Then

$$F(\zeta) = K(\zeta)T(\zeta)$$

$$T(\zeta) = \frac{F(\zeta)}{K(\zeta)}$$

and $\phi(x)$ is the inverse transform of $F(\zeta)/K(\zeta)$. The procedure must of necessity be formal, because at the outset we do not even know if $\phi(x)$ has a

Fourier transform.   Therefore, any solution which the method produces must be checked in the integral equation as a last step.

As an example of the method, consider the integral equation

$$\sqrt{2\pi}\, e^{-x^2/2} = \int_{-\infty}^{\infty} e^{-|x-\xi|}\, \phi(\xi)\, d\xi$$

The transformed equation is

$$e^{-\zeta^2/2} = \frac{2}{\sqrt{2\pi}} \frac{T(\zeta)}{1 + \zeta^2}$$

It follows that

$$T(\zeta) = \frac{\sqrt{2\pi}(1 + \zeta^2)e^{-\zeta^2/2}}{2} = \frac{\sqrt{2\pi}}{2}\, e^{-\zeta^2/2} - \frac{\sqrt{2\pi}}{2}\, (i\zeta)^2 e^{-\zeta^2/2}$$

$$\phi(x) = \frac{\sqrt{2\pi}}{2}\, e^{-x^2/2} - \frac{\sqrt{2\pi}}{2} \frac{d^2}{dx^2}\, e^{-x^2/2}$$

$$= \sqrt{2\pi}\left(e^{-x^2/2} - \frac{x^2}{2}\, e^{-x^2/2} \right)$$

Unfortunately, in many applications where the Wiener-Hopf equation arises, the function $f(x)$ is not completely known.   See, for example, the half-plane diffraction problem of Sec. 4.5.   Suppose that

$$h(x) = f(x) = \int_{-\infty}^{\infty} k(x - \xi)\phi(\xi)\, d\xi \qquad 0 < x$$

$$h(x) = g(x) = \int_{-\infty}^{\infty} k(x - \xi)\phi(\xi)\, d\xi \qquad x < 0$$

where $f(x)$ is known, but $g(x)$ is not.   In the half-plane diffraction problem, $\phi(x) = 0$ for $x < 0$.   Hence,

$$T(\zeta) = \frac{1}{\sqrt{2\pi}} \int_0^{\infty} \phi(x)e^{-i\zeta x}\, dx$$

is analytic in a lower half plane.   We shall outline the **Wiener-Hopf technique** for solving integral equations of the Wiener-Hopf type under conditions of sufficient generality to handle the half-plane problem.   For a more general discussion of Wiener-Hopf techniques see Benjamin Noble, "The Wiener-Hopf Technique," Pergamon Press, Inc., New York, 1958.

Transforming the integral equation, we have

$$H(\zeta) = F_-(\zeta) + G_+(\zeta) = K(\zeta)T(\zeta)$$

where

$$F_-(\zeta) = \frac{1}{2\pi} \int_0^{\infty} f(x)e^{-i\zeta x}\, dx$$

and is analytic in a lower half plane Im $(\zeta) < \alpha$.

$$G_+(\zeta) = \frac{1}{2\pi} \int_{-\infty}^{0} g(x)e^{-i\zeta x}\,dx$$

and is analytic in an upper half plane Im $(\zeta) > \beta$. The transformed equation will in general hold in a strip $\beta < \text{Im}\,(\zeta) < \alpha$. Suppose $K(\zeta)$ can be decomposed as follows:

$$K(\zeta) = \frac{K_-(\zeta)}{K_+(\zeta)}$$

where $K_-(\zeta)$ is analytic for Im $(\zeta) < \alpha$, and $K_+(\zeta)$ is analytic for $\beta < \text{Im}\,(\zeta)$. Then

$$K_-(\zeta)T(\zeta) = K_+(\zeta)F_-(\zeta) + K_+(\zeta)G_+(\zeta)$$

Furthermore, let us assume that the known function $K_+(\zeta)F_-(\zeta)$ can be decomposed as follows:

$$K_+(\zeta)F_-(\zeta) = P_+(\zeta) + Q_-(\zeta)$$

where $P_+(\zeta)$ is analytic for $\beta < \text{Im}\,(\zeta)$, and $Q_-(\zeta)$ is analytic for Im $(\zeta) < \alpha$. Then we can write

$$E(\zeta) = K_+(\zeta)G_+(\zeta) + P_+(\zeta) = K_-(\zeta)T(\zeta) - Q_-(\zeta)$$
$$= E_+(\zeta) = E_-(\zeta)$$

and the equation holds in the strip $\beta < \text{Im}\,(\zeta) < \alpha$. Now $E(\zeta)$ is defined by $E_+(\zeta)$ in an upper half plane and by $E_-(\zeta)$ in a lower half plane, and the two are equal in a common strip. Therefore, they provide the analytic continuation of one another to the whole plane. Hence, $E(\zeta)$ is an entire function, i.e., is analytic in the whole plane. If it can be further shown that $|E(\zeta)| \to 0$ as $|z| \to \infty$, then by Liouville's theorem $E(\zeta) \equiv 0$, and we have

$$T(\zeta) = \frac{Q_-(\zeta)}{K_-(\zeta)}$$

and we have obtained the transform of our unknown function without having to deal with the unknown $G_+(\zeta)$. The final steps are to invert the transform by complex contour integration and check the formal solution to see if it meets the conditions of the original problem, which may be a boundary-value problem from which the integral equation was derived.

To illustrate this method we shall return to the half-plane diffraction problem of Sec. 4.5. Recall that we obtained the following integral equation:

$$-2e^{ikx\cos\alpha} = i\int_{-\infty}^{\infty} H_0^{(1)}(k\,|x-\xi|)I(\xi)\,d\xi \qquad x > 0$$

$$\psi(x,0-) - \psi(x,0+) - 2e^{ikx\cos\alpha} = i\int_{-\infty}^{\infty} H_0^{(1)}(k\,|x-\xi|)I(\xi)\,d\xi \qquad x < 0$$

We can identify the present case with the general procedure outlined above as follows:

$$T(\zeta) = \frac{1}{\sqrt{2\pi}} \int_0^\infty I(x) e^{-i\zeta x} \, dx$$

$$F_-(\zeta) = -\frac{1}{\pi} \int_0^\infty e^{ikx \cos \alpha} e^{-i\zeta x} \, dx$$

$$= \frac{i}{\pi} \frac{1}{\zeta - k \cos \alpha}$$

$$G_+(\zeta) = \frac{i}{2\pi} \int_{-\infty}^0 e^{-i\zeta x} \int_{-\infty}^\infty H_0^{(1)}(k \, |x - \xi|) I(\xi) \, d\xi \, dx$$

$$K(\zeta) = \frac{i}{\sqrt{2\pi}} \int_{-\infty}^\infty H_0^{(1)}(k \, |x|) e^{-i\zeta x} \, dx$$

The transform of $i H_0^{(1)}(k \, |x|)$ exists, since for large $|x|$ it behaves like $e^{ik|x|}/|x|^{\frac{1}{2}}$ and for small $|x|$ it behaves like $\log |x|$, and the integral $\int_0^\rho \log r \, dr$ exists. To evaluate it we note that $H_0^{(1)}(kx)$ satisfies the differential equation

$$x \frac{d^2}{dx^2} H_0^{(1)}(kx) + \frac{d}{dx} H_0^{(1)}(kx) + k^2 x H_0^{(1)}(kx) = 0$$

for $x > 0$. If we make the change of variable $t = -x$, we have

$$(-t) \frac{d^2}{dt^2} H_0^{(1)}[k(-t)] - \frac{d}{dt} H_0^{(1)}[k(-t)] - k^2 t H_0^{(1)}[k(-t)] = 0$$

or $$t \frac{d^2}{dt^2} H_0^{(1)}(k \, |t|) + \frac{d}{dt} H_0^{(1)}(k \, |t|) + k^2 t H_0^{(1)}(k \, |t|) = 0$$

for $t < 0$. Hence, $H_0^{(1)}(k \, |x|)$ satisfies

$$x \frac{d^2}{dx^2} H_0^{(1)}(k \, |x|) + \frac{d}{dx} H_0^{(1)}(k \, |x|) + k^2 x H_0^{(1)}(k \, |x|) = 0$$

for $-\infty < x < \infty$ except at $x = 0$. Transforming the equation, we have

$$i \frac{d}{d\zeta} [(i\zeta)^2 K(\zeta)] + i\zeta K(\zeta) + ik^2 \frac{d}{d\zeta} K(\zeta) = 0$$

or $$K' + \frac{\zeta K}{\zeta^2 - k^2} = 0$$

$$K = \frac{C}{\sqrt{k^2 - \zeta^2}}$$

where C is a constant of integration. It can be shown that $C = \sqrt{2/\pi}$.

Hence
$$K(\zeta) = \sqrt{\frac{2}{\pi}} \frac{1}{\sqrt{k^2 - \zeta^2}}$$

In the present argument we need a common strip of analyticity for all the transforms involved. To this end we must take k complex with a small imaginary part, although k was considered real in our earlier discussions of the wave equation. Actually this is closer to physical reality than the case with real k. For r large, the scattered wave behaves as

$$\frac{e^{ikr}}{\sqrt{r}} = \frac{e^{i(k_1 + ik_2)r}}{\sqrt{r}} = \frac{e^{ik_1 r}}{\sqrt{r}} e^{-k_2 r}$$

The term $e^{-k_2 r}$ then represents a dissipation, and a more careful study of electromagnetic theory would reveal that this is the correct effect of a medium with small dissipation. For those less physically inclined, the addition of a small imaginary part can be regarded as a formal procedure introduced to obtain a solution which can be checked against the stated conditions of the problem.

Letting $k = k_1 + ik_2$, we see that $K(\zeta)$ has branch points at $\zeta = \pm(k_1 + ik_2)$. We select a branch of the square root which has branch cuts lying outside the strip $-k_2 < \text{Im}(\zeta) < k_2$. We assume that $I(x) = O(e^{\beta x})$ as $x \to \infty$ and, therefore, that $T(\zeta)$ is analytic for $\text{Im}(\zeta) < -\beta$. Since

$$H_0^{(1)}(k|x - \xi|) = O\left(\frac{e^{ik|x-\xi|}}{\sqrt{k|x-\xi|}}\right)$$

as $|x - \xi| \to \infty$, for x large and negative,

$$i\int_0^\infty H_0^{(1)}(k|x - \xi|)I(\xi)\,d\xi = O(e^{-ikx}) = O(e^{k_2 x})$$

provided $\int_0^\infty \frac{e^{ik\xi}I(\xi)}{\sqrt{\xi}}\,d\xi$ exists. This integral will exist provided $-k_2 < -\beta$. Consequently $G_+(\zeta)$ will be analytic in the half plane $-k_2 < \text{Im}(\zeta)$, and the equation

$$F_-(\zeta) + G_+(\zeta) = K(\zeta)T(\zeta)$$

will hold in the strip $-k_2 < \text{Im}(\zeta) < \min[-\beta, k_2 \cos \alpha]$. Specifically,

$$\frac{i}{\pi(\zeta - k \cos \alpha)} + G_+(\zeta) = \sqrt{\frac{2}{\pi}} \frac{T(\zeta)}{\sqrt{k^2 - \zeta^2}}$$

We write
$$K(\zeta) = \sqrt{\frac{2}{\pi}} \frac{1}{\sqrt{k^2 - \zeta^2}} = \sqrt{\frac{2}{\pi}} \frac{1}{\sqrt{k - \zeta}\sqrt{k + \zeta}}$$

and
$$\sqrt{\frac{2}{\pi}} \frac{T(\zeta)}{\sqrt{k - \zeta}} = \frac{i\sqrt{k + \zeta}}{\pi(\zeta - k \cos \alpha)} + \sqrt{k + \zeta}\, G_+(\zeta)$$

Next we write

$$\frac{i\sqrt{k+\zeta}}{\pi(\zeta-\cos\alpha)} = \frac{i\sqrt{k+k\cos\alpha}}{\pi(\zeta-k\cos\alpha)} + \frac{i\sqrt{k+\zeta}-i\sqrt{k+k\cos\alpha}}{\pi(\zeta-k\cos\alpha)}$$

$$= Q_-(\zeta) + P_+(\zeta)$$

We define $P_+(\zeta)$ at $\zeta = k\cos\alpha$ by

$$\lim_{\zeta\to k\cos\alpha} P_+(\zeta) = \frac{i}{2\pi}\frac{1}{\sqrt{k+k\cos\alpha}}$$

Then

$$P'_+(k\cos\alpha)$$

$$= \lim_{\Delta\zeta\to 0}\frac{P_+(k\cos\alpha+\Delta\zeta)-P_+(k\cos\alpha)}{\Delta\zeta}$$

$$= \frac{i}{\pi}\lim_{\Delta\zeta\to 0}\frac{(\sqrt{k+k\cos\alpha+\Delta\zeta}-\sqrt{k+k\cos\alpha})/\Delta\zeta - 1/(2\sqrt{k+k\cos\alpha})}{\Delta\zeta}$$

$$= \frac{i}{8\pi}\frac{-1}{(k+k\cos\alpha)^{\frac{3}{2}}}$$

Therefore, $P_+(\zeta)$ is analytic at $\zeta = k\cos\alpha$. It has a branch point at $\zeta = -k$ but is nevertheless analytic in an upper half plane $-k_2 < \text{Im}(\zeta)$. Finally, we have

$$\sqrt{\frac{2}{\pi}}\frac{T(\zeta)}{\sqrt{k-\zeta}} - \frac{i}{\pi}\frac{\sqrt{k+k\cos\alpha}}{\zeta-k\cos\alpha} = P_+(\zeta) + \sqrt{k+\zeta}\,G_+(\zeta)$$

The left-hand side is analytic in a lower half plane $\text{Im}(\zeta) < \min[-\beta, k\cos\alpha]$, while the right-hand side is analytic in an upper half plane $-k_2 < \text{Im}(\zeta)$. The equality holds in the strip $-k_2 < \text{Im}(\zeta) < \min[-\beta, k_2\cos\alpha]$. Therefore, one side is the analytic continuation of the other to the whole plane.

To complete the argument we have to show that the complete analytic function defined by the analytic continuation approaches zero as $|\zeta| \to \infty$. We have the following order conditions: $P_+(\zeta) = O(\zeta^{-\frac{1}{2}})$, $T(\zeta)/\sqrt{k-\zeta} = O(\zeta^{-\frac{1}{2}})$, $1/(\zeta - k\cos\alpha) = O(\zeta^{-1})$, $\sqrt{k+\zeta}\,G_+(\zeta) = O(\zeta^{\frac{1}{2}})$ in their respective half planes. Therefore, by Liouville's theorem, the complete analytic function is constant; but this constant must be zero, since it goes to zero in the lower half plane. Finally,

$$T(\zeta) = \frac{i}{\sqrt{2\pi}}\frac{\sqrt{k-\zeta}\sqrt{k+k\cos\alpha}}{\zeta-k\cos\alpha}$$

The inversion of this transform is a fairly involved problem in complex contour integration, which we shall not go into here.

The Wiener-Hopf technique can also be used to solve certain integral equations of the second kind which come up in some applications.   Suppose

$$\phi(x) = f(x) + \frac{1}{\sqrt{2\pi}} \int_0^\infty k(x - \xi)\phi(\xi) \, d\xi \qquad 0 < x$$

$$0 = g(x) + \frac{1}{\sqrt{2\pi}} \int_0^\infty k(x - \xi)\phi(\xi) \, d\xi \qquad x < 0$$

Then taking transforms

$$T(\zeta) = F_-(\zeta) + G_+(\zeta) + K(\zeta)T(\zeta)$$

where

$$T(\zeta) = \frac{1}{\sqrt{2\pi}} \int_0^\infty \phi(x)e^{-i\zeta x} \, dx$$

$$F_-(\zeta) = \frac{1}{\sqrt{2\pi}} \int_0^\infty f(x)e^{-i\zeta x} \, dx$$

$$G_+(\zeta) = \frac{1}{\sqrt{2\pi}} \int_{-\infty}^0 g(x)e^{-i\zeta x} \, dx$$

$$K(\zeta) = \frac{1}{\sqrt{2\pi}} \int_{-\infty}^\infty k(x)e^{-i\zeta x} \, dx$$

This time we write

$$[1 - K(\zeta)]T(\zeta) = F_-(\zeta) + G_+(\zeta)$$

$$1 - K(\zeta) = \frac{K_-(\zeta)}{K_+(\zeta)}$$

and proceed as before.   The actual factorization may be fairly involved in practice, but it is not our purpose here to give all the details that one might get involved with in the problem.   If the reader is interested in pursuing the subject further, he should consult additional books on the subject.   A very extensive bibliography can be found in Benjamin Noble's "The Wiener-Hopf Technique," mentioned above.

6.5   Laplace Transforms.   Applications

We have already seen in some of the applications where the function $f(x)$, whose Fourier transform we wished to compute, was zero for $x < 0$.   In this case the Fourier transform is

$$T[f] = \frac{1}{\sqrt{2\pi}} \int_0^\infty f(x)e^{-ix\zeta} \, dx = \phi(\zeta)$$

and

$$T^{-1}[\phi] = \frac{1}{\sqrt{2\pi}} \int_{-\infty + i\gamma}^{\infty + i\gamma} \phi(\zeta)e^{ix\zeta} \, d\zeta$$

The theory holds under suitable restrictions on $f(x)$. In particular, $f(x)$ must be piecewise continuous, implying that

$$\lim_{x \to 0+} f(x) = f(0+)$$

exists. If $f(x) = O(e^{\alpha x})$ as $x \to \infty$, i.e., $f(x)$ is of **exponential order,** then the transform $T[f]$ exists and is an analytic function of ζ for Im $(\zeta) < -\alpha$.

It is sometimes convenient to carry out a rotation of the ζ plane through an angle of $\pi/2$, i.e., we introduce the new variable

$$z = \sigma + i\tau = i\zeta = -s + it$$

We define the **Laplace transform** of $f(x)$ as follows:

$$\phi(z) = L[f] = \int_0^\infty f(x) e^{-i\zeta x} \, dx$$

$$= \int_0^\infty f(x) e^{(s-it)x} \, dx$$

$$= \int_0^\infty f(x) e^{-(\sigma+it)x} \, dx$$

$$= \int_0^\infty f(x) e^{-zx} \, dx$$

If $f(x)$ is piecewise continuous and of exponential order, i.e., $f(x) = O(e^{\alpha x})$ as $x \to \infty$, the Laplace transform will exist and be an analytic function of z in a right half plane Re $(z) > \alpha$.

It follows directly from the theory of Fourier transforms that if $f(x)$ and $f'(x)$ are piecewise continuous in any finite interval and $f(x) = O(e^{\alpha x})$, then

$$\tfrac{1}{2}[f(x+) + f(x-)] = \frac{1}{2\pi} \int_{-\infty}^\infty \phi(-s_0 + it) e^{i(t+is_0)x} \, dt$$

$$= \frac{1}{2\pi i} \int_{-i\infty + \sigma_0}^{i\infty + \sigma_0} \phi(\sigma_0 + i\tau) e^{(\sigma_0+i\tau)x} \, d(\sigma_0 + i\tau)$$

$$= \frac{1}{2\pi i} \int_{\sigma_0 - i\infty}^{\sigma_0 + i\infty} \phi(z) e^{zx} \, dz$$

where the integration in the z plane is along the line $\sigma_0 + i\tau$, $-\infty < t < \infty$, $\sigma_0 > \alpha$, and the value of the integral is the Cauchy principal value. Of course, where $f(x)$ is continuous, $\tfrac{1}{2}[f(x+) + f(x-)] = f(x)$. For $x = 0$ the integral converges to $\tfrac{1}{2}f(0+)$. Furthermore, if $f(x)$ is continuous, $f'(x)$ is piecewise continuous, and both are of exponential order $O(e^{\alpha x})$, then

$$f(x) = \frac{1}{2\pi i} \int_{\gamma - i\infty}^{\gamma + i\infty} \phi(z) e^{zx} \, dz$$

and the integration can be taken along *any* line $z = \gamma + i\tau$, $-\infty < t < \infty$, $\gamma > \alpha$.[1]

Now let us list some of the more important properties of the Laplace transform, which either can be verified directly or can follow from corresponding properties of the Fourier transform. All functions involved are assumed to be zero for $t < 0$, defined by their right-hand limit at $t = 0$, and of exponential order as $x \to \infty$.

1. The Laplace transform is a linear transformation, i.e.,

$$L[af + bg] = aL[f] + bL[g]$$

2. If $f(x)$ is continuous for $0 < t$, and $f'(x)$ is piecewise continuous in any finite interval,

$$L[f'] = zL[f] - f(0)$$

3. If $f(x)$ is continuous along with its first $n - 1$ derivatives and $f^{(n)}(x)$ is piecewise continuous in any finite interval,

$$L[f^{(n)}] = z^n L[f] - z^{n-1}f(0) - z^{n-2}f'(0)$$
$$- \cdots - zf^{(n-2)}(0) - f^{(n-1)}(0)$$

4. If $f(x)$ is piecewise continuous, then $\int_0^x f(\xi)\,d\xi = F(x)$ is continuous, $F(0) = 0$, and

$$L[F] = \frac{1}{z} L[f]$$

5. If $\phi(z) = L[f(x)]$, then

$$\phi(z - a) = L[e^{ax}f(x)]$$

6. Let $u(x)$ be the unit step function, i.e.,

$$u(x) = 0 \qquad x < 0$$
$$u(x) = 1 \qquad 0 \leq x$$

Then $$L[f(x - a)u(x - a)] = e^{-az}L[f(x)]$$

7. If $\phi(z) = L[f]$, then

$$\frac{d}{dz}\phi(z) = -L[xf(x)]$$

8. Let $h(x)$ be the convolution integral, i.e.,

$$h(x) = \int_0^x f(\xi)g(x - \xi)\,d\xi$$

Then $$L[h] = L[f]L[g]$$

[1] See exercise 5, Sec. 6.1.

The following are the Laplace transforms of some elementary functions:

a. $L[u(x)] = \int_0^\infty e^{-zx}\,dx = \dfrac{1}{z}$

b. $L[x^n] = n!\,z^{-(n+1)}$

c. $L[x^a] = \Gamma(a+1)z^{-(a+1)}$ $\qquad a \geq 0$

d. $L[e^{ax}] = \dfrac{1}{z-a}$

e. $L[\sin ax] = \dfrac{a}{z^2 + a^2}$

f. $L[\cos ax] = \dfrac{z}{z^2 + a^2}$

g. $L[e^{-bx}\sin ax] = \dfrac{a}{(z+b)^2 + a^2}$

h. $[Le^{-bx}\cos ax] = \dfrac{z+b}{(z+b)^2 + a^2}$

i. $L[\sinh ax] = \dfrac{a}{z^2 - a^2}$

j. $L[\cosh ax] = \dfrac{z}{z^2 - a^2}$

Formula b can be derived from a by use of property 3 plus the fact that $u(x) = \dfrac{1}{n!}\dfrac{d^n}{dx^n}f(x)$ where

$$f(x) = x^n \qquad x \geq 0$$
$$f(x) = 0 \qquad x < 0$$

Then
$$\frac{n!}{z} = L[f^{(n)}(z)] = z^n L[f]$$

$$L[f] = \frac{n!}{z^{n+1}}$$

It is also a special case of formula c, which can be established directly from the definition of the gamma function

$$\Gamma(z) = \int_0^\infty t^{z-1}e^{-t}\,dt \qquad \operatorname{Re}(z) > 0$$

Formula e can be established as follows: Let $y = \sin ax$. Then $y'' + a^2 y = 0$, and $y(0) = 0$, $y'(0) = a$. Therefore,

$$z^2 L[y] - a + a^2 L[y] = 0 \qquad \text{and} \qquad L[y] = a/(z^2 + a^2)$$

Formula g is a direct application of property 5 and formula e.

As a further example, let us find the Laplace transform of the zeroth-order Bessel function $J_0(kx)$, starting from the differential equation

$$x J_0''(kx) + J_0(kx) + k^2 x J_0(kx) = 0$$

and the initial conditions $J_0(0) = 1$, $J_0'(0) = 0$. Transforming the equation, we have

$$-\frac{d}{dz}(z^2 \phi - z) + z\phi - 1 - k^2 \frac{d}{dz}\phi = 0$$

where $\phi(z) = L[J_0(kx)]$. Then

$$\phi' + \frac{z}{k^2 + z^2}\phi = 0$$

$$\phi(z) = \frac{C}{\sqrt{k^2 + z^2}}$$

where C is a constant of integration. To evaluate C we recall that

$$\frac{d}{dx}J_0(kx) = -k J_1(kx)$$

and that $J_1(kx)$ is bounded for all x. It therefore follows from property 2 that

$$L[-k J_1(kx)] = z\phi(z) - J_0(0)$$

$$= \frac{Cz}{\sqrt{k^2 + z^2}} - 1$$

Now

$$|L[-k J_1(kx)]| \leq \int_0^\infty |k J_1(kx)|\, e^{-\sigma x}\, dx$$

$$\leq \frac{M}{\sigma}$$

Then

$$\lim_{\sigma \to \infty} L[-k J_1(kx)]_{z=\sigma} = \lim_{\sigma \to \infty} \frac{C\sigma}{\sqrt{k^2 + \sigma^2}} - 1$$

$$= C - 1 = 0$$

Therefore, $C = 1$ and

$$L[J_0(kx)] = \frac{1}{\sqrt{k^2 + z^2}}$$

We have seen how we can use the differential equation plus the initial conditions satisfied by a given function to find its Laplace transform.   Now

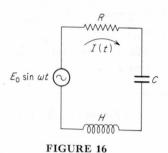

FIGURE 16

let us take the opposite point of view, i.e., to find the solution of a given differential equation by finding its Laplace transform.   Consider the simple series electrical circuit shown in Fig. 16.

The current $I(t)$ is the solution of the following integrodifferential equation:[1]

$$H\frac{dI}{dt} + RI + \frac{1}{C}\left[q_0 + \int_0^t I(\tau)\,d\tau\right] = E_0 \sin \omega t$$

Let $I(0) = I_0$, and of course $q(0) = q_0$.   Let $\phi(z) = L[I]$.

Then

$$H(z\phi - I_0) + R\phi + \frac{1}{Cz}(q_0 + \phi) = \frac{E_0\omega}{z^2 + \omega^2}$$

Solving for ϕ, we have

$$\phi(z) = \frac{E_0\omega z}{(z^2 + \omega^2)(Hz^2 + Rz + 1/C)} + \frac{HI_0z}{Hz^2 + Rz + 1/C} - \frac{q_0}{C(Hz^2 + Rz + 1/C)}$$

We can invert the transform by identifying the various parts with transforms of known elementary functions.   For example,

$$\frac{HI_0z}{Hz^2 + Rz + 1/C} = \frac{I_0z}{(z + R/2H)^2 + (1/HC - R^2/4H^2)}$$

$$= \frac{I_0(z + R/2H)}{(z + R/2H)^2 + \omega_0^2} - \frac{I_0R}{2H[(z + R/2H)^2 + \omega_0^2]}$$

where $\omega_0^2 = \dfrac{1}{HC} - \dfrac{R^2}{4H^2}$.   Now if $\omega_0^2 = 0$, we have the case of **critical damping** where

$$\frac{HI_0z}{Hz^2 + Rz + 1/C} = L\left[I_0e^{-(R/2H)t} - \frac{I_0R}{2H}te^{-(R/2H)t}\right]$$

If $\omega_0^2 < 0$, we have **overdamping** and

$$\frac{HI_0z}{Hz^2 + Rz + 1/C} = L\left[I_0e^{-(R/2H)t}\cosh\sqrt{\frac{R^2}{4H^2} - \frac{1}{HC}}\,t\right.$$

$$\left. - \frac{I_0R}{2H\sqrt{R^2/4H^2 - 1/HC}}e^{-(R/2L)t}\sinh\sqrt{\frac{R^2}{4H^2} - \frac{1}{HC}}\,t\right]$$

---

[1] We have used H for inductance to avoid the letter L designating the Laplace transform.

If $\omega_0^2 > 0$, we have **underdamping** and

$$\frac{HI_0z}{Hz^2 + Rz + 1/C} = L\left[I_0 e^{-(R/2H)t} \cos \omega_0 t - \frac{I_0R}{2H\omega_0} e^{-(R/2H)t} \sin \omega_0 t\right]$$

We see then that the nature of the solution depends on the relative values of R, H, and C. This will also be true of the other two terms in the transform. For simplicity, therefore, we shall proceed with the underdamped case only. In this case,

$$\frac{q_0}{C(Hz^2 + Rz + 1/C)} = L\left[\frac{q_0}{HC\omega_0} e^{-(R/2H)t} \sin \omega_0 t\right]$$

To identify the third term we must first perform a partial fraction expansion.[1]
Let

$$\frac{E_0\omega z}{(z^2 + \omega^2)(Hz^2 + Rz + 1/C)} = \frac{az + b}{z^2 + \omega^2} + \frac{cz + d}{Hz^2 + Rz + 1/C}$$

Then $$E_0\omega z = (az + b)\left(Hz^2 + Rz + \frac{1}{C}\right) + (cz + d)(z^2 + \omega^2)$$

implying $$\frac{b}{C} + d\omega^2 = 0$$

$$\frac{a}{C} + bR + c\omega^2 = E_0\omega$$

$$aR + bH + d = 0$$

$$aH + c = 0$$

Solving these equations, we obtain

$$a = \frac{-E_0X}{R^2 + X^2}$$

$$b = \frac{\omega E_0 R}{R^2 + X^2}$$

$$c = \frac{E_0XH}{R^2 + X^2}$$

$$d = \frac{-E_0R}{\omega C(R^2 + X^2)}$$

[1] The method of partial fraction of expansion is important in the art of inverting Laplace transforms. The procedure can be formalized through a set of theorems which can be found in Ruel V. Churchill, "Operational Mathematics," 2d ed., McGraw-Hill Book Company, Inc., New York, 1958, pp. 57–64.

where $X = \omega H - 1/\omega C$ is a quantity called the **reactance.** Let $Z = R + iX$ be the **complex impedance** and $\theta = \arg Z = \tan^{-1}(X/R)$ be the **phase.** Then

$$a = \frac{-E_0 \sin \theta}{|Z|}$$

$$b = \frac{\omega E_0 \cos \theta}{|Z|}$$

$$c = \frac{E_0 H \sin \theta}{|Z|}$$

$$d = \frac{-E_0 \cos \theta}{\omega C |Z|}$$

$$\frac{E_0 \omega z}{(z^2 + \omega^2)(Hz^2 + Rz + 1/C)} = \frac{\omega E_0 \cos \theta}{|Z|(z^2 + \omega^2)} - \frac{z E_0 \sin \theta}{|Z|(z^2 + \omega^2)}$$

$$+ \frac{z E_0 H \sin \theta}{|Z|(Hz^2 + Rz + 1/C)} - \frac{E_0 \cos \theta}{\omega C |Z|(Hz^2 + Rz + 1/C)}$$

$$\frac{E_0 \omega z}{(z^2 + \omega^2)(Hz^2 + Rz + 1/C)} = L\left[\frac{E_0}{|Z|} \sin(\omega t - \theta) + \frac{E_0}{|Z|} \sin \theta \, e^{-(R/2H)t} \cos \omega_0 t\right.$$

$$\left. - \left(\frac{E_0 R \sin\theta}{2H\omega_0 |Z|} + \frac{E_0 \cos \theta}{\omega \omega_0 CH |Z|}\right) e^{-(R/2H)t} \sin \omega_0 t\right]$$

Therefore the solution of the differential equation satisfying the initial conditions is

$$I(t) = \frac{E_0}{|Z|} \sin(\omega t - \theta) + \left(I_0 + \frac{E_0}{|Z|} \sin \theta\right) e^{-(R/2H)t} \cos \omega_0 t$$

$$+ \left(\frac{q_0}{HC\omega_0} - \frac{I_0 R}{2H\omega_0} - \frac{E_0 R \sin \theta}{2H\omega_0 |Z|} - \frac{E_0 \cos \theta}{\omega \omega_0 CH |Z|}\right) e^{-(R/2H)t} \sin \omega_0 t$$

This looks very complicated, but basically it is just the sum of the **steady-state solution** $E_0/|Z| \sin(\omega t - \theta)$ plus the **transient solution**

$$e^{-(R/2H)t}(A \cos \omega_0 t + B \sin \omega_0 t)$$

which dies out exponentially with time. The constants A and B are determined in order that the particular solution satisfy the initial conditions. One of the advantages of the Laplace transformation method is that it gives the values of A and B directly. In this particular example the work involved is such that there seems to be no advantage of the method over the conventional methods of elementary differential equations. However, the next example deals with a problem which cannot as readily be handled by the elementary methods.

Suppose the input to the circuit is a pulse of duration τ. This can be expressed as $E_0 u(t) - E_0 u(t - \tau)$ where $u(t)$ is the unit step function. The integrodifferential equation is

$$H \frac{dI}{dt} + RI + \frac{1}{C} \int_0^t I(\xi) \, d\xi = E_0 u(t) - E_0 u(t - \tau)$$

For simplicity we are assuming that $I_0 = q_0 = 0$. Transforming the equation, we have

$$zH\phi + R\phi + \frac{\phi}{Cz} = \frac{E_0}{z} - \frac{E_0 e^{-\tau z}}{z}$$

Solving for ϕ, we have

$$\phi(z) = \frac{E_0}{Hz^2 + Rz + 1/C} - \frac{E_0 e^{-\tau z}}{Hz^2 + Rz + 1/C}$$

Again we shall treat only the underdamped case. In this case,

$$\frac{E_0}{Hz^2 + Rz + 1/C} = \frac{E_0 \omega_0}{\omega_0 H[(z + R/2H)^2 + \omega_0^2]}$$

$$= L\left[\frac{E_0}{\omega_0 H} e^{-(R/2H)t} \sin \omega_0 t \right]$$

It therefore follows from property 6 that

$$\frac{E_0 e^{-\tau z}}{Hz^2 + Rz + 1/C} = L\left[\frac{E_0}{\omega_0 H} e^{-(R/2H)(t-\tau)} u(t - \tau) \sin \omega_0(t - \tau) \right]$$

and our solution is

$$I(t) = \frac{E_0}{\omega_0 H} [e^{-(R/2H)t} \sin \omega_0 t - e^{-(R/2H)(t-\tau)} u(t - \tau) \sin \omega_0(t - \tau)]$$

Laplace transform methods can also be used to advantage in solving boundary-value problems in partial differential equations. We shall consider two cases, both based on the one-dimensional wave equation. Consider the semi-infinite string $x \geq 0$ with no initial displacement or initial velocity. Starting at $t = 0$, the end at $x = 0$ is displaced according to

$$\phi(0,t) = f(t)$$

We have then to solve the following problem:

$$\frac{\partial^2 \phi}{\partial x^2} = \frac{1}{a^2} \frac{\partial^2 \phi}{\partial t^2} \qquad x > 0 \qquad t > 0$$

$$\phi(x,0) = 0$$

$$\phi_t(x,0) = 0$$

$$\phi(0,t) = f(t)$$

Let $T(x,z) = \int_0^\infty \phi(x,t)e^{-tz}\,dt$.   Then

$$\frac{d^2T}{dx^2} - \frac{z^2}{a^2}\,T = 0$$

$$T(0,z) = \int_0^\infty f(t)e^{-tz}\,dt = F(z)$$

Hence $\qquad\qquad T = Ae^{-(z/a)x} + Be^{(z/a)x}$

Any displacement of the string must propagate with a finite velocity. Therefore, $\phi(x,t) \to 0$ as $x \to \infty$ for all t, and we assume consequently that

$$\lim_{x \to \infty} T(x,z) = 0$$

for Re $(z) > 0$.   This requires that $B = 0$.   Finally, $T(0,z) = A = F(z)$. Therefore,

$$T(x,z) = F(z)e^{-z(x/a)}$$

and $\qquad\qquad \phi(x,t) = f\left(t - \frac{x}{a}\right)u\left(t - \frac{x}{a}\right)$

It can easily be shown that this is a solution of the problem provided $f(t)$ has a continuous second derivative.

As a second case let $\phi(0,t) = 0$, $\phi(x,0) = g(x)$, $\phi_t(x,0) = h(x)$.   The solution to a more general problem can be obtained by superimposing the solutions to this and the last problem.   In the present case, the transformed equation becomes

$$\frac{d^2T}{dx^2} - \frac{z^2}{a^2}\,T = -\frac{1}{a^2}\,[zg(x) + h(x)]$$

subject to $T(0,z) = 0$ and $T(x,z) \to 0$ as $x \to \infty$ for Re $(z) > 0$.   To solve the transformed problem we must develop the Green's function for the equation, i.e., we find $G(y;x)$ such that

$$\frac{d^2G}{dx^2} - \frac{z^2}{a^2}\,G = 0 \qquad 0 \le x < y \qquad y < x < \infty$$

$$G(y;0) = \lim_{x \to \infty} G = 0$$

$$G(y;y-) = G(y;y+)$$

$$G'(y;y+) - G'(y;y-) = -1$$

We therefore have

$$G(y;x) = Ae^{-(z/a)x} + Be^{(z/a)x} \qquad 0 \leq x < y$$

$$G(y;x) = Ce^{-(z/a)x} + De^{(z/a)x} \qquad y < x < \infty$$

$G(y;x) \to 0$ as $x \to \infty$ implies that $D = 0$. Also

$$G(y;0) = A + B = 0$$

$$G(y;y-) = Ae^{-(z/a)y} + Be^{(z/a)y} = G(y;y+) = Ce^{-(z/a)y}$$

$$G'(y;y+) - G'(y;y-) = -\frac{z}{a}Ce^{-(z/a)y} + \frac{z}{a}Ae^{-(z/a)y} - \frac{z}{a}Be^{(z/a)y} = -1$$

Solving for A, B, and C, we have

$$A = -\frac{a}{2z}e^{-(z/a)y}$$

$$B = \frac{a}{2z}e^{-(z/a)y}$$

$$C = -\frac{a}{2z}(e^{-(z/a)y} - e^{(z/a)y})$$

so that $\quad G(y;x) = -\dfrac{a}{2z}\left[e^{-(z/a)(x+y)} - e^{(z/a)(x-y)}\right] \qquad 0 \leq x < y$

$$G(y;x) = -\frac{a}{2z}[e^{-(z/a)(x+y)} - e^{(z/a)(y-x)}] \qquad y < x < \infty$$

In terms of the Green's function,

$$T(x,z) = \frac{1}{2a}\int_0^x g(y)[e^{-(z/a)(x-y)} - e^{-(z/a)(x+y)}]\,dy$$

$$+ \frac{1}{2a}\int_x^\infty g(y)[e^{-(z/a)(y-x)} - e^{-(z/a)(x+y)}]\,dy$$

$$+ \frac{1}{2az}\int_0^x h(y)[e^{-(z/a)(x-y)} - e^{-(z/a)(x+y)}]\,dy$$

$$+ \frac{1}{2az}\int_x^\infty h(y)[e^{-(z/a)(y-x)} - e^{-(z/a)(x+y)}]\,dy$$

$$= \frac{1}{2}\int_0^\infty g(x + a\xi)e^{-z\xi}\,d\xi + \frac{1}{2}\int_0^{x/a} g(x - a\xi)e^{-z\xi}\,d\xi$$

$$- \frac{1}{2}\int_{x/a}^\infty g(a\xi - x)e^{-z\xi}\,d\xi + \frac{1}{2z}\int_0^\infty h(x + a\xi)e^{-z\xi}\,d\xi$$

$$+ \frac{1}{2z}\int_0^{x/a} h(x - a\xi)e^{-z\xi}\,d\xi - \frac{1}{2z}\int_{x/a}^\infty h(a\xi - x)e^{-z\xi}\,d\xi$$

To identify the transform we define the functions

$$G(x) = g(x) \qquad x \geq 0$$
$$G(x) = -g(-x) \qquad x < 0$$
$$H(x) = h(x) \qquad x \geq 0$$
$$H(x) = -h(-x) \qquad x < 0$$

Then $G(-x) = -G(x)$ and $H(-x) = -H(x)$ for all x, and

$$T(x,z) = \frac{1}{2}\int_0^\infty G(x + a\xi)e^{-z\xi}\,d\xi + \frac{1}{2}\int_0^\infty G(x - a\xi)e^{-z\xi}\,d\xi$$

$$+ \frac{1}{2z}\int_0^\infty H(x + a\xi)e^{-z\xi} + \frac{1}{2z}\int_0^\infty H(x - a\xi)e^{-z\xi}\,d\xi$$

In this form we recognize the transform of

$$\phi(x,t) = \tfrac{1}{2}[G(x + at) + G(x - at)] + \tfrac{1}{2}\int_{-t}^t H(x + a\tau)\,d\tau$$

which can be verified as the solution of the problem.

Property 8, which involves taking the Laplace transform of the convolution integral, gives us a means for solving certain integral equations. Consider. for example, the integral equation of the first kind,

$$f(x) = \int_0^x k(x - \xi)\phi(\xi)\,d\xi$$

where $f(x)$ and $k(x)$ are known. $\phi(x)$ is the unknown to be found. The right-hand side is in the form of a convolution integral. Hence, we transform the equation and obtain

$$F(z) = K(z)\,T(z)$$

where $F(z)$, $K(z)$, and $T(z)$ are the transforms of $f(x)$, $k(x)$, and $\phi(x)$, respectively. Solving for $T(z)$, we have

$$T(z) = \frac{F(z)}{K(z)}$$

and we obtain $\phi(x)$ by inverting the transforms. The procedure must of necessity be formal, because at the outset we do not even know if $\phi(x)$ has a transform. The solution thus obtained can be checked in the integral equation.

Abel's integral equation is an example of this type. The equation is

$$f(x) = \int_0^x \frac{\phi(\xi)}{\sqrt{x - \xi}}\,d\xi$$

Now $k(x) = x^{-\frac{1}{2}}$ is not piecewise continuous, but nevertheless it does have a Laplace transform

$$K(z) = \int_0^\infty x^{-\frac{1}{2}} e^{-zx}\, dx = \Gamma(\tfrac{1}{2})z^{-\frac{1}{2}} = \sqrt{\pi}\, z^{-\frac{1}{2}}$$

Hence,

$$T(z) = L[\phi] = \frac{F(z)}{K(z)} = z^{\frac{1}{2}} \frac{F(z)}{\sqrt{\pi}} = \frac{z}{\pi}[\sqrt{\pi}\, z^{-\frac{1}{2}} F(z)] = \frac{z}{\pi} K(z) F(z)$$

Therefore,

$$\phi(x) = \frac{1}{\pi} \frac{d}{dx} \int_0^x \frac{f(\xi)}{\sqrt{x - \xi}}\, d\xi$$

Certain Volterra integral equations can be solved by use of the Laplace transformation.　Consider, for example, the equation

$$\phi(x) = f(x) + \int_0^x k(x - \xi)\phi(\xi)\, d\xi$$

where $f(x)$ and $k(x)$ are known and $\phi(x)$ is unknown.　Let $F(z)$, $K(z)$, and $T(z)$ be the Laplace transforms of $f(x)$, $k(x)$, and $\phi(x)$, respectively.　Then

$$T(z) = F(z) + K(z)\, T(z)$$

$$T(z) = \frac{F(z)}{1 - K(z)}$$

Inverting the transform, we obtain $\phi(x)$.　As an example of this, let us solve exercise 6, Sec. 5.3, which has a well-known solution.　The equation is

$$\phi(x) = 1 - \int_0^x (x - \xi)\phi(\xi)\, d\xi$$

Then

$$T(z) = \frac{1}{z} - \frac{T(z)}{z^2}$$

$$T(z) = \frac{z}{z^2 + 1} = L[\cos x]$$

$$\phi(x) = \cos x$$

which can be verified as the solution of the equation.

Exercises 6.5

1. Prove that the Laplace transform of a piecewise continuous function of exponential order approaches zero as Re (z) approaches infinity.

2. Let $f(x)$ be continuous for $0 < x < \infty$ and be of exponential order as $x \to \infty$ and of order x^p, $-1 < p$, as x approaches zero. Prove that $f(x)$ has a Laplace transform.

3. Show that $L[x^a] = \Gamma(a + 1)z^{-a+1}$, $-1 < a$.

4. Verify properties 4 to 7 for Laplace transforms.

5. Find the Laplace transforms of xe^{ax}, $x \sin ax$, $x^2 \cos ax$, and $e^{ax}J_0(kx)$.

6. Find the Laplace transform of $J_1(kx)$.

7. Find the inverse Laplace transforms of

$$\frac{1}{z(z^2 + a^2)} \qquad \frac{1}{z^2(z^2 - a^2)} \qquad \frac{1}{(z - a)^2(z - b)}$$

$$\frac{e^{-ax}}{z^2} \qquad \frac{z}{(z^2 + a^2)^{\frac{3}{2}}} \qquad \text{and} \qquad \frac{1}{az^2 + bz + c}$$

8–11. Solve exercises 1 to 4 of Sec. 6.2, using Laplace transforms.

12. Using Laplace transform methods, find the displacement of a vibrating string fixed at $x = 0$ and $x = L$ with initial displacement $\phi(x,0) = A \sin (\pi x/L)$ and initial velocity zero.

13. A uniform elastic bar of length L is fixed at $x = 0$ and at rest. At time $t = 0$ a force $F(t) = F_0 t^2$ is applied longitudinally at the end $x = L$. Find the longitudinal displacement of the general cross section as a function of position and time as long as the material behaves elastically.

14. Solve the generalized Abel equation $f(x) = \int_0^x \frac{\phi(\xi)}{(x - \xi)^\alpha} \, d\xi$, $0 < \alpha < 1$.

15. Solve the integral equation $\phi(x) = 1 + \int_0^x \phi(\xi) \, d\xi$.

6.6 Other Transform Techniques

Before we leave the general subject of integral transform methods, it is appropriate to mention some techniques based on other transforms. The reader should be aware of the fact that, although the Fourier and Laplace transforms are perhaps the most widely applied, there are other transforms which may be of great utility in specific applications. Some of these are the following: the **finite Fourier sine transform**, the **finite Fourier cosine transform**, the **Hankel transform**, and the **Mellin transform**. We shall discuss each of these briefly and give some examples of how they may be applied.

The **finite Fourier sine transform** of a function $f(x)$ is defined by

$$S_n[f] = \sqrt{\frac{2}{\pi}} \int_0^\pi f(x) \sin nx \, dx \qquad n = 1, 2, 3, \ldots$$

A sufficient condition for its existence is that $f(x)$ be piecewise continuous on the interval $0 \le x \le \pi$. We know from our previous work on Fourier series in Sec. 1.9 that

$$\tfrac{1}{2}[f(x+) + f(x-)] = \sqrt{\frac{2}{\pi}} \sum_{n=1}^\infty S_n \sin nx \qquad 0 \le x \le \pi$$

provided $f(x)$ and $f'(x)$ are both piecewise continuous.   At a point where $f(x)$ is continuous the series converges to the function.

Let $f(x)$ and $f'(x)$ be continuous on the interval $0 \leq x \leq \pi$, while $f''(x)$ is piecewise continuous.   Then

$$S_n[f''] = \sqrt{\frac{2}{\pi}} \int_0^\pi f''(x) \sin nx \, dx$$

$$= \sqrt{\frac{2}{\pi}} [f'(x) \sin nx]_0^\pi - n \sqrt{\frac{2}{\pi}} \int_0^\pi f'(x) \cos nx \, dx$$

$$= -n \sqrt{\frac{2}{\pi}} [f(x) \cos nx]_0^\pi - n^2 \sqrt{\frac{2}{\pi}} \int_0^\pi f(x) \sin nx \, dx$$

$$= n \sqrt{\frac{2}{\pi}} f(0) + (-1)^{n+1} n \sqrt{\frac{2}{\pi}} f(\pi) - n^2 S_n[f]$$

The **finite Fourier cosine transform** of a function $f(x)$ is defined by

$$C_n[f] = \sqrt{\frac{2}{\pi}} \int_0^\pi f(x) \cos nx \, dx \qquad n = 0, 1, 2, 3, \ldots$$

A sufficient condition for its existence is that $f(x)$ be piecewise continuous on the interval $0 \leq x \leq \pi$.   If $f(x)$ and $f'(x)$ are both piecewise continuous, then

$$\tfrac{1}{2}[f(x+) + f(x-)] = \frac{1}{\sqrt{2\pi}} C_0 + \sqrt{\frac{2}{\pi}} \sum_{n=1}^\infty C_n \cos nx \qquad 0 \leq x \leq \pi$$

Where $f(x)$ is continuous, the series converges to the function.

If $f(x)$ and $f'(x)$ are continuous while $f''(x)$ is piecewise continuous, then

$$C_n[f''] = \sqrt{\frac{2}{\pi}} \int_0^\pi f''(x) \cos nx \, dx$$

$$= \sqrt{\frac{2}{\pi}} [f'(x) \cos nx]_0^\pi + n \sqrt{\frac{2}{\pi}} \int_0^\pi f'(x) \sin nx \, dx$$

$$= \sqrt{\frac{2}{\pi}} (-1)^n f'(\pi) - \sqrt{\frac{2}{\pi}} f'(0) - n^2 \sqrt{\frac{2}{\pi}} \int_0^\pi f(x) \cos nx \, dx$$

$$= \sqrt{\frac{2}{\pi}} (-1)^n f'(\pi) - \sqrt{\frac{2}{\pi}} f'(0) - n^2 C_n[f]$$

Let $f(x)$ be continuous and $f'(x)$ be piecewise continuous on the interval $0 \le x \le 1$. Then

$$S_n[f'] = \sqrt{\frac{2}{\pi}} \int_0^\pi f'(x) \sin nx \, dx$$

$$= \sqrt{\frac{2}{\pi}} [f(x) \sin nx]_0^\pi - n\sqrt{\frac{2}{\pi}} \int_0^\pi f(x) \cos nx \, dx$$

$$= -nC_n[f]$$

$$C_n[f'] = \sqrt{\frac{2}{\pi}} \int_0^\pi f'(x) \cos nx \, dx$$

$$= \sqrt{\frac{2}{\pi}} [f(x) \cos nx]_0^\pi + n\sqrt{\frac{2}{\pi}} \int_0^\pi f(x) \sin nx \, dx$$

$$= \sqrt{\frac{2}{\pi}} (-1)^n f(\pi) - \sqrt{\frac{2}{\pi}} f(0) + nS_n[f]$$

The finite Fourier sine transform is ideally suited for solving for the vibrations of a finite string. Consider the following boundary-value problem:

$$\frac{\partial^2 \phi}{\partial x^2} = \frac{1}{a^2} \frac{\partial^2 \phi}{\partial t^2} \qquad 0 \le x \le \pi \qquad 0 < t$$

$$\phi(0,t) = \phi(\pi,t) = 0$$

$$\phi(x,0) = f(x)$$

$$\phi_t(x,0) = g(x)$$

Let

$$S_n(t) = \sqrt{\frac{2}{\pi}} \int_0^\pi \phi(x,t) \sin nx \, dx$$

Then

$$-n^2 S_n(t) = \frac{1}{a^2} \ddot{S}_n(t)$$

$$S_n(t) = A_n \cos ant + B_n \sin ant$$

$$S_n(0) = F_n = A_n$$

$$\dot{S}_n(0) = G_n = anB_n$$

where

$$F_n = \sqrt{\frac{2}{\pi}} \int_0^\pi f(x) \sin nx \, dx \qquad G_n = \sqrt{\frac{2}{\pi}} \int_0^\pi g(x) \sin nx \, dx$$

Inverting, we have

$$\phi(x,t) = \sqrt{\frac{2}{\pi}} \sum_{n=1}^\infty \left(F_n \cos ant + \frac{G_n}{an} \sin ant \right) \sin nx$$

Next consider the following ordinary differential equation with constant coefficients:

$$ay''(x) + by'(x) + cy(x) = f(x)$$

Let $f(x)$ be periodic with period 2π, i.e., $f(x + 2\pi) = f(x)$. We look for a periodic solution of the differential equation. This will not in general be the complete solution, but the general solution of the homogeneous equation can be added to it, giving the complete solution. First we write

$$y(x) = \tfrac{1}{2}[y(x) + y(-x)] + \tfrac{1}{2}[y(x) - y(-x)]$$
$$= y_e(x) + y_o(x)$$

where $y_e(x)$ is even and $y_o(x)$ is odd. We shall assume that $y(x)$ is continuous. This implies that $y_o(0) = y_o(\pi) = 0$. The differential equation becomes

$$ay_e''(x) + ay_o''(x) + by_e'(x) + by_o'(x) + cy_e(x) + cy_o(x) = f_e(x) + f_o(x)$$

where we have similarly decomposed $f(x)$. We first take the sine transform of the equation, and then the cosine transform.

$$-an^2 S_n[y_o] - nbC_n[y_e] + cS_n[y_o] = S_n[f_o]$$
$$-an^2 C_n[y_e] + nbS_n[y_o] + cC_n[y_e] = C_n[f_e]$$

Solving for $S_n[y_o]$ and $C_n[y_e]$, we have

$$S_n[y_o] = \frac{(c - an^2)S_n[f_o] + nbC_n[f_e]}{(c - an^2)^2 + n^2 b^2}$$

$$C_n[y_e] = \frac{(c - an^2)C_n[f_e] - nbS_n[f_o]}{(c - an^2)^2 + n^2 b^2}$$

Then

$$y(x) = y_e(x) + y_o(x) = \frac{1}{\sqrt{2\pi}} C_0 + \sqrt{\frac{2}{\pi}} \sum_{n=1}^{\infty} C_n \cos nx + \sqrt{\frac{2}{\pi}} \sum_{n=1}^{\infty} S_n \sin nx$$

The nature of the convergence of the series and the existence of the first and second derivatives can be determined when $f(x)$ is given.

The **Hankel transform** of a function $f(x)$ is defined by

$$H[f] = \int_0^{\infty} xf(x)J_\nu(tx)\, dx \qquad \nu \geq -\tfrac{1}{2}$$

It exists if $f(x)$ is piecewise continuous in any finite interval and absolutely integrable. If, in addition, $f'(x)$ is piecewise continuous in any finite interval we have the intersion integral[1]

$$\tfrac{1}{2}[f(x+) + f(x-)] = \int_0^{\infty} tH(t)J_\nu(tx)\, dt$$

[1] Ian N. Sneddon, "Fourier Transforms," McGraw-Hill Book Company, Inc., New York, 1951.

Consider the following ordinary differential equation:

$$x\frac{d^2y}{dx^2} + \frac{dy}{dx} - \frac{v^2}{x}y = f(x)$$

Assume that $f(x)$ is absolutely integrable on $0 \le x < \infty$, that $y(0)$ and $y'(0)$ are finite, and that $y(x) = O(1/x)$ as $x \to \infty$. We obtain a formal solution by the use of the Hankel transform.

$$F(t) = \int_0^\infty f(x)J_v(tx)\,dx = \int_0^\infty J_v(tx)\left[\frac{d}{dx}\left(x\frac{dy}{dx}\right) - \frac{v^2}{x}y\right]dx$$

$$= [xJ_v(tx)y']_0^\infty - \int_0^\infty \left(xy'J_v' + \frac{v^2}{x}yJ_v\right)dx$$

$$= -[xyJ_v'(tx)]_0^\infty + \int_0^\infty y\left[(xJ_v')' - \frac{v^2}{x}J_v\right]dx$$

$$= -t^2\int_0^\infty xy(x)J_v(tx)\,dx = -t^2H[y]$$

Hence, $H[y] = -F(t)/t^2$ and

$$y(x) = -\int_0^\infty \frac{F(t)J_v(xt)}{t}\,dt$$

The **Mellin transform** of a function $f(x)$ is defined by

$$M[f] = \int_0^\infty x^{z-1}f(x)\,dx = \phi(z)$$

Suppose $f(x)$ is piecewise continuous in any finite interval and

$$\int_0^\infty x^{\xi-1}|f(x)|\,dx$$

exists, where $\xi = \text{Re}\,(z)$. This will be true in general in some strip

$$0 < \text{Re}\,(z) < \beta.$$

Then $\phi(z)$ will be an analytic function of z in this strip. Consider

$$\frac{1}{2\pi i}\int_{\gamma-i\infty}^{\gamma+i\infty} x^{-z}\phi(z)\,dz$$

with $0 < \gamma < \beta$. Let $z = \xi + i\eta$ and $x = e^t$. Then

$$\frac{1}{2\pi i}\int_{\gamma-i\infty}^{\gamma+i\infty} x^{-z}\phi(z)\,dz = \frac{1}{2\pi}\int_{-\infty}^\infty e^{-t(\gamma+i\eta)}\int_{-\infty}^\infty e^{\tau(\gamma+i\eta)}f(e^\tau)\,d\tau\,d\eta$$

$$= \frac{e^{-t\gamma}}{2\pi}\int_{-\infty}^\infty e^{-it\eta}\int_{-\infty}^\infty e^{i\tau\eta}e^{\gamma\tau}f(e^\tau)\,d\tau\,d\eta$$

$$= e^{-t\gamma}e^{t\gamma}\frac{f(e^{t+}) + f(e^{t-})}{2} = \tfrac{1}{2}[f(x+) + f(x-)]$$

provided $e^{\gamma t} f(e^t)$ satisfies the conditions of the Fourier integral theorem, i.e.,

$$\int_{-\infty}^{\infty} e^{\gamma t} |f(e^t)| \, dt = \int_{0}^{\infty} x^{\gamma-1} |f(x)| \, dx$$

exists and $f(x)$ and $f'(x)$ are piecewise continuous in any finite interval. The convergence of the integral is guaranteed, since $0 < \gamma < \beta$. We have thus obtained the inversion integral for the Mellin transform.

As an application of the Mellin transform, consider the following boundary-value problem:

$$\nabla^2 \phi = 0 \qquad z = 0 \qquad -\infty < x < \infty \qquad 0 < y$$

$$\phi = f(|x|) \qquad y = 0$$

$$\phi = O\left(\frac{1}{\sqrt{r}}\right) \qquad \text{as } r \to \infty$$

In polar coordinates this problem becomes

$$\frac{\partial^2 \phi}{\partial r^2} + \frac{1}{r}\frac{\partial \phi}{\partial r} + \frac{1}{r^2}\frac{\partial^2 \phi}{\partial \theta^2} = 0 \qquad 0 < \theta < \pi \qquad 0 < r$$

$$\phi(r,0) = \phi(r,\pi) = f(r)$$

$$\phi = O\left(\frac{1}{\sqrt{r}}\right) \qquad \text{as } r \to \infty$$

We take the Mellin transform with respect to the variable r. Let

$$M(z,\theta) = \int_{0}^{\infty} r^{z-1} \phi(r,\theta) \, dr$$

$$\frac{\partial^2 M}{\partial \theta^2} = \int_{0}^{\infty} r^{z-1} \frac{\partial^2 \phi}{\partial \theta^2} \, dr$$

$$= -\int_{0}^{\infty} r^z \frac{\partial}{\partial r}\left(r \frac{\partial \phi}{\partial r}\right) dr$$

$$= -\left[r^{z+1} \frac{\partial \phi}{\partial r}\right]_{0}^{\infty} + z\int_{0}^{\infty} r^z \frac{\partial \phi}{\partial r} \, dr$$

$$= [z r^z \phi]_{0}^{\infty} - z^2 \int_{0}^{\infty} r^{z-1} \phi \, dr$$

$$= -z^2 M$$

Let $\qquad F(z) = \int_{0}^{\infty} r^{z-1} f(r) \, dr = M(z,0) = M(z,\pi)$

Solving and using the boundary conditions, we have

$$M(z,\theta) = A \cos z\theta + B \sin z\theta$$

$$F(z) = A$$

$$F(z) = A \cos \pi z + B \sin \pi z$$

$$F(z)(1 - \cos \pi z) = B \sin \pi z$$

$$2 \sin^2 \frac{\pi z}{2} F(z) = 2B \cos \frac{\pi z}{2} \sin \frac{\pi z}{2}$$

$$B = F(z) \tan \frac{\pi z}{2}$$

$$M(z, \theta) = F(z) \frac{\cos z(\theta - \pi/2)}{\cos(\pi z/2)}$$

Inverting, we have

$$\phi(r,\theta) = \frac{1}{2\pi i} \int_{\gamma - i\infty}^{\gamma + i\infty} r^{-z} \frac{F(z) \cos z(\theta - \pi/2)}{\cos(\pi z/2)} dz$$

where $0 < \gamma < \frac{1}{2}$.

We could give other examples of integral transform techniques, but there seems to be little point in doing so. By now the reader should be familiar with the general aspects of integral transform methods. For a variety of other applications he may wish to refer to the book by Sneddon already cited.

Exercises 6.6

1. Solve the following boundary-value problem using the finite Fourier cosine transform:

$$\frac{\partial^2 \phi}{\partial x^2} = \frac{1}{a^2} \frac{\partial^2 \phi}{\partial t^2} \qquad 0 < x < \pi \qquad 0 < t$$

$$\phi_x(0,t) = \phi_x(\pi,t) = 0$$

$$\phi(x,0) = f(x)$$

$$\phi_t(x,0) = 0$$

What transform could be used if the interval is changed to $0 < x < L$?

2. Define the **finite Fourier transform** as

$$F_n[f] = \frac{1}{\sqrt{2\pi}} \int_{-\pi}^{\pi} f(x) e^{-inx} dx$$

State an inversion theorem giving sufficient conditions on $f(x)$ for its validity.

3. Solve the following boundary-value problem using the Hankel transform and cylindrical coordinates:

$$\nabla^2 \phi = 0 \qquad 0 < r \qquad 0 \leq \theta \leq 2\pi \qquad 0 < z$$

$$\phi(r,\theta,0) = f(r)$$

$$\phi = O\left(\frac{1}{r}\right) \qquad \text{as } r \to \infty$$

References

Campbell, George A., and Ronald M. Foster: "Fourier Integrals for Practical Applications," D. Van Nostrand Company, Inc., Princeton, N.J., 1948.

Churchill, Ruel V.: "Operational Mathematics," 2d ed., McGraw-Hill Book Company, Inc., New York, 1958.

Noble, Benjamin: "The Wiener-Hopf Technique," Pergamon Press, Inc., New York, 1958.

Sneddon, Ian N.: "Fourier Transforms," McGraw-Hill Book Company, Inc., New York, 1951.

Titchmarsh, E. C.: "The Theory of Functions," 2d ed., Oxford University Press, New York, 1937.

Widder, David V.: "The Laplace Transform," Princeton University Press, Princeton, N.J., 1941.

Wiener, Norbert: "The Fourier Integral," Cambridge University Press, New York, 1933.

Index